Journeys Through Bookland

He Turned His Face and Kissed
Her Climbing

Geraint and Enid

Journeys Through Bookland

A NEW AND ORIGINAL
PLAN FOR READING APPLIED TO THE
WORLD'S BEST LITERATURE
FOR CHILDREN

BY

CHARLES H. SYLVESTER

Author of English and American Literature

VOLUME FIVE
New Edition

Chicago
BELLOWS-REEVE COMPANY
PUBLISHERS

CONTENTS

		PAGE
JONATHAN SWIFT		1
GULLIVER'S TRAVELS	Jonathan Swift	6
THE BALLAD OF AGINCOURT	Michael Drayton	95
SOME CHILDREN'S BOOKS OF THE PAST	Grace E. Sellon	101
LEAD, KINDLY LIGHT	Cardinal Newman	110
LET SOMETHING GOOD BE SAID	James Whitcomb Riley	111
POLONIUS' ADVICE	Shakespeare	112
KING ARTHUR		113
BALIN AND BALAN		130
GERAINT AND ENID	Alfred Tennyson	148
THE HOLY GRAIL	Adapted from Thomas Malory	207
DISSENSIONS AT KING ARTHUR'S COURT		232
THE PASSING OF ARTHUR	Alfred Tennyson	237
HENRY HUDSON'S FOURTH VOYAGE	Henry R. Cleveland	254
THE RISE OF ROBERT BRUCE	Sir Walter Scott	278
BRUCE AND THE SPIDER	Bernard Arton	314
THE HEART OF BRUCE	William E. Aytoun	316
THE SKELETON IN ARMOR	Henry Wadsworth Longfellow	327
HOW THEY BROUGHT THE GOOD NEWS FROM GHENT TO AIX	Robert Browning	335
REMINISCENCES OF A PIONEER	Edwin D. Coe	340
THE BUCCANEERS		359
CAPTAIN MORGAN AT MARACAIBO		365
BRADDOCK'S DEFEAT	Benjamin Franklin	379
READING HISTORY		394
THE AMERICAN FLAG	Joseph Rodman Drake	396
BATTLE HYMN OF THE REPUBLIC	Julia Ward Howe	399
"STONEWALL" JACKSON'S WAY	J. W. Palmer	400
BARON MUNCHAUSEN		403
THE FIDDLING PARSON	Davy Crockett	440
WE PLAN A RIVER TRIP	Jerome K. Jerome	443
ON COMIC SONGS	Jerome K. Jerome	455
THE INCHCAPE ROCK	Robert Southey	465
TOM BROWN AT RUGBY	Thomas Hughes	469
PRONUNCIATION OF PROPER NAMES		497

The Classification of Selections, see General Index, at end of
Volume X

ILLUSTRATIONS

PAGE

HE TURN'D HIS FACE AND KISS'D HER CLIMBING (Color Plate) . .
. . . . *Donn P. Crane* FRONTISPIECE
JONATHAN SWIFT (Halftone) 4
GULLIVER'S JOURNEY TO THE METROPOLIS . . . *Iris Weddell White* 17
THE EMPEROR VISITS GULLIVER . . . . *Iris Weddell White* 23
GULLIVER AND THE PISTOL (Color Plate) . . . . . . *G. H. Mitchell* 30
GULLIVER'S WATCH IS BORNE AWAY . . . . . *Iris Weddell White* 32
GULLIVER TAKES THE ENEMY'S FLEET . . . . . *Iris Weddell White* 43
GULLIVER BRINGS IN THE DRIFTING BOAT . . . . *Harry L. Gage* 49
THE BABY SEIZES GULLIVER . . . . *Iris Weddell White* 66
A GALE WITH THEIR FANS . . . . *Iris Weddell White* 75
GULLIVER AND THE KING . . . . *Iris Weddell White* 79
"VICTOR I WILL REMAIN" . . . . *R. F. Babcock* 97
CHILDREN WITH HORNBOOKS . . . . *Laura K. Deal* 103
ARTHUR DRAWS THE SWORD . . . . *Jessie Arms* 115
KING ARTHUR (Halftone) 116
THE WEDDING OF ARTHUR AND GUINEVERE . . . . . *Jessie Arms* 121
MERLIN SAVES ARTHUR . . . . *Donn P. Crane* 125
ARTHUR RECEIVES EXCALIBUR . . . . *Donn P. Crane* 128
THE DAMSEL LET FALL HER MANTLE . . . . . . *Donn P. Crane* 133
THE FIGHT . . . . *Donn P. Crane* 145
ALFRED, LORD TENNYSON (Halftone) 148
GERAINT HEARS ENID SINGING . . . . *Donn P. Crane* 159
ENID LEADS THE WAY . . . . *Donn P. Crane* 177
ENID WATCHING BY GERAINT . . . . *Donn P. Crane* 195
GALAHAD GETS HIS SHIELD . . . . *Donn P. Crane* 219
THE SHIP APPROACHES THE CITY OF SARRAS . . . . *Jessie Arms* 227
THE LAST APPEARANCE OF THE SANGREAL. . . . . *Donn P. Crane* 229
THE BARGE MOVED FROM THE BRINK . . . . . . *Donn P. Crane* 253
CUT ADRIFT IN HUDSON'S BAY . . . . *R. F. Babcock* 271
SAVAGES ON THE SHORE . . . . *R. F. Babcock* 276
BRUCE KILLS COMYN . . . . *Donn P. Crane* 281
SHE BROUGHT HER TWO SONS . . . . *Donn P. Crane* 296
THE ASCENT TO THE CASTLE OF EDINBURGH . . . . *Donn P. Crane* 303
BRUCE SLAYS SIR HENRY DE BOHUN . . . . . . *Donn P. Crane* 309
BRUCE BEHELD A SPIDER . . . . *Donn P. Crane* 315
I SAW A PILGRIM STAND . . . . *Donn P. Crane* 319
HELD THE HEART ALOFT . . . . *Donn P. Crane* 325
I WAS A VIKING OLD . . . . *R. F. Babcock* 329
THREE WEEKS WE WESTWARD BORE . . . . . . *R. F. Babcock* 333
I CAST LOOSE MY BUFF COAT . . . . *Donn P. Crane* 337

HALF A DOZEN INDIANS BOLTED IN. . . . . *R. F. Babcock* 345
HE FISHED OUT AN OLD BUNGTOWN CENT. . . . . . *R. F. Babcock* 351
CHASING THE GEESE TO GET A NEW QUILL . . . . . *R. F. Babcock* 356
THE FIRE SHIP GRAPPLED THE SPANIARD . . . . . *Everett E. Lowry* 371
BENJAMIN FRANKLIN (Halftone) 380
ON THE MARCH . . . . *Everett E. Lowry* 388
THE AMBUSH . . . . *Everett E. Lowry* 389
"STONEWALL" JACKSON (Halftone) 400
THE LION HAD JUMPED INTO THE CROCODILE'S MOUTH
. . . . *Donn P. Crane* 408
I BEHELD A NOBLE STAG . . . . *Donn P. Crane* 413
THE HIND PART OF THE POOR CREATURE WAS MISSING
. . . . *Donn P. Crane* 417
WARRIORS OF THE MOON . . . . *Donn P. Crane* 428
WE DESCENDED SAFELY ON A MOUNTAIN OF ICE . . *Donn P. Crane* 438
THE PARSON FIDDLED . . . . *Donn P. Crane* 442
"AIN'T YOU GOING TO PUT THE BOOK IN?" . . . *Herbert N. Rudeen* 453
"WHEN I WAS YOUNG" . . . . *Herbert N. Rudeen* 459
ONE DREADFUL SOUND HE SEEMED TO HEAR . . . . *R. F. Babcock* 468
RUGBY SCHOOL (Color Plate) 472
THE BULLY CAUGHT IT ON HIS ELBOW . . . . *Louis Grell* 471
"A FIGHT!" . . . . *Louis Grell* 485
TOM SITS ON MARTIN'S KNEE . . . . *Louis Grell* 487

JONATHAN SWIFT

HE father of Jonathan Swift was a Dublin lawyer who died just as he was beginning what might have been a profitable career, and before his only son was born. The widow was left with so little money that when her son was born in November, 1667, she was not able to take care of him. Her brother-in-law undertook to provide for mother and child.

He procured a nurse who became so attached to her little charge that when she received a small sum of money from a relative in England and was compelled to go to that country, she stole the baby and took him with her across the channel. It was more than three years before Jonathan was brought back to Dublin, but he had been tenderly cared for, and though but five years of age had been taught to spell and to read in the Bible.

A year later he was sent to a good school, where he made rapid progress. However, he could not have been always studious, for visitors to the school are still shown a desk in which his name is deeply cut.

He was fourteen years old when he entered the University of Dublin, where his record was not a very satisfactory one. When it came time for him to graduate, his standing was too poor for him to take his degree, but after some delay it was given him "by special favor," a term then used in Dublin to show that a candidate did not pass in his examinations.

After this, Swift remained three years at the University under the pretense of studying, but he was chiefly notorious for his connection with a gang of wild and disobedient students who were often under censure of the faculty for their irregularities. For one offense Swift was severely censured and compelled upon his knees to beg pardon of the dean. This punishment he did not forgive, and long afterward he wrote bitter things about Dr. Allen, the dean.

Yet while indulging in these follies, Swift learned to write well and became noted for a peculiar satirical style that afterward made him much feared by the government.

When the uncle who had first supported Swift had died, a second uncle and his son took up the burden. At one time this cousin sent Swift quite a large sum of money, a fact which seemed to change the nature of the wild young spendthrift, who thereafter remained economical; in fact, he became niggardly in his saving.

Swift's second degree from the University was earned creditably, and he was much pleased with the praise and respect with which he was received. This was owing to two years of diligent study which he spent at the home of Sir William Temple, a leading statesman of the time and a distant relative by marriage of Swift's mother.

Discouraged by his fruitless attempt to enter public life, he began to study for the ministry, and, ultimately, he received a church appointment, of which he wearied after a short experience.

Until 1710, he led a varied life, sometimes dependent upon his relatives, and at others making his way in various political positions. From the date above he was embroiled in heated political controversies in which his bitter writings made him feared even by his friends and fiercely hated by his enemies. But he steadily rose in power and influence, and when his party triumphed he was rewarded for his political services by being appointed dean of Saint Patrick's Cathedral in Ireland.

His appointment was exceedingly unpopular, even in Ireland, for few believed him at all suited for a position in the church, much less for one so high and important. On the day he was installed, some bitter verses, of which the following are three, were found posted on the door of the cathedral:

> To-day this temple gets a dean,
> Of parts and fame uncommon;
> Used both to pray and to profane,
> To serve both God and Mammon.

> * * * * *

> This place he got by wit and rhyme,
> And many ways most odd;
> And might a bishop be in time,
> Did he believe in God.

> * * * * *

> And now when'er his deanship dies,
> Upon his tomb be graven—
> A man of God here buried lies,
> Who never thought of heaven.

Unfortunately there was too much truth in the charges against Swift's character, and his career, in spite of his genius, is a pitiful one. He was admired for his wit and brilliancy, and courted by the noble and powerful, but he was never able to gratify his ambitions, though he did secure many devoted friends. From his disappointments he became moody, bitter and discontented. This state of mind, together with other causes, finally broke his health, destroyed his mind and left him but the sad wreck of a brilliant manhood, and an old age of helpless imbecility. Such a life has little that is attractive for anyone, but it does show us that even a brilliant intellect cannot save a man who persistently neglects to guard his character, and that fame does not always bring happiness.

But Swift was by no means all bad, and his great services to Ireland are still deservedly recognized by that devoted people. He really laid the foundation for their prosperity and may be said to have created constitutional liberty for them.

It is, however, as a wit and a writer that Swift is now chiefly famous. Many are the stories told of his readiness in repartee, his bright sallies in conversation, and of his skill in quick and caustic rhyming. It is said that one day, when traveling in the south of Ireland, he stopped to give his horse water at a brook which crossed the road; a gentleman of the neighborhood halted for the same purpose, and saluted him, a courtesy which was politely returned. They parted, but the gentleman, struck by the dean's figure, sent his servant to inquire who the man was. The messenger rode up to the dean and said, "Please, sir, master would be obliged if you would tell him who you are."

"Willingly," replied the dean. "Tell your master I am the person that bowed to him when we were giving our horses water at the brook yonder."

JONATHAN SWIFT
1667–1745

Swift's interests lay rather with the common people than with the Irish aristocracy, who, he thought, were arrant "grafters." Of one in particular he said,

> "So great was his bounty—
> He erected a bridge—at the expense of the county."

The last thing Swift wrote was an epigram. It was in almost the final lucid interval between periods of insanity that he was riding in the park with his physician. As they drove along, Swift saw, for the first time, a building that had recently been put up.

"What is that?" he inquired.

"That," said the physician, "is the new magazine in which are stored arms and powder for the defence of the city."

"Oh!" said the dean, pulling out his notebook. "Let me take an item of that; this is worth remarking: 'My tablets!' as Hamlet says, 'my tablets! Memory put down that.' " Then he scribbled the following lines, the last he ever penned:

> "Behold a proof of Irish sense!
> Here Irish wit is seen!
> When nothing's left that's worth defence,
> We build a magazine."

With the exception of *Gulliver's Travels,* very little that Dean Swift wrote is now read by anyone but students.

GULLIVER'S TRAVELS

INTRODUCTION

ULLIVER'S TRAVELS was published in 1726 and without any allusion to the real author, though many knew that the work must have come from the pen of Dean Swift. Though the dean was habitually secretive in what he did, he had some reason for not wishing to say in public that he had written so bitter a satire on the government and on mankind.

The work was immediately popular, not only in the British Isles but on the Continent as well. No such form of political satire had ever appeared, and everyone was excited over its possibilities. Not all parts of the work were considered equally good; some parts were thought to be failures, and the Fourth Voyage was as a whole deservedly unpopular. The Voyages to Lilliput and to Brobdingnag were considered the best, and to them is to be attributed the greater part of the author's fame. Their popularity continues with the years.

Lemuel Gulliver is represented as a British sailor who had been educated as a doctor but whose wandering instincts led him back to the sea. On his return from his voyages he writes the account of his adventures; and the manner in which this account is written is so masterly that we almost believe the things he tells.

In describing the manners, customs, and governments of the several countries, he shows in his inimitable way the weakness of his king, prince, nobles, government and mankind in general.

While the scholar and the man of affairs may still be interested in the political significance of what is said and in a study of the keen knowledge of human nature shown by the writer, yet it is principally as a story that the work is now popular. Everybody enjoys reading about the wonderful people who existed only in the imagination of the great dean of Saint Patrick's.

In this volume are printed some of the most enjoyable parts of the first and second voyages. About the only changes from the original text are in the omission of those passages which contribute nothing to the narrative or which for other reasons it seems inadvisable to reprint. These omissions put the real fictitious narrative into so small a compass that children will be entertained from beginning to end.

The *Voyage to Lilliput* was directed against the policy of the English Court during the reign of George I. The real differences between the parties were trifling; not more, to Swift's idea, than that between *High-heels* and *Low-heels* in the court of Lilliput; and the controversies between the churches were not greater than those between the *Big-endians* and the *Little-endians*. As the Prince of Wales was thought to favor a union of parties, he was typified in the heir-apparent of Lilliput who wore one shoe with a high heel and one with a low heel. This explanation will give an idea of the nature of Swift's milder satire.

The *Voyage to Brobdingnag* advocates the principles then held by the Tory party in England and attacks those of the Whigs.

The *Voyage to Laputa,* from which we give no selections, was not generally understood and hence was not popular. Its chief purpose was to ridicule the proceedings of the Royal Society, but Swift was not well enough acquainted with music and some of the other sciences fostered by the Society to attack them to advantage.

The *Voyage to the Houyhnhnms* was a bitter screed against mankind, and is in many respects disgusting. It showed Swift's venom against the world and something of the approach of the malady which finally hurried him into insanity.

The following selections are somewhat condensed from the original story, chiefly by the omission of passages of no interest to people of to-day.

ADVENTURES IN LILLIPUT

I. The Arrival

E set sail from Bristol, May 4, 1699, and our voyage at first was very prosperous.

It would not be proper, for some reasons, to trouble the reader with the particulars of our adventures; let it suffice to inform him, that, in our passage to the East Indies, we were driven by a violent storm to the northwest of Van Diemen's Land.[1] By an observation we found ourselves in the lati-

1. *Van Diemen's Land* is the old name for Tasmania, an island off the coast of Australia.

tude of 30 degrees 2 minutes south. Twelve of our crew were dead by immoderate labor and ill food; the rest were in a very weak condition.

On the 5th of November, which was the beginning of summer in those parts, the weather being very hazy, the seamen spied a rock within half a cable's length of the ship; but the wind was so strong that we were driven directly upon it, and immediately split. Six of the crew, of whom I was one, having let down the boat into the sea, made a shift to get clear of the ship and the rock. We rowed, by my computation, about three leagues, till we were able to work no longer, being already spent with labor while we were in the ship. We, therefore, trusted ourselves to the mercy of the waves; and in about half an hour the boat was overset by a sudden flurry from the north. What became of my companions in the boat, as well as those who escaped on the rock, or were left in the vessel, I cannot tell, but conclude they were all lost.

For my own part, I swam as Fortune directed me, and was pushed forward by wind and tide. I often let my legs drop, and could feel no bottom; but when I was almost gone, and able to struggle no longer, I found myself within my depth; and by this time the storm was much abated. The declivity was so small, that I walked near a mile before I got to the shore, which I conjectured was about eight o'clock in the evening. I then advanced forward near half a mile, but could not discover any sign of houses or inhabitants; at least I was in so weak a condition that I did not observe them. I was extremely tired; and with that, and the heat of the weather, and about half a pint of brandy that I drank as I left the ship, I found myself much inclined to sleep. I lay down on the grass, which was very short and soft, where I slept sounder than ever I remember to have done in my life, and, as I reckoned, above nine hours; for when I awaked it was just daylight.

I attempted to rise, but was not able to stir; for as I happened to lie on my back, I found my arms and legs were strongly fastened on each side to the ground, and my hair, which was long and thick, tied down in the same manner. I likewise felt several slender ligatures across my body, from my armpits to my thighs. I could only look upward; the sun began to grow hot, and the light offended mine eyes. I heard a confused noise about me, but, in the posture I lay, could see nothing except the sky.

In a little time I felt something alive moving on my left leg, which, advancing gently forward over my breast, came almost up to my chin; when, bending mine eyes downward as much as I could, I perceived it to be a human creature not six inches high, with a bow and arrow in his hands, and a quiver at his back. In the meantime, I felt at least forty more of the same kind (as I conjectured) following the first. I was in the utmost astonishment, and roared so loud that they all ran back in a fright; and some of them, as I was afterward told, were hurt with the falls they got by leaping from my sides upon the ground. However, they soon returned; and one of them, who ventured so far as to get a full sight of my face, lifting up his hands and eyes by way of admiration, cried out, in a shrill but distinct voice, "Hekinah degul." The others repeated the same words several times; but I then knew not what they meant. I lay all this while, as the reader may believe, in great uneasiness.

At length, struggling to get loose, I had the fortune to break the strings and wrench out the pegs that fastened my left arm to the ground; for, by lifting it up to my face, I discovered the methods they had taken to bind me, and, at the same time, with a violent pull, which gave me excessive pain, I a little loosened the strings that tied down my hair on the left side, so that I was just able to turn my head about two inches. But the creatures ran off a second time, before I could seize them; whereupon there was a great shout, in a very shrill accent, and, after it ceased, I heard one of them cry aloud, "Tolgo phonac"; when, in an instant, I felt above an hundred arrows discharged on my left hand, which pricked me like so many needles; and, besides, they shot another flight into the air, as we do bombs in Europe; whereof many, I suppose, fell on my body (though I felt them not), and some on my face, which I immediately covered with my left hand.

When this shower of arrows was over, I fell a-groaning with grief and pain; and then, striving again to get loose, they discharged another volley, larger than the first, and some of them attempted, with spears, to stick me in the sides; but, by good luck, I had on me a buff² jerkin, which they could not pierce. I thought it the most prudent method to lie still; and my design was to continue so till night, when, my left hand being already loose, I could easily free myself; and as for the inhabitants,

2. *Buff* is the name given to a kind of leather, made originally of buffalo hide, but later of the skins of other animals.

I had reason to believe I might be a match for
the greatest armies they could bring against me, if
they were all of the same size with him that I saw.

But fortune disposed otherwise of me. When
the people observed I was quiet, they discharged
no more arrows; but, by the noise I heard, I knew
their numbers increased; and about four yards from
me, over against my right ear, I heard a knocking
for above an hour, like that of people at work;
when, turning my head that way, as well as the
pegs and strings would permit me, I saw a stage
erected about a foot and a half from the ground,
capable of holding four of the inhabitants, with two
or three ladders to mount it; from whence one of
them, who seemed to be a person of quality, made
me a long speech, whereof I understood not one
syllable.

But I should have mentioned that, before the
principal person began his oration, he cried out
three times, "Langro dehul san" (these words and
the former were afterward repeated and explained
to me) ; whereupon, immediately, about fifty of the
inhabitants came and cut the strings that fastened
the left side of my head, which gave me the liberty
of turning it to the right, and of observing the person and gesture of him that was to speak. He appeared to be of a middle age, and taller than any
of the other three who attended him; whereof one
was a page, that held up his train, and seemed to
be somewhat longer than my middle finger; the
other two stood one on each side to support him.
He acted every part of an orator; and I could observe many periods of threatenings, and others of
promises, pity, and kindness.

I answered in a few words, but in the most submissive manner, lifting up my left hand and both mine eyes to the sun, as calling him for a witness: and being almost famished with hunger, having not eaten a morsel for some hours before I left the ship, I found the demands of nature so strong upon me that I could not forbear showing my impatience (perhaps against the strict rules of decency) by putting my finger frequently on my mouth, to signify that I wanted food.

The *hurgo* (for so they call a great lord, as I afterward learned) understood me very well. He descended from the stage, and commanded that several ladders should be applied to my sides, on which above an hundred of the inhabitants mounted, and walked toward my mouth, laden with baskets full of meat, which had been provided and sent thither by the king's orders, upon the first intelligence he received of me. I observed there was the flesh of several animals, but could not distinguish them by the taste. There were shoulders, legs, and loins, shaped like those of mutton, and very well dressed, but smaller than the wings of a lark. I eat them by two or three at a mouthful, and took three loaves at a time, about the bigness of musket-bullets. They supplied me as fast as they could, showing a thousand marks of wonder and astonishment at my bulk and appetite.

I then made another sign, that I wanted drink. They found by my eating that a small quantity would not suffice me; and, being a most ingenious people, they slung up, with great dexterity, one of their largest hogsheads, then rolled it toward my hand, and beat out the top. I drank it off at a draught, which I might well do, for it did not hold half a pint, and tasted like a small wine of Burgundy, but much more delicious. They brought me a second hogshead, which I drank in the same manner, and made signs for more; but they had none to give me.

When I had performed these wonders, they shouted for joy, and danced upon my breast, repeating several times, as they did at first, "Hekinah degul." They made me a sign that I should throw down the two hogsheads, but first warning the people below to stand out of the way, crying aloud, "Borach mivolah"; and when they saw the vessels in the air there was an universal shout of "Hekinah degul."

I confess I was often tempted, while they were passing backward and forward on my body, to seize forty or fifty of the first that came in my reach, and dash them against the ground. But the remembrance of what I had felt, which probably might not be the worst they could do, and the promise of honor I made them—for so I interpreted my submissive behavior—soon drove out these imaginations. Besides, I now considered myself as bound by the laws of hospitality to a people who had treated me with so much expense and magnificence. However, in my thoughts I could not sufficiently wonder at the intrepidity of these diminutive mortals, who durst venture to mount and walk upon my body, while one of my hands was at liberty, without trembling at the very sight of so prodigious a creature as I must appear to them.

After some time, when they observed that I made no more demands for meat, there appeared before

me a person of high rank from his imperial majesty.
His excellency, having mounted on the small of my
right leg, advanced forward up to my face, with
about a dozen of his retinue; and producing his
credentials, under the signet-royal, which he applied
close to mine eyes, spoke about ten minutes without
any signs of anger, but with a kind of determinate
resolution; often pointing forward; which, as I afterward found, was toward the capital city, about
half a mile distant, whither it was agreed by his
majesty in council that I must be conveyed.

I answered in few words, but to no purpose, and
made a sign with my hand that was loose, putting
it to the other (but over his excellency's head, for
fear of hurting him or his train), and then to my
own head and body, to signify that I desired my
liberty.

It appeared that he understood me well enough,
for he shook his head by way of disapprobation,
and held his hand in a posture to show that I
must be carried as a prisoner. However, he made
other signs, to let me understand that I should have
meat and drink enough, and very good treatment.
Whereupon, I once more thought of attempting to
break my bonds; but again, when I felt the smart
of their arrows upon my face and hands, which
were all in blisters, and many of the darts still sticking in them, and observing likewise that the number of my enemies increased, I gave tokens to let
them know that they might do with me what they
pleased.

Upon this, the *hurgo* and his train withdrew,
with much civility and cheerful countenances. Soon
after, I heard a general shout, with frequent

repetitions of the words "Peplom selan," and I felt
great numbers of the people on my left side, re-
laxing the cords to such a degree that I was able to
turn upon my right. But before this they had
daubed my face and both my hands with a sort of
ointment, very pleasant to the smell, which, in a
few minutes, removed all the smart of their arrows.
These circumstances, added to the refreshment I
had received by their victuals and drink, which were
very nourishing, disposed me to sleep. I slept about
eight hours, as I was afterward assured; and it
was no wonder, for the physicians, by the emperor's
order, had mingled a sleepy potion in the hogsheads of wine.

It seems that upon the first moment I was discovered sleeping on the ground, after my landing,
the emperor had early notice of it by an express,
and determined in council that I should be tied in
the manner I have related (which was done in the
night, while I slept), that plenty of meat and drink
should be sent to me, and a machine prepared to
carry me to the capital city.

This resolution, perhaps, may appear very bold
and dangerous, and I am confident would not be
imitated by any prince in Europe, on the like occasion. However, in my opinion, it was extremely
prudent, as well as generous; for supposing these
people had endeavored to kill me with their spears
and arrows while I was asleep, I should certainly
have awaked with the first sense of smart, which
might so far have roused my rage and strength as
to have enabled me to break the strings wherewith
I was tied; after which, as they were not able to
make resistance, so they could expect no mercy.

GULLIVER'S JOURNEY TO THE METROPOLIS

These people are most excellent mathematicians,
and arrived to a great perfection in mechanics, by
the countenance and encouragement of the emperor,
who is a renowned patron of learning. This prince
has several machines fixed on wheels, for the carriage of trees and other great weights. He often
builds his largest men-of-war, whereof some are
nine feet long, in the woods where the timber grows,
and has them carried on these engines, three or four
hundred yards, to the sea.

Five hundred carpenters and engineers were immediately set at work to prepare the greatest engine they had. It was a frame of wood raised three
inches from the ground, about seven feet long, and
four wide, moving upon twenty-two wheels. The
shout I heard was upon the arrival of this engine,
which, it seems, set out in four hours after my landing. It was brought parallel to me as I lay. But
the principal difficulty was to raise and place me in
this vehicle. Eighty poles, each of one foot high,
were erected for this purpose, and very strong cords,
of the bigness of pack-thread, were fastened by
hooks to many bandages, which the workmen had
girt round my neck, my hands, my body, and my
legs. Nine hundred of the strongest men were employed to draw up these cords, by many pulleys
fastened on the poles; and thus, in less than three
hours, I was raised and slung into the engine, and
there tied fast. All this I was told; for, while the
whole operation was performing, I lay in a pro-
found sleep, by the force of that soporiferous medicine infused into my liquor. Fifteen hundred of
the emperor's largest horses, each about four inches
and a half high, were employed to draw me toward

the metropolis, which, as I said, was half a mile distant. About four hours after we began our journey,
I awaked by a very ridiculous accident; for the carriage being stopped awhile to adjust something that
was out of order, two or three of the young natives
had the curiosity to see how I looked when I was
asleep; they climbed up into the engine, and advancing very softly to my face, one of them, an
officer in the guards, put the sharp end of his half-
pike a good way up into my nostril, which tickled
my nose like a straw, and made me sneeze violently;
whereupon they stole off unperceived, and it was
three weeks before I knew the cause of my awaking
so suddenly.

We made a long march the remaining part of that
day,[3] and rested at night with five hundred guards
on each side of me, half with torches, and half with
bows and arrows, ready to shoot me if I should offer to stir. The next morning at sunrise we continued our march, and arrived within two hundred
yards of the city gates about noon. The emperor
and all his court came out to meet us, but his great
officers would by no means suffer his majesty to
endanger his person by mounting on my body.

At the place where the carriage stopped there
stood an ancient temple, esteemed to be the largest
in the whole kingdom; which, having been polluted
some years before by an unnatural murder, was,
according to the zeal of those people, looked on as
profane, and therefore had been applied to common

3. Notice the skill with which Swift adjusts all things to his
tiny Lilliputians. The half-mile journey would have been but a
few minutes' walk for Gulliver, but the six-inch men and the
four-and-one-half-inch horses spent almost a day and a half in
covering the distance.

use, and all the ornaments and furniture carried away. In this edifice it was determined I should lodge. The great gate fronting to the north was about four foot high, and about two foot wide, through which I could easily creep. On each side of the gate was a small window, not above six inches from the ground: into that on the left side the king's smiths conveyed fourscore and eleven chains, like those that hang to a lady's watch in Europe, and almost as large, which were locked to my left leg with thirty-six padlocks.

Over against this temple, on t'other side of the great highway, at twenty foot distance, there was a turret at least five foot high. Here the emperor ascended, with many principal lords of his court, to have an opportunity of viewing me, as I was told, for I could not see them. It was reckoned that above an hundred thousand inhabitants came out of the town upon the same errand; and, in spite of my guards, I believe there could not be fewer than ten thousand at several times, who mounted upon my body by the help of ladders. But a proclamation was soon issued to forbid it upon pain of death.

When the workmen found it was impossible for me to break loose they cut all the strings that bound me; whereupon I rose up, with as melancholy a disposition as ever I had in my life. But the noise and astonishment of the people, at seeing me rise and walk, are not to be expressed. The chains that held my left leg were about two yards long, and gave me not only the liberty of walking backward and forward in a semicircle, but, being fixed within four inches of the gate, allowed me to creep in and lie at my full length in the temple.

II. *Imprisonment*

HEN I found myself on my feet I looked about me, and must confess I never beheld a more entertaining prospect. The country round appeared like a continued garden, and the enclosed fields, which were generally forty foot square, resembled so many beds of flowers. These fields were intermingled with woods of half a stang,[4] and the tallest trees, as I could judge, appeared to be seven foot high. I viewed the town on my left hand, which looked like the painted scene of a city in a theater.

The emperor was already descended from the tower, and advancing on horseback toward me, which had like to have cost him dear, for the beast, though very well trained, yet wholly unused to such a sight, which appeared as if a mountain moved before him, reared up on his hinder feet; but that prince, who is an excellent horseman, kept his seat till his attendants ran in and held the bridle while his majesty had time to dismount.

When he alighted he surveyed me round with great admiration, but kept beyond the length of my chain. He ordered his cooks and butlers, who were already prepared, to give me victuals and drink, which they pushed forward in sorts of vehicles upon wheels till I could reach them. I took these vehicles, and soon emptied them all; twenty of them were filled with meat, and ten with liquor;

4. *Stang* is an old name for a pole, or perch, sixteen and one-half feet.

each of the former afforded me two or three good mouthfuls, and I emptied the liquor of ten vessels, which was contained in earthen vials, into one vehicle, drinking it off at a draught. The empress and young princes of the blood, of both sexes, attended by many ladies, sat at some distance in their chairs, but upon the accident that happened to the emperor's horse they alighted and came near his person, which I am now going to describe.

He is taller, by almost the breadth of my nail, than any of his court, which is alone enough to strike an awe into the beholders. His features are strong and masculine, with an Austrian lip and arched nose; his complexion olive, his countenance erect, his body and limbs well proportioned, all his motions graceful, and his deportment majestic. He was then past his prime, being twenty-eight years and three-quarters old,[5] of which he had reigned about seven in great felicity, and generally victorious. For the better convenience of beholding him I lay on my side, so that my face was parallel to his, and he stood but three yards off; however, I have had him since many times in my hand, and therefore cannot be deceived in the description. His dress was very plain and simple, and the fashion of it between the Asiatic and the European; but he had on his head a light helmet of gold, adorned with jewels, and a plume on the crest. He held his sword drawn in his hand to defend himself if I should happen to break loose; it was almost three inches long, the hilt and scabbard were gold enriched with

5. Swift uses his reducing imagination even on the time, perceiving that it would not seem natural for his tiny manikins to have as long lives as the "man mountain" on which they gazed with such wonder.

diamonds. His voice was shrill, but very clear and articulate, and I could distinctly hear it when I stood up.

THE EMPEROR VISITS GULLIVER

The ladies and courtiers were all most magnificently clad, so that the spot they stood upon seemed to resemble a petticoat spread on the ground embroidered with figures of gold and silver.

His imperial majesty spoke often to me, and I
returned answers, but neither of us could understand a syllable. There were several of his priests
and lawyers present (as I conjectured by their
habit), who were commanded to address themselves
to me, and I spoke to them in as many languages
as I had the least smattering of, which were High
and Low Dutch, Latin, French, Spanish, Italian,
and Lingua Franca,[6] but all to no purpose.

After about two hours the court retired, and I
was left with a strong guard to prevent the impertinence and probably the malice of the rabble, who
were very impatient to crowd about me as near as
they durst, and some of them had the impudence to
shoot their arrows at me as I sat on the ground by
the door of my house, whereof one very narrowly
missed my left eye. But the colonel ordered six of
the ringleaders to be seized, and thought no punishment so proper as to deliver them bound into my
hands, which some of his soldiers accordingly did,
pushing them forward with the butt ends of their
pikes into my reach. I took them all in my right
hand, put five of them into my coat pocket, and as
to the sixth, I made a countenance as if I would
eat him alive. The poor man squalled terribly, and
the colonel and his officers were in much pain, especially when they saw me take out my penknife;
but I soon put them out of fear, for looking mildly,
and immediately cutting the strings he was bound
with, I set him gently on the ground, and away he
ran. I treated the rest in the same manner, taking

6. *Lingua Franca* was the name given to a mixed dialect used
in some parts of the Mediterranean coasts as means of communication between people of different nationalities. It consisted
largely of corrupted Italian words.

them one by one out of my pocket, and I observed both the soldiers and people were highly delighted at this mark of my clemency, which was represented very much to my advantage at court.

Toward night I got with some difficulty into my house, where I lay on the ground, and continued to do so about a fortnight, during which time the emperor gave orders to have a bed prepared for me. Six hundred beds of the common measure were brought in carriages, and worked up in my house; an hundred and fifty of their beds sewn together made up the breadth and length, and these were four double, which, however, kept me but very indifferently from the hardness of the floor, that was of smooth stone. By the same computation they provided me with sheets, blankets, and coverlets, tolerable enough for one who had been so long inured to hardships as I.

In the meantime the emperor held frequent councils, to debate what course should be taken with me; and I was afterward assured by a particular friend, a person of great quality, who was looked upon to be as much in the secret as any, that the court was under many difficulties concerning me. They apprehended my breaking loose; that my diet would be very expensive, and might cause a famine. Sometimes they determined to starve me, or at least to shoot me in the face and hands with poisoned arrows, which would soon despatch me.

In the midst of these consultations, several officers of the army went to the door of the great council-chamber, and two of them, being admitted, gave an account of my behavior to the six criminals above mentioned, which made so favorable an im-

pression in the breast of his majesty and the whole
board in my behalf, that an imperial commission
was issued out obliging all the villages nine hundred
yards round the city to deliver in every morning
six beeves, forty sheep, and other victuals for my
sustenance; together with a proportionable quantity of bread, and wine, and other liquors; for the
payment of which his majesty gave orders upon his
treasury. An establishment was also made of six
hundred persons to be my domestics, who had board
wages allowed for their maintenance, and tents
built for them, very conveniently on each side of my
door. It was likewise ordered that three hundred
tailors should make me a suit of clothes, after the
fashion of the country; that six of his majesty's
greatest scholars should be employed to instruct me
in their language; and, lastly, that the emperor's
horses, and those of the nobility, and troops of
guard, should be frequently exercised in my sight,
to accustom themselves to me.

All these orders were duly put in execution; and
in about three weeks I made a great progress in
learning their language; during which time the emperor frequently honored me with his visits, and
was pleased to assist my masters in teaching me.
We began already to converse together in some
sort: and the first words I learned were to express
my desire that he would please to give me my liberty; which I every day repeated on my knees. His
answer, as I could apprehend it, was, that this must
be a work of time, not to be thought on without
the advice of his council, and that first I must swear
a peace with him and his kingdom. However, that
I should be used with all kindness. And he ad-

vised me to acquire, by my patience and discreet behavior, the good opinion of himself and his subjects.

He desired I would not take it ill, if he gave orders to certain proper officers to search me; for probably I might carry about me several weapons, which must needs be dangerous things, if they answered the bulk of so prodigious a person. I said his majesty should be satisfied; for I was ready to strip myself, and turn up my pockets before him. This, I delivered part in words and part in signs.

He replied, that by the laws of the kingdom, I must be searched by two of his officers; that he knew this could not be done without my consent and assistance; that he had so good an opinion of my generosity and justice as to trust their persons in my hands; that whatever they took from me should be returned when I left the country, or paid for at the rate which I would set upon them.

I took up the two officers in my hands, put them first into my coat pockets, and then into every other pocket about me, except my two fobs,[7] and another secret pocket I had no mind should be searched, wherein I had some little necessaries that were of no consequence to any but myself. In one of my fobs there was a silver watch, and in the other a small quantity of gold in a purse.

These gentlemen, having pen, ink, and paper about them, made an exact inventory of everything they saw; and when they had done desired I would set them down, that they might deliver it to the

7. In England this word means not the ribbon or guard which hangs from a watch, but the small pocket in the waistband of the trousers, in which the watch is carried.

emperor. This inventory I afterwards translated into English, and is word for word as follows:

"*Imprimis*,[8] in the right coat pocket of the great man-mountain (for so I interpret the words *quinbus flestrin*), after the strictest search, we found only one great piece of coarse cloth, large enough to be a footcloth for your majesty's chief room of state.

"In the left pocket we saw a huge silver chest, with a cover of the same metal, which we, the searchers, were not able to lift. We desired it should be opened, and one of us, stepping into it, found himself up to the mid-leg in a sort of dust, some part whereof, flying up to our faces, set us both a-sneezing for several times together.

"In his right waistcoat pocket we found a prodigious bundle of white, thin substances, folded one over another, about the bigness of three men, tied with a strong cable, and marked with black figures, which we humbly conceive to be writings, every letter almost half as large as the palm of our hands.

"In the left there was a sort of engine, from the back of which were extended twenty long poles, resembling the palisadoes before your majesty's court; wherewith we conjecture the man-mountain combs his head; for we did not always trouble him with questions, because we found it a great difficulty to make him understand us.

"In the large pocket, on the right side of his middle cover (so I translate the word *ranfu-lo*, by which they meant my breeches), we saw a hollow pillar of iron, about the length of a man, fastened

8. *Imprimis* is a word from the Latin, and means *in the first place.*

to a strong piece of timber larger than the pillar; and upon one side of the pillar were huge pieces of iron sticking out, cut into strange figures, which we know not what to make of.

"In the left pocket, another engine of the same kind.

"In the smaller pocket, on the right side, were several round, flat pieces of white and red metal, of different bulk; some of the white, which seemed to be silver, were so large and heavy that my comrade and I could hardly lift them.

"In the left pocket were two black pillars irregularly shaped; we could not, without difficulty, reach the top of them, as we stood at the bottom of his pocket. One of them was covered and seemed all of a piece; but at the upper end of the other there appeared a white, round substance, about twice the bigness of our heads. Within each of these was enclosed a prodigious plate of steel; which, by our orders, we obliged him to show us, because we apprehended they might be dangerous engines. He took them out of their cases, and told us that, in his own country, his practice was to shave his beard with one of these, and to cut his meat with the other.

"There were two pockets which we could not enter; these he called his fobs; they were two large slits cut into the top of his middle cover, but squeezed close by the pressure of his belly. Out of the right fob hung a great silver chain, with a wonderful kind of engine at the bottom. We directed him to draw out whatever was at the end of that chain, which appeared to be a globe, half silver, and half of some transparent metal; for, on the transparent side, we saw certain strange figures circularly drawn, and thought we could touch them, till we found our fingers stopped by that lucid substance. He put this engine to our ears, which made an incessant noise like that of a water-mill: and we conjecture it is either some unknown animal, or the god that he worships; but we are more inclined to the latter opinion, because he assured us (if we understood him right, for he expressed himself very imperfectly), that he seldom did anything without consulting it. He called it his oracle, and said it pointed out the time for every action of his life.

"From the left fob he took out a net, almost large enough for a fisherman, but contrived to open and shut like a purse, and served him for the same use: we found therein several massy pieces of yellow metal, which, if they be real gold, must be of immense value.

"Having thus, in obedience to your majesty's commands, diligently searched all his pockets, we observed a girdle about his waist, made of the hide of some prodigious animal, from which, on the left side, hung a sword of the length of five men; and on the right, a bag or pouch divided into two cells, each cell capable of holding three of your majesty's subjects. In one of these cells were several globes or balls, of a most ponderous metal, about the bigness of our heads, and required a strong hand to lift them; the other cell contained a heap of certain black grains, but of no great bulk or weight, for we could hold above fifty of them in the palms of our hands.

"This is an exact inventory of what we found about the body of the man-mountain, who used us with great civility, and due respect to your majes-

GULLIVER AND THE PISTOL

ty's commission. Signed and sealed on the fourth
day of the eighty-ninth moon of your majesty's
auspicious reign.

"CLEFREN FRELOCK,   MARSI FRELOCK."

When this inventory was read over to the emperor he directed me, although in very gentle terms,
to deliver up the several particulars. He first
called for my scimitar, which I took out, scabbard
and all. In the meantime he ordered three thousand
of his choicest troops (who then attended him) to
surround me at a distance, with their bows and arrows just ready to discharge; but I did not observe
it, for mine eyes were wholly fixed upon his majesty. He then desired me to draw my scimitar,
which, although it had got some rust by the sea-
water, was in most parts exceeding bright. I did
so, and immediately all the troops gave a shout between terror and surprise: for the sun shone clear,
and the reflection dazzled their eyes, as I waved
the scimitar to and fro in my hand. His majesty,
who is a most magnanimous prince, was less daunted than I could expect: he ordered me to return it
into the scabbard, and cast it on the ground as gently as I could, about six foot from the end of my
chain.

The next thing he demanded was one of the hollow iron pillars: by which he meant my pocket pistols. I drew it out, and at his desire, as well as I
could, expressed to him the use of it; and charging
it only with powder, which, by the closeness of my
pouch, happened to escape wetting in the sea (an
inconvenience against which all prudent mariners
take special care to provide), I first cautioned the

emperor not to be afraid, and then I let it off in
the air. The astonishment here was much greater
than at the sight of my scimitar. Hundreds fell
down as if they had been struck dead; and even the
emperor, although he stood his ground, could not
recover himself in time. I delivered up both my

GULLIVER'S WATCH IS BORNE AWAY

pistols in the same manner as I had done my scimitar, and then my pouch of powder and bullets; beg-
ging him that the former might be kept from the
fire, for it would kindle with the smallest spark, and
blow up his imperial palace into the air.

I likewise delivered up my watch, which the emperor was very curious to see, and commanded two
of his tallest yeomen of the guards to bear it on a
pole upon their shoulders, as draymen in England
do a barrel of ale. He was amazed at the continual
noise it made, and the motion of the minute-hand,
which he could easily discern; for their sight is
much more acute than ours: and asked the opinions
of his learned men about him, which were various

and remote, as the reader may well imagine without my repeating; although, indeed, I could not perfectly understand them.

I then gave up my silver and copper money, my purse with nine large pieces of gold and some smaller ones; my knife and razor, my comb and silver snuffbox, my handkerchief, and journal-book. My scimitar, pistols, and pouch were conveyed in carriages to his majesty's stores; but the rest of my goods were returned to me.

I had, as I before observed, one private pocket, which escaped their search, wherein there was a pair of spectacles (which I sometimes use for the weakness of mine eyes), a pocket perspective,[9] and several other little conveniences; which being of no consequence to the emperor, I did not think myself bound in honor to discover, and I apprehended they might be lost or spoiled if I ventured them out of my possession.

About two or three days before I was set at liberty, there arrived an express to inform his majesty that some of his subjects, riding near the place where I was first taken up, had seen a great black substance lying on the ground, very oddly shaped, extending its edges round, as wide as his majesty's bedchamber, and rising up in the middle as high as a man; that it was no living creature, as they at first apprehended, for it lay on the grass without motion, and some of them had walked round it several times; that, by mounting upon each other's shoulders, they had got to the top, which was flat and even, and stamping upon it, they found it was hollow within; that they humbly conceived it might be

9. *Perspective* is an old name for telescope.

something belonging to the man-mountain; and, if his majesty pleased, they would undertake to bring it with only five horses.

I presently knew what they meant, and was glad at heart to receive this intelligence. It seems, upon my first reaching the shore after our shipwreck I was in such confusion that, before I came to the place where I went to sleep, my hat, which I had fastened with a string to my head while I was rowing, and which had stuck on all the time I was swimming, fell off after I came to land; the string, as I conjecture, breaking by some accident which I never observed, but thought my hat had been lost at sea. I entreated his imperial majesty to give orders it might be brought to me as soon as possible, describing to him the use and the nature of it: and the next day the wagoners arrived with it, but not in a very good condition; they had bored two holes in the brim, within an inch and a half of the edge, and fastened two hooks in the holes; these hooks were tied by a long cord to the harness, and thus my hat was dragged along for above half an English mile; but the ground in that country being extremely smooth and level, it received less damage than I expected.[10]

10. Can you see any reason for introducing this long account of the finding of Gulliver's hat? We have grown accustomed, in the pages past, to thinking of the Lilliputians in contrast with Gulliver, but does it not give us a new idea of their diminutive size to see them thus contrasted with Gulliver's hat?

III. *The War with Blefuscu*

I HAD sent so many memorials and petitions for my liberty, that his majesty at length mentioned the matter, first in the cabinet, and then in a full council; where it was opposed by none except Skyresh Bolgolam, who was pleased, without any provocation, to be my mortal enemy. But it was carried against him by the whole board, and confirmed by the emperor. That minister was *galbet,* or admiral of the realm, very much in his master's confidence, and a person well versed in affairs, but of a morose and sour complexion.[11] However, he was at length persuaded to comply; but prevailed that the articles and conditions upon which I should be set free, and to which I must swear, should be drawn up by himself.

These articles were brought to me by Skyresh Bolgolam in person, attended by two under-secretaries and several persons of distinction. After they were read, I was demanded to swear to the performance of them; first in the manner of my own country, and afterward in the method prescribed by their laws; which was, to hold my right foot in my left hand, to place the middle finger of my right hand on the crown of my head, and my thumb on the tip of my right ear.

I swore and subscribed to these articles with great cheerfulness and content, although some of them

11. *Complexion* here means *disposition.*

were not so honorable as I could have wished; which proceeded wholly from the malice of Skyresh Bolgolam, the high admiral; whereupon my chains were immediately unlocked, and I was at full liberty. The emperor himself in person did me the honor to be by at the whole ceremony. I made my acknowledgments by prostrating myself at his majesty's feet: but he commanded me to rise; and after many gracious expressions, which, to avoid the censure of vanity I shall not repeat, he added, that he hoped I should prove a useful servant, and well deserve all the favors he had already conferred upon me, or might do for the future.

One morning, about a fortnight after I had obtained my liberty, Reldresal, principal secretary (as they style him) of private affairs, came to my house, attended only by one servant. He ordered his coach to wait at a distance, and desired I would give him an hour's audience; which I readily consented to, on account of his quality and personal merits, as well as of the many good offices he had done me during my solicitations at court. I offered to lie down, that he might the more conveniently reach my ear; but he chose rather to let me hold him in my hand during our conversation. He began with compliments on my liberty; said he might pretend to some merit in it; but, however, added, that if it had not been for the present situation of things at court perhaps I might not have obtained it so soon.

"For," said he, "as flourishing a condition as we may appear to be in to foreigners, we labor under two mighty evils; a violent faction at home, and the danger of an invasion by a most potent enemy from abroad. As to the first, you are to understand that for above seventy moons[12] past there have been two struggling parties in this empire, under the names *Tramecksan* and *Slamecksan*, from the high and low heels of their shoes, by which they distinguish themselves. It is alleged, indeed, that the high heels are most agreeable to our ancient constitution; but, however this be, his majesty hath determined to make use of only low heels in the administration of the government, and all offices in the gift of the crown, as you cannot but observe; and particularly that his majesty's imperial heels are lower, at least by a *drurr,* than any of his court *(drurr* is a measure about the fourteenth part of an inch). The animosities between these two parties run so high that they will neither eat nor drink, nor talk with each other. We compute the *Tramecksan,* or high heels, to exceed us in number; but the power is wholly on our side. We apprehend his imperial highness, the heir to the crown, to have some tendency toward the high heels; at least we can plainly discover one of his heels higher than the other, which gives him a hobble in his gait.

"Now, in the midst of these intestine disquiets, we are threatened with an invasion from the island of Blefuscu, which is the other great empire of the universe, almost as large and powerful as this of his majesty. For, as to what we have heard you affirm, that there are other kingdoms and states in the world, inhabited by human creatures as large as yourself, our philosophers are in much doubt,

12. These little people measure time by *moons* or months, rather than by the longer division of years.

and would rather conjecture that you dropped from the moon or one of the stars; because it is certain that an hundred mortals of your bulk would in a short time destroy all the fruits and cattle of his majesty's dominions; besides, our histories of six thousand moons make no mention of any other regions than the two great empires of Lilliput and Blefuscu; which two mighty powers have, as I was going to tell you, been engaged in a most obstinate war for thirty-six moons past. It began upon the following occasion:

"It is allowed on all hands that the primitive way of breaking eggs, before we eat them, was upon the larger end; but his present majesty's grandfather, while he was a boy, going to eat an egg, and breaking it according to the ancient practice, happened to cut one of his fingers; whereupon, the emperor, his father, published an edict, commanding all his subjects, upon great penalties, to break the smaller end of their eggs. The people so highly resented this law that our histories tell us there have been six rebellions raised on that account; wherein one emperor lost his life, and another his crown.

"These civil commotions were constantly fomented by the monarchs of Blefuscu; and when they were quelled the exiles always fled for refuge to that empire. It is computed that eleven thousand persons have at several times suffered death rather than submit to break their eggs at the smaller end. Many hundred large volumes have been published upon this controversy; but the books of the Big-endians have been long forbidden, and the whole party rendered incapable by law of holding employments. During the course of these troubles, the emperors of Blefuscu did frequently expostulate by their ambassadors, accusing us of making a schism in religion by offending against a fundamental doctrine of our great prophet Lustrog, in the fifty-fourth chapter of the Blundecral (which is their Alcoran).[13] This, however, is thought to be a mere strain upon the text; for the words are these: that all true believers shall break their eggs at the convenient end. And which is the convenient end seems, in my humble opinion, to be left to every man's conscience, or at least in the power of the chief magistrate to determine.

"Now, the Big-endian exiles have found so much credit in the emperor of Blefuscu's court, and so much private assistance and encouragement from their party here at home, that a bloody war hath been carried on between the two empires for thirty-six moons with various success; during which time we have lost forty capital ships, and a much greater number of smaller vessels, together with thirty thousand of our best seamen and soldiers; and the damage received by the enemy is reckoned to be somewhat greater than ours. However, they have now equipped a numerous fleet, and are just preparing to make a descent upon us; and his imperial majesty, placing great confidence in your valor and strength, hath commanded me to lay this account of his affairs before you."

I desired the secretary to present my humble duty to the emperor; and to let him know that I thought it would not become me, who was a foreigner, to

13. The Alcoran, or, as it is more commonly called, the Koran. is the Mohammedan Bible.

interfere with parties; but I was ready, with the hazard of my life, to defend his person and state against all invaders.

The empire of Blefuscu is an island, situated to the northeast of Lilliput, from which it is parted only by a channel of eight hundred yards wide. I had not yet seen it, and upon this notice of an intended invasion I avoided appearing on that side of the coast, for fear of being discovered by some of the enemy's ships, who had received no intelligence of me; all intercourse between the two empires having been strictly forbidden during the war, upon pain of death. I communicated to his majesty a project I had formed, of seizing the enemy's whole fleet; which, as our scouts assured us, lay at anchor in the harbor, ready to sail with the first fair wind. I consulted the most experienced seamen upon the depth of the channel, which they had often plumbed; who told me that in the middle, at high-water, it was seventy *glumgluffs* deep, which is about six foot of European measure; and the rest of it fifty *glumgluffs* at most.

I walked toward the northeast coast, over against Blefuscu, and, lying down behind a hillock, took out my small pocket perspective glass, and viewed the enemy's fleet at anchor, consisting of about fifty men-of-war, and a great number of transports: I then came back to my house, and gave order (for which I had a warrant) for a great quantity of the strongest cable and bars of iron. The cable was about as thick as packthread, and the bars of the length and size of a knitting-needle. I trebled the cable to make it stronger, and for the same reason I twisted three of the iron bars together, bending the extremities into a hook. Having thus fixed fifty hooks to as many cables, I went back to the northeast coast, and, putting off my coat, shoes, and stockings, walked into the sea, in my leathern jerkin, about half an hour before high-water.

I waded with what haste I could, and swam in the middle, about thirty yards, till I felt ground. I arrived at the fleet in less than half an hour. The enemy was so frighted when they saw me that they leaped out of their ships, and swam to shore, where there could not be fewer than thirty thousand souls: I then took my tackling, and, fastening a hook to the hole at the prow of each, I tied all the cords together at the end. While I was thus employed the enemy discharged several thousand arrows, many of which stuck in my hands and face; and, besides the excessive smart, gave me much disturbance in my work. My greatest apprehension was for mine eyes, which I should have infallibly lost, if I had not suddenly thought of an expedient. I kept, among other little necessaries, a pair of spectacles in a private pocket, which, as I observed before, had escaped the emperor's searchers. These I took out, and fastened as strongly as I could upon my nose, and, thus armed, went on boldly with my work, in spite of the enemy's arrows, many of which struck against the glasses of my spectacles, but without any other effect further than a little to discompose them.

I had now fastened all the hooks, and, taking the knot in my hand, began to pull; but not a ship would stir, for they were all too fast held by their anchors, so that the bold part of my enterprise remained. I therefore let go the cord, and, leaving

the hooks fixed to the ships, I resolutely cut with
my knife the cables that fastened the anchors, receiving about two hundred shots in my face and
hands; then I took up the knotted end of the cables,
to which my hooks were tied, and with great ease
drew fifty of the enemy's largest men-of-war after
me.

The Blefuscudians, who had not the least imagination of what I intended, were at first confounded
with astonishment. They had seen me cut the cables, and thought my design was only to let the ships
run adrift, or fall foul on each other; but when
they perceived the whole fleet moving in order, and
saw me pulling at the end, they set up such a scream
of grief and despair that it is almost impossible to
describe or conceive. When I had got out of danger I stopped a while to pick out the arrows that
stuck in my hands and face; and rubbed on some
of the ointment that was given me at my first arrival, as I have formerly mentioned. I then took
off my spectacles, and, waiting about an hour, till
the tide was a little fallen, I waded through the middle with my cargo, and arrived safe at the royal
port of Lilliput.

The emperor and his whole court stood on the
shore, expecting the issue of this great adventure.
They saw the ships move forward in a large half-
moon, but could not discern me, who was up to my
breast in water. When I advanced to the middle
of the channel they were yet more in pain, because
I was under water to my neck. The emperor concluded me to be drowned, and that the enemy's fleet
was approaching in a hostile manner: but he was
soon eased of his fears; for, the channel growing

GULLIVER TAKES THE ENEMY'S FLEET

shallower every step I made, I came in a short time within hearing, and, holding up the end of the cable by which the fleet was fastened, I cried in a loud voice, "Long live the most puissant Emperor of Lilliput!" This great prince received me at my landing with all possible encomiums, and created me a *nardac* upon the spot, which is the highest title of honor among them.

His majesty desired I would take some other opportunity of bringing all the rest of the enemy's ships into his ports. And so unmeasurable is the ambition of princes, that he seemed to think of nothing else than reducing the whole empire of Blefuscu into a province, and governing it by a viceroy; of destroying the Big-endian exiles, and compelling that people to break the smaller end of their eggs, by which he would remain the sole monarch of the whole world. But I endeavored to divert him from this design, by many arguments drawn from the topics of policy as well as justice; and I plainly protested that I would never be an instrument of bringing a free and brave people into slavery. And, when the matter was debated in council, the wisest part of the ministry were of my opinion.

This open, bold declaration of mine was so opposite to the schemes and politics of his imperial majesty that he could never forgive it. He mentioned it in a very artful manner at council, where I was told that some of the wisest appeared at least, by their silence, to be of my opinion; but others, who were my secret enemies, could not forbear some expressions which, by a side-wind, reflected on me. And from this time began an intrigue between his majesty and a junto of ministers, maliciously bent against me, which broke out in less than two months, and had like to have ended in my utter destruction. Of so little weight are the greatest services to princes when put into the balance with a refusal to gratify their passions.

About three weeks after this exploit there arrived a solemn embassy from Blefuscu, with humble offers of a peace; which was soon concluded, upon conditions very advantageous to our emperor, wherewith I shall not trouble the reader.

IV. The Escape and the Return

EFORE I proceed to give an account of my leaving this kingdom, it may be proper to inform the reader of a private intrigue which had been for two months forming against me.

When I was just preparing to pay my attendance on the emperor of Blefuscu, a considerable person at court (to whom I had been very serviceable at a time when he lay under the highest displeasure of his imperial majesty) came to my house very privately at night, in a close chair, and, without sending his name, desired admittance. The chairmen were dismissed; I put the chair, with his lordship in it, into my coat pocket; and giving orders to a trusty servant to say I was indisposed and gone to sleep, I fastened the door of my house, placed the chair on the table, according to my usual custom, and sate down by it. After the common salutations were over, observing his lordship's countenance full of concern, and inquiring into the reason, he desired I would hear

him with patience, in a matter that highly concerned my honor and my life. His speech was to
the following effect, for I took notes of it as soon
as he left me:

"You are to know," said he, "that several com-
mittees of council have been lately called, in the
most private manner, on your account; and it is
but two days since his majesty came to a full
resolution.

"You are very sensible that Skyresh Bolgolam
(*galbet,* or high admiral) hath been your mortal
enemy almost ever since your arrival. His original
reasons I know not; but his hatred is much increased since your great success against Blefuscu,
by which his glory as admiral is obscured. This
lord, in conjunction with Flimnap the high treas-
urer, Limtoc the general, Lalcon the chamberlain,
and Balmuff the grand justiciary have prepared
articles of impeachment against you, for treason
and other capital crimes.

"In three days your friend the secretary will be
directed to come to your house, and read before
you the articles of impeachment; and then to signify the great lenity and favor of his majesty and
council, whereby you are only condemned to the
loss of your eyes, which his majesty doth not question you will gratefully and humbly submit to; and
twenty of his majesty's surgeons will attend in
order to see the operation well performed, by dis-
charging very sharp-pointed arrows into the balls
of your eyes, as you lie on the ground.

"I leave to your prudence what measures you
will take; and, to avoid suspicion, I must immediately return in as private a manner as I came."

His lordship did so; and I remained alone, under many doubts and perplexities of mind.

I took the opportunity, before the three days were elapsed, to send a letter to my friend the secretary, signifying my resolution of setting out that morning for Blefuscu, pursuant to the leave I had got; and, without waiting for an answer, I went to that side of the island where our fleet lay. I seized a large man-of-war, tied a cable to the prow, and, lifting up the anchors, I stripped myself, put my clothes (together with my coverlet, which I brought under my arm) into the vessel, and, drawing it after me, between wading and swimming, arrived at the royal port of Blefuscu, where the people had long expected me: they lent me two guides to direct me to the capital city, which is of the same name. I held them in my hands till I came within two hundred yards of the gate, and desired them to signify my arrival to one of the secretaries, and let him know I there waited his majesty's command. I had an answer in about an hour, that his majesty, attended by the royal family, and great officers of the court, was coming out to receive me. I advanced a hundred yards. The emperor and his train alighted from their horses; the empress and ladies from their coaches; and I did not perceive they were in any fright or concern. I lay on the ground to kiss his majesty's and the empress' hand. I told his majesty that I was come, according to my promise, and with the license of the emperor my master, to have the honor of seeing so mighty a monarch, and to offer him any service in my power, consistent with my duty to my own prince; not mentioning a word of my disgrace, be-

cause I had hitherto no regular information of it,
and might suppose myself wholly ignorant of any
such design; neither could I reasonably conceive
that the emperor would discover the secret while
I was out of his power.

Three days after my arrival, walking out of
curiosity to the northeast coast of the island, I
observed, about half a league off in the sea, somewhat that looked like a boat overturned. I pulled
off my shoes and stockings, and, wading two or
three hundred yards, I found the object to approach nearer by force of the tide; and then plainly
saw it to be a real boat, which I supposed might
by some tempest have been driven from a ship:
whereupon I returned immediately toward the city,
and desired his imperial majesty to lend me twenty
of the tallest vessels he had left, after the loss of his
fleet, and three thousand seamen under the command of the vice-admiral.

This fleet sailed round, while I went back the
shortest way to the coast, where I first discovered
the boat. I found the tide had driven it still nearer.
The seamen were all provided with cordage, which
I had beforehand twisted to a sufficient strength.
When the ships came up, I stripped myself, and
waded till I came within an hundred yards of the
boat, after which I was forced to swim till I got up
to it. The seamen threw me the end of the cord,
which I fastened to a hole in the fore part of the
boat, and the other end to a man-of-war, but I
found all my labor to little purpose; for, being out
of my depth, I was not able to work. In this necessity, I was forced to swim behind, and push the boat
forward, as often as I could, with one of my hands;

and the tide favoring me, I advanced so far that I
could just hold up my chin and feel the ground. I
rested two or three minutes, and then gave the boat

GULLIVER BRINGS IN THE DRIFTING BOAT

another shove, and so on, till the sea was no higher
than my armpits, and now, the most laborious part
being over, I took out my other cables, which were

stowed in one of the ships, and fastened them first
to the boat, and then to nine of the vessels which
attended me; the wind being favorable, the seamen
towed and I shoved, till we arrived within forty
yards of the shore; and waiting till the tide was out,
I got dry to the boat, and, by the assistance of two
thousand men, with ropes and engines, I made a
shift to turn it on its bottom, and found it was but
little damaged.

I shall not trouble the reader with the difficulties
I was under, by the help of certain paddles, which
cost me ten days' making, to get my boat to the
royal port of Blefuscu, where a mighty concourse
of people appeared upon my arrival, full of wonder
at the sight of so prodigious a vessel. I told the
emperor that my good fortune had thrown this boat
in my way to carry me some place from whence I
might return into my native country; and begged
his majesty's orders for getting materials to fit it
up, together with his license to depart; which, after
some kind expostulations, he was pleased to grant.

Five hundred workmen were employed to make
two sails to my boat, according to my directions, by
quilting thirteen folds of their strongest linen together. I was at the pains of making ropes and
cables by twisting ten, twenty or thirty of the
thickest and strongest of theirs. A great stone that
I happened to find served me for an anchor. I had
the tallow of three hundred cows for greasing my
boat, and other uses. I was at incredible pains in
cutting down some of the largest timber-trees for
oars and masts; wherein I was much assisted by his
majesty's ship carpenters, who helped me in smooth-
ing them after I had done the rough work.

In about a month, when all was prepared, I sent to receive his majesty's commands, and to take my leave. The emperor and royal family came out of the palace: I lay on my face to kiss his hand, which he very graciously gave me: so did the empress and young princes of the blood. His majesty presented me with fifty purses of two hundred *sprugs* apiece, together with his picture at full length, which I put immediately into one of my gloves, to keep it from being hurt. The ceremonies at my departure were too many to trouble the reader with at this time.

I stored the boat with the carcasses of an hundred oxen and three hundred sheep, with bread and drink proportionable, and as much meat ready dressed as four hundred cooks could provide. I took with me six cows and two bulls alive, with as many ewes and rams, intending to carry them into my own country, and propagate the breed. And, to feed them on board, I had a good bundle of hay and a bag of corn. I would gladly have taken a dozen of the natives, but this was a thing which the emperor would by no means permit; and, besides a diligent search into my pockets, his majesty engaged my honor not to carry away any of his subjects, although with their own consent and desire.

Having thus prepared all things as well as I was able, I set sail on the 24th day of September, 1701, at six in the morning; and when I had gone about four leagues to the northward, the wind being at southeast, at six in the evening I descried a small island, about half a league to the northwest. I advanced forward, and cast anchor on the lee-side of the island, which seemed to be uninhabited. I then took some refreshment, and went to my rest. I slept well, and I conjecture at least six hours, for I found the day broke in two hours after I awaked. It was a clear night. I eat my breakfast before the sun was up; and, heaving anchor, the wind being favorable, I steered the same course that I had done the day before, wherein I was directed by my pocket compass. My intention was to reach, if possible, one of those islands which I had reason to believe lay to the northeast of Van Diemen's Land.[14]

I discovered nothing all that day; but upon the next, about three in the afternoon, when I had, by my computation, made twenty-four leagues from Blefuscu, I described a sail steering to the southeast; my course was due east. I hailed her, but could get no answer; yet I found I gained upon her, for the wind slackened. I made all the sail I could, and in half an hour she spied me, then hung out her ancient,[15] and discharged a gun. It is not easy to express the joy I was in, upon the unexpected hope of once more seeing my beloved country, and the dear pledges I left in it. The ship slackened her sails, and I came up with her between five and six in the evening, September 26; but my heart leaped within me to see her English colors. I put my cows and sheep into my coat pockets, and got on board with all my little cargo of provisions.

The vessel was an English merchantman, returning from Japan by the North and South Seas; the captain, Mr. John Biddel of Deptford, a very civil man and an excellent sailor. We were now in the latitude of thirty degrees south; there were about

14. Australia is a short distance from Tasmania, or Van Diemen's Land. There are no islands to the northeast for a long distance.

15. *Ancient* is an old word for *ensign*.

fifty men in the ship; and I met an old comrade of mine, one Peter Williams, who gave me a good character to the captain. This gentleman treated me with kindness, and desired I would let him know what place I came from last, and whither I was bound; which I did in few words, but he thought I was raving, and that the dangers I underwent had disturbed my head; whereupon I took my black cattle and sheep out of my pocket, which, after great astonishment, clearly convinced him of my veracity. I then showed him the gold given me by the Emperor of Blefuscu, together with his majesty's picture at full length, and some other rarities of that country. I gave him two purses of two hundred *sprugs* each, and promised, when we arrived in England, to make him a present of a cow and a sheep.

I shall not trouble the reader with a particular account of this voyage, which was very prosperous for the most part. We arrived in the Downs on the 13th of April, 1702. I had only one misfortune, that the rats on board carried away one of my sheep; I found her bones in a hole, picked clean from the flesh. The rest of my cattle I got safe on shore, and set them a-grazing in a bowling green at Greenwich, where the fineness of the grass made them feed very heartily, though I had always feared the contrary; neither could I possibly have preserved them in so long a voyage, if the captain had not allowed me some of his best biscuit, which, rubbed to powder and mingled with water, was their constant food. The short time I continued in England, I made a considerable profit by showing my cattle to many persons of quality and others; and

before I began my second voyage, I sold them for
six hundred pounds. Since my last return I find
the breed is considerably increased, especially the
sheep, which I hope will prove much to the advantage of the woolen manufacture, by the fineness
of the fleeces.

ADVENTURES IN BROBDINGNAG

I. Among the Giants

HAVING been condemned, by nature
and fortune, to an active and restless
life, in two months after my return I
again left my native country, and took
shipping in the Downs, on the 20th
day of June, 1702, in the *Adventure,*
Captain John Nicholas, a Cornish-
man, commander, bound for Surat.

We had a very prosperous gale till we arrived
at the Cape of Good Hope, where we landed for
fresh water; but discovering a leak, we unshipped
our goods and wintered there; for the captain falling sick of an ague, we could not leave the Cape
till the end of March. We then set sail, and had a
good voyage till we passed the Straits of Madagas-
car; but having got northward of that island, and
to about five degrees south latitude, the winds,
which in those seas are observed to blow a constant
equal gale between the north and west, from the
beginning of December to the beginning of May, on
the 19th of April began to blow with much greater
violence, and more westerly than usual, continuing

so for twenty days together; during which time we were driven a little to the east of the Molucca Islands,[16] and about three degrees northward of the line, as our captain found by an observation he took the 2d of May, at which time the wind ceased, and it was a perfect calm; whereat I was not a little rejoiced. But he, being a man well experienced in the navigation of those seas, bid us all prepare against a storm, which accordingly happened the day following; for a southern wind, called the Southern monsoon,[17] began to set in, and soon it was a very fierce storm.

During this storm, which was followed by a strong wind west-southwest, we were carried, by my computation, about five hundred leagues to the east, so that the oldest sailor on board could not tell in what part of the world we were. Our provisions held out well, our ship was staunch, and our crew all in good health; but we lay in the utmost distress for water. We thought it best to hold on the same course, rather than turn more northerly, which might have brought us to the northwest parts of Great Tartary, and into the Frozen Sea.

On the 16th day of June, 1703, a boy on the topmast discovered land. On the 17th we came in full view of a great island, or continent (for we knew not whether), on the south side whereof was a small neck of land jutting out into the sea, and a creek too shallow to hold a ship of above one hundred tons. We cast anchor within a league of this creek,

16. They could not really have been driven to the east of the Molucca Islands without passing Sumatra, Java, Borneo or other islands.

17. *Monsoons* are winds that blow part of the year in one direction, and the rest of the year in the opposite direction.

and our captain sent a dozen of his men well armed in the longboat, with vessels for water, if any could be found. I desired his leave to go with them, that I might see the country, and make what discoveries I could.

When we came to land we saw no river or spring, nor any sign of inhabitants. Our men therefore wandered on the shore to find out some fresh water near the sea, and I walked alone about a mile on the other side, where I observed the country all barren and rocky. I now began to be weary, and, seeing nothing to entertain my curiosity, I returned gently down toward the creek; and the sea being full in my view, I saw our men already got into the boat, and rowing for life to the ship.

I was going to halloo after them, although it had been to little purpose, when I observed a huge creature walking after them in the sea, as fast as he could; he waded not much deeper than his knees, and took prodigious strides; but our men had got the start of him half a league, and the sea thereabouts being full of sharp-pointed rocks, the monster was not able to overtake the boat. This I was afterward told, for I durst not stay to see the issue of that adventure; but ran as fast as I could the way I first went, and then climbed up a steep hill, which gave me some prospect of the country. I found it fully cultivated; but that which first surprised me was the length of the grass, which in those grounds that seemed to be kept for hay was above twenty foot high.

I fell into a highroad, for so I took it to be, though it served to the inhabitants only as a footpath through a field of barley. Here I walked on for some time, but could see little on either side, it being now near harvest, and the corn rising at least forty foot. I was an hour walking to the end of this field, which was fenced in with a hedge of at least one hundred and twenty foot high, and the trees so lofty that I could make no computation of their altitude. There was a stile to pass from this field into the next. It had four steps, and a stone to cross over when you came to the uppermost. It was impossible for me to climb this stile, because every step was six foot high, and the upper stone above twenty.

I was endeavoring to find some gap in the hedge, when I discovered one of the inhabitants in the next field, advancing toward the stile, of the same size with him whom I saw in the sea pursuing our boat. He appeared as tall as an ordinary spire steeple, and took about ten yards at every stride, as near as I could guess. I was struck with the utmost fear and astonishment, and ran to hide myself in the corn, from whence I saw him at the top of the stile, looking back into the next field on the right hand, and heard him call in a voice many degrees louder than a speaking-trumpet; but the noise was so high in the air that at first I certainly thought it was thunder. Whereupon seven monsters, like himself, came toward him with reaping hooks in their hands, each hook about the largeness of six scythes. These people were not so well clad as the first, whose servants or laborers they seemed to be; for, upon some words he spoke, they went to reap the corn in the field where I lay.

I kept from them at as great a distance as I could, but was forced to move with extreme difficulty, for the stalks of the corn were sometimes not above a foot distant, so that I could hardly squeeze my body betwixt them. However, I made a shift to go forward till I came to a part of the field where the corn had been laid by the rain and wind. Here it was impossible for me to advance a step; for the stalks were so interwoven that I could not creep through, and the beards of the fallen ears so strong and pointed that they pierced through my clothes into my flesh. At the same time I heard the reapers not above an hundred yards behind me. Being quite dispirited with toil, and wholly overcome by grief and despair, I lay down between two ridges, and heartily wished I might there end my days. I bemoaned my desolate widow and fatherless children. I lamented my own folly and willfulness in attempting a second voyage, against the advice of all my friends and relations.

In this terrible agitation of mind I could not forbear thinking of Lilliput, whose inhabitants looked upon me as the greatest prodigy that ever appeared in the world; where I was able to draw an imperial fleet in my hand, and perform those other actions which will be recorded forever in the chronicles of that empire, while posterity shall hardly believe them, although attested by millions. I reflected what a mortification it must prove to me to appear as inconsiderable in this nation as one single Lilliputian would be among us. But this I conceived was to be the least of my misfortunes; for, as human creatures are observed to be more savage and cruel in proportion to their bulk, what could I expect but to be a morsel in the mouth of the first among these enormous barbarians that

should happen to seize me? Undoubtedly philosophers are in the right when they tell us that nothing
is great or little otherwise than by comparison. It
might have pleased fortune to let the Lilliputians
find some nation, where the people were as diminutive with respect to them as they were to me. And
who knows but that even this prodigious race of
mortals might be equally overmatched in some
distant part of the world, whereof we have yet no
discovery.

Scared and confounded as I was, I could not forbear going on with these reflections, when one of
the reapers, approaching within ten yards of the
ridge where I lay, made me apprehend that with
the next step I should be squashed to death under
his foot, or cut in two with his reaping-hook. And
therefore when he was again about to move, I
screamed as loud as fear could make me; whereupon the huge creature trod short, and, looking
round about under him for some time, at last espied
me as I lay on the ground. He considered awhile,
with the caution of one who endeavors to lay hold
on a small dangerous animal in such a manner that
it may not be able either to scratch or to bite him,
as I myself have sometimes done with a weasel in
England.

At length he ventured to take me up behind, by
the middle, between his forefinger and thumb, and
brought me within three yards of his eyes, that he
might behold my shape more perfectly. I guessed
his meaning, and my good fortune gave me so much
presence of mind that I resolved not to struggle in
the least as he held me in the air above sixty foot
from the ground, although he grievously pinched

my sides, for fear I should slip through his fingers.
All I ventured was to raise mine eyes toward the
sun, and place my hands together in a supplicating
posture, and to speak some words in an humble,
melancholy tone, suitable to the condition I then
was in; for I apprehended every moment that he
would dash me against the ground, as we usually
do any little hateful animal which we have a mind
to destroy. But my good star would have it that
he appeared pleased with my voice and gestures,
and began to look upon me as a curiosity, much
wondering to hear me pronounce articulate words,
although he could not understand them. In the
meantime I was not able to forbear groaning and
shedding tears, and turning my head toward my
sides; letting him know as well as I could how
cruelly I was hurt by the pressure of his thumb
and finger. He seemed to apprehend my meaning;
for, lifting up the lappet of his coat, he put me
gently into it, and immediately ran along with me
to his master, who was a substantial farmer, and
the same person I had first seen in the field.

The farmer having (as I supposed by their talk)
received such an account of me as his servant could
give him, took a piece of a small straw, about the
size of a walking-staff, and therewith lifted up the
lappets of my coat; which, it seems, he thought to
be some kind of covering that nature had given me.
He blew my hairs aside to take a better view of my
face. He called his hinds about him, and asked
them, as I afterward learned, whether they had ever
seen in the fields any little creature that resembled
me. He then placed me softly on the ground upon
all four, but I got immediately up, and walked

slowly backward and forward, to let those people
see I had no intent to run away.

They all sate down in a circle about me, the
better to observe my motions. I pulled off my hat,
and made a low bow toward the farmer. I fell on
my knees, and lifted up my hands and eyes, and
spoke several words as loud as I could; I took a
purse of gold out of my pocket, and humbly presented it to him. He received it on the palm of his
hand, then applied it close to his eye to see what
it was, and afterward turned it several times with
the point of a pin (which he took out of his sleeve),
but could make nothing of it. Whereupon I made
a sign that he should place his hand on the ground.
I then took the purse, and opening it, poured all
the gold into his palm. There were six Spanish
pieces of four pistoles[18] each, besides twenty or
thirty smaller coins. I saw him wet the tip of his
little finger upon his tongue, and take up one of my
largest pieces, and then another; but he seemed to
be wholly ignorant what they were. He made me
a sign to put them again into my purse, and the
purse again into my pocket, which, after offering
to him several times, I thought it best to do.

The farmer, by this time, was convinced I must
be a rational creature. He spoke often to me; but
the sound of his voice pierced my ears like that of a
water-mill, yet his words were articulate enough.
I answered as loud as I could in several languages,
and he often laid his ear within two yards of me;
but all in vain, for we were wholly unintelligible to
each other. He then sent his servants to their work,
and taking his handkerchief out of his pocket, he

18. A *pistole* is equivalent to about four dollars.

doubled, and spread it on his left hand, which he placed flat on the ground, with the palm upward, making me a sign to step into it, as I could easily do, for it was not above a foot in thickness. I thought it my part to obey; and for fear of falling laid myself at full length upon the handkerchief, with the remainder of which he lapped me up to the head for further security, and in this manner carried me home to his house.

There he called his wife, and showed me to her; but she screamed and ran back, as women in England do at the sight of a toad or a spider. However, when she had awhile seen my behavior, and how well I observed the signs her husband made, she was soon reconciled, and by degrees grew extremely tender of me.

II.   Adventures in the Farmer's Home

I T was about twelve at noon, and a servant brought in dinner. It was only one substantial dish of meat (fit for the plain condition of an husbandman), in a dish of about twenty-four foot diameter. The company were, the farmer and his wife, three children, and an old grandmother. When they were sat down, the farmer placed me at some distance from him on the table, which was thirty foot high from the floor. I was in a terrible fright, and kept as far as I could from the edge, for fear of falling. The wife minced a bit of meat, then crumbled some bread on a trencher, and placed it before me. I made her a low bow, took out my knife and fork, and fell to eat, which gave them exceeding delight. The mistress sent her maid for a small dram-cup, which held about two gallons, and filled it with drink; I took up the vessel with much difficulty in both hands, and in a most respectful manner drank to her ladyship's health, expressing the words as loud as I could in English, which made the company laugh so heartily, that I was almost deafened with the noise. This liquor tasted like a small cider, and was not unpleasant. Then the master made me a sign to come to his trencher side: but as I walked on the table, being in great surprise all the time, as the indulgent reader will easily conceive and excuse, I happened to stumble against a crust, and fell flat on my face, but received no hurt. I got up immediately, and observing the good people to be in much concern, I took my hat (which I held under my arm out of good manners), and waving it over my head, made three huzzas, to show I had got no mischief by my fall.

But advancing forward toward my master (as I shall henceforth call him), his youngest son, who sate next him, an arch boy of about ten years old, took me up by the legs, and held me so high in the air that I trembled in every limb; but his father snatched me from him, and at the same time gave him such a box on the left ear as would have felled an European troop of horse to the earth, ordering him to be taken from the table. But, being afraid the boy might owe me a spite, and well remembering how mischievous all children among us naturally are to sparrows, rabbits, young kittens, and puppy-dogs, I fell on my knees, and, pointing to the boy, made my master to understand, as well as I could, that I desired his son might be pardoned. The father complied, and the lad took his seat again, whereupon I went to him, and kissed his hand, which my master took, and made him stroke me gently with it.

In the midst of dinner my mistress' favorite cat leaped into her lap. I heard a noise behind me like that of a dozen stocking-weavers at work; and turning my head I found it proceeded from the purring of this animal, who seemed to be three times larger than an ox, as I computed by the view of her head and one of her paws, while her mistress was feeding and stroking her. The fierceness of this creature's countenance altogether discomposed me though I stood at the further end of the table, above fifty foot off; and although my mistress held her fast, for fear she might give a spring, and seize me in her talons. But it happened there was no danger; for the cat took not the least notice of me when my master placed me within three yards of her. And, as I have been always told, and found true by experience in my travels, that flying or discovering fear before a fierce animal is a certain way to make it pursue or attack you, so I resolved, in this dangerous juncture, to show no manner of concern. I walked with intrepidity five or six times before the very head of the cat, and came within half a yard of her; whereupon she draw herself back, as if she were more afraid of me.

I had less apprehension concerning the dogs, whereof three or four came into the room as it is usual in farmers' houses; one of which was a mastiff, equal in bulk to four elephants, and a greyhound, somewhat taller than the mastiff, but not so large.

When dinner was almost done the nurse came in with a child of a year old in her arms, who immediately spied me, and began a squall that you might have heard from London Bridge to Chelsea, after the usual oratory of infants, to get me for a plaything.

The mother, out of pure indulgence, took me up, and put me toward the child, who presently seized me by the middle and got my head in his mouth, where I roared so loud that the urchin was frighted, and let me drop, and I should infallibly have broke my neck, if the mother had not held her apron under me. The nurse, to quiet her babe, made use of a rattle, which was a kind of hollow vessel filled with great stones, and fastened by a cable to the child's waist.

The vast creatures are not deformed: for I must do them justice to say they are a comely race of people; and particularly the features of my master's countenance, although he was but a farmer, when I beheld him from the height of sixty foot, appeared very well-proportioned.

When dinner was done my master went out to his laborers, and, as I could discover by his voice and gesture, gave his wife a strict charge to take care of me. I was very much tired, and disposed to sleep, which my mistress perceiving she put me on her own bed, and covered me with a clean white handkerchief, but larger and coarser than the mainsail of a man-of-war.

I slept about two hours, and dreamed I was at home with my wife and children, which aggravated my sorrows when I awaked and found myself alone in a vast room, between two and three hundred foot wide, and above two hundred high, lying in a bed twenty yards wide. My mistress was gone about her household affairs, and had locked me in. The bed was eight yards from the floor. I wished to get down, but durst not presume to call; and if I had it would have been in vain, with such a voice as

THE BABY SEIZED GULLIVER

mine, at so great a distance as from the room where I lay to the kitchen where the family kept.

While I was under these circumstances two rats crept up the curtains, and ran smelling backward and forward on the bed. One of them came up almost to my face, whereupon I rose in a fright, and drew out my hanger[19] to defend myself. These

19. *Hanger* is the name given to a kind of short, broad sword which was formerly carried.

horrible animals had the boldness to attack me on both sides, and one of them held his forefeet at my collar; but I had the good fortune to rip up his belly before he could do me any mischief. He fell down at my feet; and the other, seeing the fate of his comrade, made his escape, but not without one good wound on the back, which I gave him as he fled, and made the blood run trickling from him. After this exploit I walked gently to and fro on the bed, to recover my breath and loss of spirits. These creatures were of the size of a large mastiff, but infinitely more nimble and fierce; so that, if I had taken off my belt before I went to sleep, I must have infallibly been torn to pieces and devoured. I measured the tail of the dead rat, and found it to be two yards long, wanting an inch; but it went against my stomach to drag the carcass off the bed, where it lay still bleeding; I observed it had yet some life, but with a strong slash across the neck I thoroughly despatched it.[20]

Soon after my mistress came into the room, who, seeing me all bloody, ran and took me up in her hand. I pointed to the dead rat, smiling, and making other signs to show I was not hurt; whereat she was extremely rejoiced, calling the maid to take up the dead rat with a pair of tongs, and throw it out of the window. Then she set me on a table, where I showed her my hanger all bloody, and wiping it on the lappet of my coat, returned it to the scabbard.

20. Gulliver told how, as he was returning from Lilliput, an ordinary rat carried off a Lilliputian sheep; here he tells of rats large enough to kill and eat a man. It is by such violent contrasts as these that Swift impresses on us the difference in size between the Lilliputians and the giants.

I hope the gentle reader will excuse me for dwelling on these and the like particulars, which, however insignificant they may appear to groveling vulgar minds, yet will certainly help a philosopher to enlarge his thoughts and imagination, and apply them to the benefit of public as well as private life, which was my sole design in presenting this and other accounts of my travels to the world; wherein I have been chiefly studious of truth, without affecting any ornaments of learning or of style. But the whole scene of this voyage made so strong an impression on my mind, and is so deeply fixed in my memory, that, in committing it to paper, I did not omit one material circumstance: however, upon a strict review, I blotted out several passages of less moment, which were in my first copy, for fear of being censured as tedious and trifling, whereof travelers are often, perhaps not without justice, accused.

My mistress had a daughter of nine years old, a child of towardly parts for her age, very dexterous at her needle, and skillful in dressing her baby.[21] Her mother and she contrived to fit up the baby's cradle for me against night; the cradle was put into a small drawer of a cabinet, and the drawer placed upon a hanging shelf for fear of the rats. This was my bed all the time I stayed with those people, though made more convenient by degrees, as I began to learn their language, and make my wants known. She made me seven shirts and some other linen, of as fine cloth as could be got, which indeed was coarser than sackcloth; and these she constantly washed for me with her own hands. She was like-

21. That is, her doll.

wise my schoolmistress, to teach me the language;
when I pointed to anything she told me the name
of it in her own tongue, so that in a few days I was
able to call for whatever I had a mind to. She was
very good-natured, and not above forty foot high,
being little for her age. I called her my *Glumdalclitch*, or little nurse, and I should be guilty of great
ingratitude if I omitted this honorable mention of
her care and affection toward me, which I heartily
wish it lay in my power to requite as she deserves.

A most ingenious artist, according to my directions, in three weeks finished for me a wooden
chamber, of sixteen foot square, and twelve high,
with sash windows, a door, and two closets, like a
London bedchamber. The board that made the
ceiling was to be lifted up and down by two hinges,
to put in a bed, ready furnished by her majesty's
upholsterer, which Glumdalclitch took out every
day to air, made it with her own hands, and letting
it down at night, locked up the roof over me. A
workman, who was famous for little curiosities,
undertook to make me two chairs, with backs and
frames, of a substance not unlike ivory, and two
tables, with a cabinet to put my things in. The
room was quilted on all sides, as well as the floor
and the ceiling, to prevent any accident from the
carelessness of those who carried me, and to break
the force of a jolt when I went in a coach. I desired
a lock for my door, to prevent rats and mice from
coming in. The smith made the smallest that ever
was seen among them, for I have known a larger at
the gate of a gentleman's house in England. I made
a shift to keep the key in a pocket of my own,
fearing Glumdalclitch might lose it.

III.   *Adventures at the Royal Court*

I SHOULD have lived happily enough in that country if my littleness had not exposed me to several ridiculous and troublesome accidents; some of which I shall venture to relate. Glumdalclitch often carried me into the gardens of the court in a smaller box, and would sometimes take me out of it, and hold me in her hand, or set me down to walk. I remember the queen's dwarf followed us one day into those gardens, and my nurse having set me down, he and I being close together, near some dwarf apple trees, I must needs show my wit, by a silly allusion between him and the trees, which happens to hold in their language as it does in ours. Whereupon, the malicious rogue, watching his opportunity when I was walking under one of them, shook it directly over my head, by which a dozen apples, each of them near as large as a Bristol barrel, came tumbling about my ears; one of them hit me on the back as I chanced to stoop, and knocked me down flat on my face; but I received no other hurt, and the dwarf was pardoned at my desire, because I had given the provocation.

Another day Glumdalclitch left me on a smooth grassplot to divert myself, while she walked at some distance with her governess. In the meantime there suddenly fell such a violent shower of hail that I was immediately, by the force of it, struck to the ground; and when I was down the hailstones gave me such cruel bangs all over the body, as if I had

been pelted with tennis balls; however, I made a
shift to creep on all four, and shelter myself, by
lying flat on my face, on the lee-side of a border
of lemon-thyme; but so bruised from head to foot
that I could not go abroad in ten days. Neither is
this at all to be wondered at, because nature in that
country, observing the same proportion through all
her operations, a hailstone is near eighteen hundred
times as large as one in Europe; which I can assert
upon experience, having been so curious as to weigh
and measure them.

But a more dangerous accident happened to me
in the same garden, where my little nurse, believing
she had put me in a secure place (which I often
entreated her to do, that I might enjoy my own
thoughts), and having left my box at home to avoid
the trouble of carrying it, went to another part of
the gardens, with her governess and some ladies of
her acquaintance. While she was absent, and out
of hearing, a small white spaniel, belonging to one
of the chief gardeners, having got by accident into
the garden, happened to range near the place where
I lay; the dog following the scent came directly up,
and taking me in his mouth, ran straight to his
master, wagging his tail, and set me gently on the
ground. By good fortune he had been so well
taught that I was carried between his teeth without
the least hurt, or even tearing my clothes. But the
poor gardener, who knew me well, and had a great
kindness for me, was in a terrible fright; he gently
took me up in both his hands, and asked me how I
did, but I was so amazed and out of breath that I
could not speak a word. In a few minutes I came
to myself, and he carried me safe to my little nurse,

who by this time had returned to the place where she left me, and was in cruel agonies when I did not appear nor answer when she called. She severely reprimanded the gardener on account of his dog.

This accident absolutely determined Glumdalclitch never to trust me abroad for the future out of her sight. I had been long afraid of this resolution, and therefore concealed from her some little unlucky adventures that happened in those times when I was left by myself. Once a kite hovering over the garden made a stoop at me, and if I had not resolutely drawn my hanger, and run under a thick espalier, he would have certainly carried me away in his talons.

Another time, walking to the top of a fresh molehill, I fell to my neck in the hole through which that animal had cast up the earth, and coined some lie, not worth remembering, to excuse myself for spoiling my clothes. I likewise broke my right shin against the shell of a snail, which I happened to stumble over, as I was walking alone, and thinking on poor England.

I cannot tell whether I were more pleased or mortified to observe, in those solitary walks, that the smaller birds did not appear to be at all afraid of me, but would hop about within a yard distance, looking for worms and other food, with as much indifference and security as if no creature at all were near them. I remember, a thrush had the confidence to snatch out of my hand, with his bill, a piece of cake that Glumdalclitch had just given me for my breakfast. When I attempted to catch any of these birds they would boldly turn against me, endeavoring to peck my fingers, which I durst not venture within their reach; and then they would turn back unconcerned, to hunt for worms or snails, as they did before. But one day I took a thick cudgel, and threw it with all my strength so luckily at a linnet that I knocked him down, and seizing him by the neck with both my hands, ran with him in triumph to my nurse. However, the bird, who had only been stunned, recovering himself, gave me so many boxes with his wings on both sides of my head and body, though I held him at arm's length, and was out of the reach of his claws, that I was twenty times thinking to let him go. But I was soon relieved by one of our servants, who wrung off the bird's neck, and I had him next day for dinner. This linnet, as near as I can remember, seemed to be somewhat larger than an English swan.

The queen, who often used to hear me talk of my sea voyages, and took all occasions to divert me when I was melancholy, asked me whether I understood how to handle a sail or an oar, and whether a little exercise of rowing might not be convenient for my health. I answered that I understood both very well; for although my proper employment had been to be surgeon or doctor to the ship, yet often upon a pinch I was forced to work like a common mariner. But I could not see how this could be done in their country, where the smallest wherry was equal to a first-rate man-of-war among us; and such a boat as I could manage would never live in any of their rivers. Her majesty said, if I would contrive a boat, her own joiner should make it, and she would provide a place for me to sail in. The fellow was an ingenious work-man, and by my instructions, in ten days finished a pleasure-boat, with all its tackling, able conveniently to hold eight Europeans. When it was finished the queen was so delighted that she ran with it in her lap to the king, who ordered it to be put into a cistern full of water, with me in it, by way of trial, where I could not manage my two sculls, or little oars, for want of room.

But the queen had before contrived another project. She ordered the joiner to make a wooden trough of three hundred foot long, fifty broad, and eight deep; which, being well pitched, to prevent leaking, was placed on the floor, along the wall, in an outer room of the palace. It had a cock near the bottom to let out the water, when it began to grow stale; and two servants could easily fill it in half an hour. Here I often used to row for my own diversion, as well as that of the queen and her ladies, who thought themselves well entertained with my skill and agility. Sometimes I would put up my sails, and then my business was only to steer, while the ladies gave me a gale with their fans; and, when they were weary, some of their pages would blow my sail forward with their breath, while I showed my art by steering starboard or larboard as I pleased. When I had done, Glumdalclitch always carried back my boat into her closet, and hung it on a nail to dry.

One time, one of the servants, whose office it was to fill my trough every third day with fresh water, was so careless as to let a huge frog (not perceiving it) slip out of his pail. The frog lay concealed till I was put into my boat, but then, seeing a resting place, climbed up, and made it lean so much on one side that I was forced to balance it with all my

weight on the other, to prevent overturning. When
the frog was got in it hopped at once half the length
of the boat; and then over my head, backward and
forward, daubing my face and clothes with odious
slime. The largeness of its features made it appear
the most deformed animal that can be conceived.
However, I desired Glumdalclitch to let me deal

A GALE WITH THEIR FANS

with it alone. I banged it a good while with one
of my sculls, and at last forced it to leap out of
the boat.

But the greatest danger I ever underwent in that
kingdom was from a monkey, who belonged to one
of the clerks of the kitchen. Glumdalclitch had
locked me up in her closet, while she went somewhere upon business or a visit. The weather being

very warm, the closet window was left open, as well as the windows and the door of my bigger box, in which I usually lived, because of its largeness and conveniency. As I sat quietly meditating at my table I heard something bounce in at the closet window, and skip about from one side to the other: whereat, although I was much alarmed, yet I ventured to look out, but not stirring from my seat; and then I saw this frolicsome animal frisking and leaping up and down, till at last he came to my box, which he seemed to view with great pleasure and curiosity, peeping in at the door and every window. I retreated to the further corner of my room or box; but the monkey, looking in at every side, put me into such a fright that I wanted presence of mind to conceal myself under the bed, as I might easily have done. After some time spent in peeping, grinning, and chattering, he at last espied me; and, reaching one of his paws in at the door, as a cat does when she plays with a mouse, although I often shifted place to avoid him, he at length caught hold of the lappet of my coat (which, being made of that country cloth, was very thick and strong), and dragged me out. He took me up in his right forefoot, and held me, just as I have seen the same sort of creature do with a kitten in Europe; and when I offered to struggle he squeezed me so hard that I thought it more prudent to submit. I have good reason to believe that he took me for a young one of his own species, by his often stroking my face very gently with his other paw. In these diversions he was interrupted by a noise at the closet door, as if somebody were opening it, whereupon he suddenly leaped up to the window at which he had come

in, and thence upon the leads and gutters, walking
upon three legs, and holding me in the fourth, till
he clambered up to a roof that was next to ours.
I heard Glumdalclitch give a shriek at the moment
he was carrying me out. The poor girl was almost
distracted; that quarter of the palace was all in an
uproar; the servants ran for ladders; the monkey
was seen by hundreds in the court sitting upon the
ridge of a building, holding me like a baby in one
of his forepaws, and feeding me with the other, by
cramming into my mouth some victuals he had
squeezed out of the bag on one side of his chaps,
and patting me when I would not eat; whereat the
rabble below could not forbear laughing; neither
do I think they justly ought to be blamed, for without question the sight was ridiculous enough to
everybody but myself.

Some of the people threw up stones, hoping to
drive the monkey down; but this was strictly forbidden, or else, very probably, my brains had been
dashed out.

The ladders were now applied, and mounted by
several men, which the monkey observing, and finding himself almost encompassed, not being able to
make speed enough with his three legs, let me drop
on a ridge tile, and made his escape. Here I sat
for some time, three hundred yards from the
ground, expecting every moment to be blown down
by the wind, or to fall by my own giddiness, and
come tumbling over and over from the ridge to the
eaves; but an honest lad, one of my nurse's footmen,
climbed up, and, putting me into his breeches
pocket, brought me down safe.

I was so weak and bruised in the sides by the

squeezes given me by this odious animal that I was
forced to keep my bed a fortnight. The king,
queen, and all the court, sent every day to inquire
after my health; and her majesty made me several
visits during my sickness. The monkey was killed,
and an order made that no such animal should be
kept about the palace.

When I attended the king after my recovery, to
return him thanks for his favors, he was pleased
to rally me a good deal upon this adventure. He
asked me what my thoughts and speculations were
while I lay in the monkey's paw; how I liked the
victuals he gave me; his manner of feeding; and
whether the fresh air on the roof had sharpened my
stomach. He desired to know what I would have
done upon such an occasion in my own country.

I told his majesty that in Europe we had no
monkeys, except such as were brought for curiosities from other places, and so small that I could
deal with a dozen of them together, if they pre-
sumed to attack me. And as for that monstrous
animal with whom I was so lately engaged (it was
indeed as large as an elephant), if my fear had
suffered me to think so far as to make use of my
hanger (looking fiercely, and clapping my hand
upon the hilt as I spoke), when he poked his paw
into my chamber, perhaps I should have given him
such a wound as would have made him glad to withdraw it with more haste than he put it in. This I
delivered in a firm tone, like a person who was
jealous lest his courage should be called in question.
However, my speech produced nothing else besides
a loud laughter, which all the respect due to his
majesty from those about him could not make them

contain.   This made me reflect how vain an attempt
it is for a man to endeavor doing himself honor
among those who are out of all degree of equality

GULLIVER AND THE KING

or comparison with him.   And yet I have seen the
moral of my own behavior very frequent in England since my return; where a little, contemptible
varlet, without the least title to birth, person, wit,

or common sense, shall presume to look with importance, and put himself upon a foot with the
greatest persons of the kingdom.[22]

IV. A Wonderful Escape

I HAD always a strong impulse that I
should some time recover my liberty,
though it was impossible to conjecture
by what means, or to form any project
with the least hope of succeeding. The
ship in which I sailed was the first
ever known to be driven within sight
of that coast, and the king had given strict orders
that if at any time another appeared it should be
taken ashore, and, with all its crew and passengers,
brought in a tumbrel to the capital. I was indeed
treated with much kindness; I was the favorite of
a great king and queen, and the delight of the
whole court; but it was upon such a foot as ill became the dignity of human kind. I could never
forget those domestic pledges I had left behind me.
I wanted to be among people with whom I could
converse upon even terms, and walk about the
streets and fields without fear of being trod to death
like a frog or a young puppy. But my deliverance
came sooner than I expected, and in a manner not
very common; the whole story and circumstances
of which I shall faithfully relate.

I had now been two years in the country; and
about the beginning of the third Glumdalclitch and

22. Gulliver's hatred of mankind betrays him, even in the
midst of his mildest satire, into such sharp, biting remarks as
this.

I attended the king and queen in a progress to the south coast of the kingdom. I was carried, as usual, in my traveling-box, a very convenient closet of twelve foot wide.

And I had ordered a hammock to be fixed, by silken ropes, from the four corners at the top, to break the jolts when a servant carried me before him on horseback, as I sometimes desired; and would often sleep in my hammock while we were upon the road. On the roof of my closet, not directly over the middle of the hammock, I ordered the joiner to cut out a hole of a foot square, to give me air in hot weather, as I slept; which hole I shut at pleasure with a board that drew backward and forward through a groove.

When we came to our journey's end, the king thought proper to pass a few days at a palace he hath near Flanflasnic, a city within eighteen English miles of the seaside. Glumdalclitch and I were much fatigued: I had gotten a small cold, but the poor girl was so ill as to be confined to her chamber. I longed to see the ocean, which must be the only scene of my escape, if ever it should happen. I pretended to be worse than I really was, and desired leave to take the fresh air of the sea, with a page whom I was very fond of, and who had sometimes been trusted with me. I shall never forget with what unwillingness Glumdalclitch consented, nor the strict charge she gave the page to be careful of me, bursting at the same time into a flood of tears, as if she had some foreboding of what was to happen.

The boy took me out in my box, about half an hour's walk from the palace, toward the rocks on

the seashore.[23]   I ordered him to set me down, and
lifting up one of my sashes, cast many a wistful,
melancholy look toward the sea.   I found myself
not very well, and told the page that I had a mind
to take a nap in my hammock, which I hoped would
do me good.   I got in, and the boy shut the window
close down, to keep out the cold.   I soon fell asleep,
and all I can conjecture is, that while I slept the
page, thinking no danger. could happen, went
among the rocks to look for bird's eggs, having
before observed him from my window searching
about, and picking up one or two in the clefts.

Be that as it will, I found myself suddenly
awaked with a violent pull upon the ring, which
was fastened at the top of my box for the conveniency of carriage.   I felt my box raised very
high in the air, and then borne forward with prodigious speed.   The first jolt had like to have
shaken me out of my hammock, but afterward the
motion was easy enough.   I called out several times
as loud as I could raise my voice, but all to no
purpose.

I looked toward my windows, and could see
nothing but the clouds and sky.   I heard a noise
just over my head, like the clapping of wings, and
then began to perceive the woeful condition I was
in; that some eagle had got the ring of my box in
his beak, with an intent to let it fall on a rock, like
a tortoise in a shell, and then pick out my body, and
devour it: for the sagacity and smell of this bird
enable him to discover his quarry at a great distance,

23. Here again we have a striking contrast—the "half an
hour's walk" of eighteen miles set over against the day and a
half's ride of one-half mile in Lilliput.

though better concealed than I could be within a
two-inch board.

In a little time I observed the noise and flutter
of wings to increase very fast, and my box was
tossed up and down, like a sign in a windy day.
I heard several bangs or buffets, as I thought, given
to the eagle (for such, I am certain, it must have
been that held the ring of my box in his beak), and
then, all on a sudden, felt myself falling perpendicularly down for above a minute, but with such incredible swiftness that I almost lost my breath. My
fall was stopped by a terrible squash, that sounded
louder to my ears than the cataract of Niagara;
after which I was quite in the dark for another
minute, and then my box began to rise so high that
I could see light from the tops of my windows. I
now perceived that I was fallen into the sea. My
box, by the weight of my body, the goods that were
in it, and the broad plates of iron fixed for strength
at the four corners of the top and bottom, floated
above five foot deep in water. I did then, and do
now, suppose that the eagle, which flew away with
my box, was pursued by two or three others, and
forced to let me drop, while he was defending himself against the rest, who hoped to share in the prey.
The plates of iron fastened at the bottom of the box
(for those were the strongest) preserved the balance
while it fell, and hindered it from being broken on
the surface of the water. Every joint of it was
well grooved; and the door did not move on hinges,
but up and down like a sash, which kept my closet
so tight that very little water came in. I got, with
much difficulty, out of my hammock, having first
ventured to draw back the slip-board on the roof,

already mentioned, contrived on purpose to let in air, for want of which I found myself almost stifled.

How often did I then wish myself with my dear Glumdalclitch, from whom one single hour had so far divided me! And I may say with truth, that, in the midst of my own misfortunes, I could not forbear lamenting my poor nurse, the grief she would suffer for my loss, the displeasure of the queen, and the ruin of her fortune. Perhaps many travelers have not been under greater difficulties and distress than I was at this juncture, expecting every moment to see my box dashed in pieces, or, at least, overset by the first violent blast, or a rising wave. A breach in one single pane of glass would have been immediate death: nor could anything have preserved the windows, but the strong lattice wires, placed on the outside, against accidents in traveling. I saw water ooze in at several crannies, although the leaks were not considerable, and I endeavored to stop them as well as I could. I was not able to lift up the roof of my closet, which otherwise I certainly should have done, and sat on top of it; where I might at least preserve myself some hours longer, than by being shut up (as I may call it) in the hold. Or, if I escaped these dangers for a day or two, what could I expect but a miserable death of cold and hunger? I was four hours under these circumstances, expecting, and indeed wishing, every moment to be my last.

There were two strong staples fixed upon that side of my box which had no window, and into which the servant, who used to carry me on horseback, would put a leathern belt, and buckle it about his waist. Being in this disconsolate state, I heard, or at least thought I heard, some kind of grating noise on that side of my box where the staples were fixed; and soon after I began to fancy that the box was pulled or towed along in the sea; for I now and then felt a sort of tugging, which made the waves rise near the tops of my windows, leaving me almost in the dark. This gave me some faint hopes of relief, although I was not able to imagine how it could be brought about. I ventured to unscrew one of my chairs, which were always fastened to the floor; and having made a hard shift to screw it down again, directly under the slipping-board that I had lately opened, I mounted on the chair, and, putting my mouth as near as I could to the hole, I called for help in a loud voice, and in all the languages I understood. I then fastened my handkerchief to a stick I usually carried, and, thrusting it up the hole waved it several times in the air, that, if any boat or ship were near, the seamen might conjecture some unhappy mortal to be shut up in this box.

I found no effect from all I could do, but plainly perceived my closet to be moved along; and in the space of an hour, or better, that side of the box where the staples were, and had no windows, struck against something that was hard. I apprehended it to be a rock, and found myself tossed more than ever. I plainly heard a noise upon the cover of my closet like that of a cable, and the grating of it as it passed through the ring. I then found myself hoisted up, by degrees, at least three foot higher than I was before. Whereupon I again thrust up my stick and handkerchief, calling for help till I was almost hoarse. In return to which I heard a great shout repeated three times, giving me such transports of joy as are not to be conceived but by those who feel them. I now heard a trampling over my head, and somebody calling through the hole with a loud voice, in the English tongue, if there be anybody below, let them speak.

I answered, I was an Englishman, drawn, by ill fortune, into the greatest calamity that ever any creature underwent, and begged, by all that was moving, to be delivered out of the dungeon I was in. The voice replied, I was safe, for my box was fastened to their ship, and the carpenter should immediately come and saw a hole in the cover, large enough to pull me out. I answered, that was needless, and would take up too much time; for there was no more to be done, but let one of the crew put his finger into the ring, and take the box out of the sea into the ship, and so into the captain's cabin. Some of them, upon hearing me talk so wildly, thought I was mad; others laughed; for indeed it never came into my head that I was now got among people of my own stature and strength. The carpenter came, and, in a few minutes, sawed a passage about four foot square, then let down a small ladder, upon which I mounted, and from thence was taken into the ship in a very weak condition.

The sailors were all in amazement, and asked me a thousand questions, which I had no inclination to answer. I was equally confounded at the sight of so many pigmies, for such I took them to be, after having so long accustomed mine eyes to the monstrous objects I had left. But the captain, Mr. Thomas Wilcocks, an honest, worthy Shropshireman, observing I was ready to faint, took me into his cabin, gave me a cordial to comfort me, and made me turn in upon his own bed, advising me to take a little rest, of which I had great need.

Before I went to sleep I gave him to understand that I had some valuable furniture in my box, too good to be lost; a fine hammock—an handsome field bed—two chairs—a table—and a cabinet. That my closet was hung on all sides, or rather quilted with silk and cotton; that, if he would let one of the crew bring my closet into his cabin, I would open it there before him, and show him my goods. The captain, hearing me utter these absurdities, concluded I was raving; however (I suppose to pacify me), he promised to give order as I desired, and going upon deck, sent some of his men down into my closet, from whence (as I afterward found) they drew up all my goods, and stripped off the quilting; but the chairs, cabinet, and bedstead, being screwed to the floor, were much damaged by the ignorance of the seamen, who tore them up by force. Then they knocked off some of the boards for the use of the ship, and when they had got all they had a mind for, let the hull drop into the sea, which, by reason of many breaches made in the bottom and sides, sunk to rights.[24] And, indeed, I was glad not to have been a spectator of the havoc they made, because I am confident it would have sensibly touched me, by bringing former passages into my mind, which I had rather forget.

I slept some hours, but perpetually disturbed with dreams of the place I had left, and the dangers I had escaped. However, upon waking, I found

24. *To rights* means *directly*.

myself much recovered. It was now about eight
o'clock at night, and the captain ordered supper immediately, thinking I had already fasted too long.
He entertained me with great kindness, observing
me not to look wildly, or talk inconsistently; and,
when we were left alone, desired I would give him
a relation of my travels, and by what accident I came
to be set adrift in that monstrous wooden chest. He
said that about twelve o'clock at noon, as he was
looking through his glass, he spied it at a distance,
and thought it was a sail, which he had a mind to
make, being not much out of his course, in hopes
of buying some biscuit, his own beginning to fall
short; that, upon coming nearer, and finding his
error, he sent out his longboat to discover what it
was; that his men came back in a fright, swearing
that they had seen a swimming house; that he
laughed at their folly, and went himself in the boat,
ordering his men to take a strong cable along with
them; that the weather being calm, he rowed round
me several times, observed my windows, and the
wire lattice that defended them; that he discovered two staples upon one side, which was all of
boards, without any passage for light. He then
commanded his men to row up to that side, and
fastening a cable to one of the staples, ordered them
to tow my chest, as they called it, toward the ship.
When it was there, he gave directions to fasten another cable to the ring fixed in the cover, and to
raise up my chest with pulleys, which all the sailors
were not able to do above two or three foot. He
said they saw my stick and handkerchief thrust out
of the hole, and concluded that some unhappy man
must be shut up in the cavity.

I asked whether he or the crew had seen any prodigious birds in the air about the time he first discovered me. To which he answered, that discoursing this matter with the sailors while I was asleep, one of them said he had observed three eagles flying toward the north, but remarked nothing of their being larger than the usual size; which, I suppose, must be imputed to the great height they were at; and he could not guess the reason of my question. I then asked the captain how far he reckoned we might be from land. He said by the best computation he could make, we were, at least, an hundred leagues. I assured him that he must be mistaken by almost half, for I had not left the country from whence I came above two hours before I dropped into the sea. Whereupon, he began again to think that my brain was disturbed, of which he gave me a hint, and advised me to go to bed in a cabin he had provided.

I assured him I was well refreshed with his good entertainment and company, and as much in my senses as ever I was in my life. He then grew serious, and desired to ask me freely, whether I were not troubled in mind by the consciousness of some enormous crime, for which I was punished, at the command of some prince, by exposing me in that chest; as great criminals, in other countries, have been forced to sea in a leaky vessel, without provisions; for although he should be sorry to have taken so ill a man into his ship, yet he would engage his word to set me safe on shore at the first port where we arrived. He added that his suspicions were much increased by some very absurd speeches I had delivered at first to the sailors, and afterward to himself, in relation to my closet or chest, as well as by my odd looks and behavior while I was at supper.

I begged his patience to hear me tell my story, which I faithfully did, from the last time I left England to the moment he first discovered me. And as truth always forceth its way into rational minds, so this honest, worthy gentleman, who had some tincture of learning and very good sense, was immediately convinced of my candor and veracity.

But further to confirm all I had said, I entreated him to give order that my cabinet should be brought, of which I had the key in my pocket; for he had already informed me how the seamen disposed of my closet. I opened it in his own presence, and showed him the small collection of rarities I made in the country from whence I had been so strangely delivered. There was a comb I had contrived out of the stumps of the king's beard, and another of the same materials, but fixed into a paring of her majesty's thumb-nail, which served for the back. There was a collection of needles and pins, from a foot to half a yard long; four wasp's stings, like joiner's tacks; a gold ring, which one day she made me a present of, in a most obliging manner, taking it from her little finger, and throwing it over my head like a collar. I desired the captain would please to accept this ring in return of his civilities, which he absolutely refused. I showed him a corn that I had cut off, with my own hand, from a maid of honor's toe; it was the bigness of a Kentish pippin, and grown so hard that, when I returned to England, I got it hollowed into a cup, and set in silver. Lastly, I desired him to see the breeches I had then on, which were made of a mouse's skin.

I could force nothing on him but a footman's tooth, which I observed him to examine with great curiosity, and found he had a fancy for it. He received it with abundance of thanks, more than such a trifle could deserve. It was drawn by an unskillful surgeon in a mistake, from one of Glumdalclitch's men, who was afflicted with the toothache, but it was as sound as any in his head. I got it cleaned, and put it in my cabinet. It was about a foot long and four inches in diameter.

The captain wondered at one thing very much, which was, to hear me speak so loud; asking me whether the king or queen of that country were thick of hearing. I told him it was what I had been used to for above two years past, and that I wondered as much at the voices of him and his men, who seemed to me only to whisper, and yet I could hear them well enough. But when I spoke in that country it was like a man talking in the street to another looking out from the top of a steeple, unless when I was placed on a table, or held in any person's hand.

I told him I had likewise observed another thing, that, when I first got into the ship, and the sailors stood all about me, I thought they were the most contemptible little creatures I had ever beheld. For, indeed, while I was in that prince's country I could never endure to look in a glass after mine eyes had been accustomed to such prodigious objects, because the comparison gave me so despicable a conceit of myself.

The captain said that while we were at supper he observed me to look at everything with a sort of wonder, and that I often seemed hardly able to con-

tain my laughter, which he knew not well how to
take, but imputed it to some disorder in my brain.

I answered, it was very true: and I wondered
how I could forbear when I saw his dishes of the
size of a silver threepence, a leg of pork hardly a
mouthful, a cup not so big as a nutshell; and so I
went on, describing the rest of his household stuff
and provisions, after the same manner. For, although the queen had ordered a little equipage of
all things necessary for me, while I was in her
service, yet my ideas were wholly taken up with
what I saw on every side of me, and I winked at
my own littleness as people do at their own faults.

The captain understood my raillery very well,
and merrily replied with the old English proverb,
that he doubted mine eyes were bigger than my
belly, for he did not observe my stomach so good,
although I had fasted all day; and continuing in his
mirth, protested, that he would have gladly given
a hundred pounds to have seen my closet in the
eagle's bill, and afterward in its fall from so great
a height into the sea, which would certainly have
been a most astonishing object, worthy to have the
description of it transmitted to future ages; and the
comparison of Phaëthon [25] was so obvious that he
could not forbear applying it, although I did not
much admire the conceit.

The captain having been at Tonquin was in his

25. *Phaëthon* was, according to Greek mythology, the son of
Apollo, the sun god. One day he prevailed upon his father to
allow him to mount the chariot of the sun and drive the white
cloud-horses across the heavens. He was unable to guide his
steeds, however, and they worked great havoc by dragging the
sun up and down and from one side of the sky to the other. Finally,
Jupiter hurled the youth into a river.

return to England driven north-eastward to the latitude of 44 degrees, and of longitude 143. But meeting a trade-wind two days after I came on board him, we sailed southward a long time, and coasting New Holland kept our course west-southwest, and then south-south-west till we doubled the Cape of Good Hope. Our voyage was very prosperous, but I shall not trouble the reader with a journal of it. The captain called in at one or two ports, and sent in his long boat for provisions and fresh water, but I never went out of the ship, till we came into the Downs which was on the third day of June, 1706, about nine months after my escape. I offered to leave my goods in security for payment of my freight; but the captain protested he would not receive one farthing. We took kind leave of each other, and I made him promise he would come to see me at my house. I hired a horse and guide for five shillings, which I borrowed of the captain.

As I was on the road, observing the littleness of the horses, the trees, the cattle, and the people, I began to think myself in Lilliput. I was afraid of trampling on every traveler I met, and often called aloud to have them stand out of the way, so that I had like to have gotten one or two broken heads for my impertinence.

When I came to my own house, for which I was forced to inquire, one of the servants opening the door, I bent down to go in (like a goose under a gate), for fear of striking my head. My wife ran out to embrace me, but I stooped lower than her knees, thinking she could otherwise never be able to reach my mouth. My daughter kneeled to ask my blessing, but I could not see her till she arose,

having been so long used to stand with my head
and eyes erect to above sixty feet; and then I went
to take her up with one hand by the waist. I looked
down upon the servants, and one or two friends who
were in the house, as if they had been pigmies, and
I a giant. I told my wife, "she had been too thrifty,
for I found she had starved herself and her daughter
to nothing." In short, I behaved myself so unac-
countably that they were all of the captain's opinion when he first saw me, and concluded I had lost
my wits. This I mention as an instance of the great
power of habit and prejudice.

In a little time, I and my family and friends
came to a right understanding; but my wife protested I should never go to sea any more; although
my evil destiny so ordered, that she had not power
to hinder me.

THE BALLAD OF AGINCOURT

By MICHAEL DRAYTON[1]

AIR stood the wind for France,[2]
When we our sails advance,
Nor now to prove our chance
    Longer will tarry;
But putting to the main,
At Kaux, the mouth of Seine,
With all his martial train,
    Landed King Harry.[3]

And taking many a fort,
Furnished in warlike sort,
Marched towards Agincourt[4]
    In happy hour,—
Skirmishing day by day

1. Michael Drayton was an English poet who lived from 1563 to 1631. Little is known of his life beyond the fact that he served as a page in the household of some nobleman, and that he tried in vain to gain the patronage of King James I. This *Ballad of Agincourt* is one of the finest of the English martial ballads.

2. From 1337 to 1453 the French and the English were engaged in a series of struggles to which the name of *The Hundred Years' War* has been given. The cause of the conflict was the attempt of the English kings to establish their rule over France.

3. This was Henry V, king of England from 1413 to 1422. He was a general of great ability, and the battle described in this ballad was one of his chief victories.

4. The English army numbered but 14,000, while the French were about 50,000 strong. Henry, to save his men, was willing to make terms with the French, who, however, demanded unconditional surrender. The two armies met for battle near the little village of Agincourt.

With those that stopped his way,
Where the French general lay
   With all his power,

Which in his height of pride,
King Henry to deride,
His ransom to provide
   To the king sending;
Which he neglects the while,
As from a nation vile,
Yet, with an angry smile,
   Their fall portending.

And turning to his men,
Quoth our brave Henry then:
"Though they to one be ten,
   Be not amazed;
Yet have we well begun,—
Battles so bravely won
Have ever to the sun
   By fame been raised.

"And for myself," quoth he,
"This my full rest shall be;
England ne'er mourn for me,
   Nor more esteem me.
Victor I will remain,
Or on this earth lie slain;
Never shall she sustain
   Loss to redeem me.

"Poitiers[5] and Cressy[6] tell,
When most their pride did swell,
Under our swords they fell;
   No less our skill is

Than when our grandsire[7] great,
Claiming the regal seat,
By many a warlike feat
        Lopped the French lilies." [8]

"VICTOR I WILL REMAIN"

5. The Battle of Poitiers was fought in 1356. The English under the Black Prince, son of Edward III of England, defeated the French under King John, though the French outnumbered them more than five to one.

The Duke of York so dread
The eager vaward[9] led;
With the main Henry sped,
    Amongst his henchmen.
Excester had the rear,—
A braver man not there:
O Lord! how hot they were
    On the false Frenchmen!

They now to fight are gone;
Armor on armor shone;
Drum now to drum did groan,—
    To hear was wonder;
That with the cries they make
The very earth did shake;
Trumpet to trumpet spake,
    Thunder to thunder.

Well it thine age became,
O noble Erpingham!
Which did the signal aim
    To our hid forces;
When, from a meadow by,
Like a storm suddenly,
The English archery
    Struck the French horses,

6. In the Battle of Cressy, which was fought in 1346, 35,000 English under King Edward III defeated 75,000 French under Philip VI. About 30,000 of the French army were slain.

7. The great-grandfather of Henry V was Edward III, the hero of the early part of the Hundred Years' War.

8. The lily, or fleur-de-lis, is the national flower of France. *Lopped the French lilies* is a poetical way of saying *defeated the French.*

9. *Vaward* is an old word for *vanward*, or *advance-guard.*

With Spanish yew so strong,
Arrows a cloth-yard long,
That like to serpents stung,
   Piercing the weather;
None from his fellow starts,
But playing manly parts,
And like true English hearts
   Stuck close together.

When down their bows they threw,
And forth their bilboes[10] drew,
And on the French they flew,
   Not one was tardy;
Arms were from shoulders sent;
Scalps to the teeth were rent;
Down the French peasants went;
   Our men were hardy.

This while our noble king,
His broadsword brandishing,
Down the French host did ding,[11]
   As to o'erwhelm it;
And many a deep wound lent,
His arms with blood besprent,
And many a cruel dent
   Bruisèd his helmet.

Glo'ster, that duke so good,
Next of the royal blood,
For famous England stood,
   With his brave brother,—
Clarence, in steel so bright,

10. *Bilboes* is a poetical word for *swords*.
11. To *ding* is to *strike*.

Though but a maiden knight,
Yet in that furious fight
    Scarce such another.

Warwick in blood did wade;
Oxford the foe invade,
And cruel slaughter made,
    Still as they ran up.
Suffolk his axe did ply;
Beaumont and Willoughby
Bare them right doughtily,
    Ferrers and Fanhope.

Upon Saint Crispin's[12] day
Fought was this noble fray,
Which fame did not delay
    To England to carry;
O, when shall Englishmen
With such acts fill a pen,
Or England breed again
    Such a King Harry!

12. Crispin was a Christian saint who suffered martyrdom in
the third century. The 25th of October was made sacred to him.
It was on Saint Crispin's day, 1415, that the Battle of Agincourt
was fought.

SOME CHILDREN'S BOOKS OF THE PAST

By GRACE E. SELLON

PROBABLY somewhere about your home, put away so far from sight that you never think of them any more, are some of the A B C books and the alphabet blocks and the brightly colored story books about horses, dogs and other familiar animals that used to amuse you when you were just learning to say the alphabet and to spell a few three-letter words. Perhaps you can remember how much you liked to have the stories read to you and how much fun there was in repeating your A B C's when you could point out the big, colored letters in your book or on your blocks. But have you ever thought that you were any more fortunate than other children of other ages in having these interesting things to help you? Have you ever wondered whether, far back in history before our country was discovered and settled by white men, boys and girls had the same kinds of picture books and drawing-slates, alphabet games and other playthings that used to delight you in the days when you were going to kindergarten or learning your first simple lessons from your mother?

If you have never thought enough about this matter to ask some older person about it, you will find

101

the lesson books and story books used by children
of even a hundred years ago very curious. Suppose
we go farther back, to 1620, the year of the May-
flower, let us say. You could never imagine what
a child then living in England was given to learn his
letters from. As soon as he was able to remember
the first little things that children are taught, his
mother would fasten to his belt a string from which
was suspended what she would call his *hornbook*.
This was not at all what we think of to-day as a
book, for it was made of a piece of cardboard covered on one side with a thin sheet of horn, and surrounded by a frame with a handle. Through the
covering of horn the little boy could see the alphabet written on the cardboard in both large and small
letters. After these would come rows of syllables
to help him in learning to pronounce simple combi-
nations of sounds. Probably last on the sheet there
would be the Lord's Prayer, which he must be
taught to say without a mistake. As he went about
he could easily take up his hornbook once in a while
and say over to himself the letters and the rows of
syllables. Sometimes—especially if he had been
obedient and had studied well—he was given a hornbook made of gingerbread; and then, of course, he
would find that the tiresome lines of letters had all
at once become very attractive.

The hornbook must have done its work well, or
at least no better way of teaching the alphabet had
been found when the Puritans came to America,
for it was not many years before little folks in the
New World were being taught from the famous
New England Primer, which joined to what had
been in the hornbook a catechism and various moral

teachings.   With its rude illustrations and its dry
contents, this little book would probably be laughed
at by school-children of to-day, if they did not stop

CHILDREN WITH HORNBOOKS

to think how very many of the writers, statesmen
and soldiers who have made our country great
learned their first lessons from its pages.   Somewhere between 1687 and 1690 it was first published,

and for a hundred years from that time it was the schoolbook found in almost every New England home and classroom.

Can you imagine what kind of reading lessons were in this primer? If you think they were like the lively little stories and the pleasing verses printed in your readers, you will be a good deal surprised to find that they are stern and gloomy tales that were meant to frighten children into being good, rather than to entertain them.

First of all in the little book came the alphabet and the lists of syllables, as in the hornbook. There was this difference, however. At the beginning of the first line of letters in the hornbooks was placed a cross, as the symbol of Christianity, and from this fact the first line was called the *Christ-cross,* or *criss-cross row.* But the Puritans strictly kept the cross out of the *Primer,* for to them it stood in a disagreeable way for the older churches from which they had separated themselves.

Then came a series of sentences from the Bible teaching moral lessons and illustrating the use of the letters of the alphabet, one being made prominent in each verse. The Lord's Prayer and the Apostle's Creed might appear next, followed by twenty-four alphabet rhymes with accompanying pictures. Most of these verses were upon Bible subjects, as in the case of the letter *R,* for example, illustrated by the lines:

> "Young pious Ruth
> Left all for Truth."

One of the best-loved rhymes was one put into the series after the Revolution to stir the pride of every young American by reminding him that

"Great Washington brave
His country did save."

In the pages that followed were to be found an illustrated poem telling of the awful fate of John Rogers, burned at the stake while his wife and their ten children looked on, and a dialogue between Christ, a youth and the devil, in which the youth was finally overcome by Satan's temptations.

This story of the terrifying fate of the youth was placed after the shorter Westminster catechism, possibly as a warning to all children who would not obey their religious teachings. The one hundred seven questions of the catechism must be answered correctly, even though the five-syllable words were even harder to understand than to pronounce.

Religious songs and pictures and descriptions of good and of bad children were also scattered through the book, and in some copies is to be found the little prayer beginning: "Now I lay me down to sleep," which was probably published for the first time in the *Primer*.

As the years went on, pictures and verses and little articles about the objects of nature and the everyday things that children are interested in began to take the place of the Bible verses and subjects; and at length when people saw how well children liked this new way of teaching, better books than the *Primer* took its place.

While the young folks in New England families were thus being warned in story and verse against the awful temptations that lay all around them, the children in old England were being entertained by popular penny-books that treated of all kinds of subjects, from the *History of Joseph and his*

Brother to *The Old Egyptian Fortune Teller's Last Legacy.*   These books were of a size scarcely larger than that of the letter-paper made for little folks, and they contained usually from sixteen to twenty-four pages.   Illustrations that looked a good deal like the pictures made by a small boy in his schoolbooks adorned the rough little volumes.

In every city and town and even in the villages peddlers went along the streets selling these chap-books, as they were called.   Imagine how the children, and the grown people too, must have flocked around the peddler as he began taking out one after another of his queer little books, for he had something to please every one.   The boys might choose stories like *The Mad Pranks of Tom Tram, A Wonderful and Strange Relation of a Sailor* or *The True Tale of Robin Hood,* and we can see them almost getting into a brawl over the possession of *The Merry Life and Mad Exploits of Captain James Hind, the Great Robber of England.*   Probably the girls would choose *Patient Grissel, The History of Mother Bunch* or *Cinderella.*   For the small children there were, for example, the *History of Two Children in the Wood, The Pleasant History of Jack Horner* and *Tom Thumb.*   Most likely it was only the pennies of much-tried mothers and fathers that were spent for *A Timely Warning to Rash and Disobedient Children.*

The chapman or peddler we may well believe did not stand silently looking on as he disposed of his stock.   He had at the tip of his tongue such a fair-sounding advertisement for every book that everybody, young and old, came under the spell of his words and bought of his wares.

After he had departed with his traveling library, we can picture the children taking themselves off to quiet places with their new chapbooks. Perhaps you are wondering why it was that they were so eager to read them. If so, you may like to look into a few of these rare old story books. As you read, notice how quaint the wording seems when compared with that of the stories of to-day.

(Extract from *The History of Tom Long the Carrier*.)

As Tom Long the Carrier was travelling between Dover and Westchester, he fortuned to pass something near a House, where was kept a great Mastiff Dog, who, as soon as he espied Tom, came running open-mouthed at him, and so furiously assaulted him, as if he meant to devour him at a bite. But Tom, having in his Hand a good Pikestaff, most valiantly defended himself like a Man, and to withstand the danger he thrust the Pike-end of his Staff into his Throat and so killed him. Whereupon the Owner thereof, seeing the Dog lost, comes earnestly unto Tom, and between threatening and chiding, asking him why he struck him not with the great End of the staff. 'Marry,' quoth he, 'because your Dog runs not at me with his tail.'

(Extract from *The Kentish Miracle, or, A Seasonable Warning to all Sinners*.) Shewn in the Wonderful Relation of one Mary Moore whose Husband died some time ago, and left her with two children, and who was reduced to great want. How she wandered about the Country asking relief and went two Days without any Food—How the Devil

appeared to her and the many great offers he made
her to deny Christ and enter into his service, and
how she confounded Satan by powerful Argument.
How she came to a well of water when she fell down
on her knees to pray to God that He would give
that Vertue to the Water that it might refresh and
satisfy her Children's Hunger, with an Account
how an Angel appeared to her, and relieved her,
also declared many Things that shall happen in the
Month of March next.   Shewing likewise what
strange and surprising Accidents shall happen by
means of the present War, and concerning a dreadful Earthquake, etc.

(Extract from *A Timely Warning to Rash and
Disobedient Children.*)
As this Child went to School one Day
Through the Churchyard she took her Way
When lo, the Devil came and said
Where are you going to, my pretty Maid
To School I am going Sir, said she
Pish, Child, don't mind the same saith he,
But haste to your Companions dear
And learn to lie and curse and swear.
They bravely spend their Time in Play
God they don't value—no, not they.
It is a Fable, Child, he cry'd
At which his cloven Foot she spy'd.
I'm sure there is a God, saith she
Who from your Power will keep me free,
And if you should this Thing deny
Your cloven Foot gives you the Lie.
Satan, avaunt, hence, out of hand,
In Name of Jesus I command.

At which the Devil instantly
In Flames of Fire away did fly.

(Extract from *Wonder of Wonders,* being a strange and wonderful Relation of a Mermaid that was seen and spoke with by one John Robinson, Mariner, who was tossed on the Ocean for 6 Days and Nights. All the other Mariners perished.)

He was in great Fear and dreadful Fright in the main Ocean . . . . . . but to his great Amazement he espy'd a beautiful young Lady combing her Head and toss'd on the Billows, cloathed all in green (but by chance he got the first Word from her). Then She with a Smile came on Board and asked how he did. The young Man, being Something Smart and a Scholar reply'd—Madam, I am the better to see you in good Health, in great hopes trusting you will be a Comfort and Assistance to me in this my low Condition: and so caught hold of her Comb and Green Girdle that was about her Waist. To which she reply'd, Sir, you ought not to rob a young Woman of her Riches and then expect a Favour at her Hands, but if you will give me my Comb and Girdle again, what lies in my Power, I will do for you. She presents him with a Compass, told him to steer S. W., made an Appointment for following Friday, and jumped in the sea. He arrives safely home, and while musing on his promise She appeared to him with a smiling Countenance, and (by his Misfortune) she got the first Word of him, so that he could not speak one Word and was quite Dumb, and she began to sing, after which she departed, taking from him the Compass. She took a Ring from her Finger and gave him.   (The young man went home, fell ill and died 5 days after), to the wonderful Admiration of all People who saw the young Man.

AFTER the eighteenth century the chapbooks gradual-ly went out of favor, and since then in England, as in America, more and more careful attention has been given to writing good stories for children and printing these attractively.   These better books could not have come, however, had it not been that for generation after generation crude little primers and storybooks, such as the interesting kinds that have been described, helped to point out to people, little by little, how to make children's reading both instructive and pleasing.

LEAD, KINDLY LIGHT
By CARDINAL NEWMAN

Of this poem, Newman has written: "I was ach-ing to get home; yet for want of a vessel, I was kept at Palermo for three weeks.   At last I got off on an orange boat, bound for Marseilles.   Then it was that I wrote the lines, *Lead, Kindly Light,* which have since become well known."

Again, he has said: "This is one full of light, re-joicing in suffering with our Lord.   This is what those who like *Lead, Kindly Light* must come to— they have to learn it."

LEAD, kindly light, amid the encircling gloom,
    Lead thou me on;
The night is dark and I am far from home;
    Lead thou me on;
Keep thou my feet; I do not ask to see
The distant scene; one step enough for me.

I was not ever thus, nor prayed that thou
    Shouldst lead me on;
I loved to choose and see my path; but now
    Lead thou me on;
I loved the garish day, and, spite of fears,
Pride ruled my will. Remember not past years.

So long thy power has blest me, sure it still
    Will lead me on
O'er moor and fen, o'er crag and torrent till
    The night is gone,
And with the morn those angel faces smile
Which I have loved long since, and lost the while.

LET SOMETHING GOOD BE SAID*

By JAMES WHITCOMB RILEY

WHEN over the fair fame of friend or foe
    The shadows of disgrace shall fall; instead
Of words of blame, or proof of so and so,
    Let something good be said.
Forget not that no fellow-being yet
    May fall so low but love may lift his head;
Even the cheek of shame with tears is wet,
    If something good be said.
No generous heart may vainly turn aside
    In ways of sympathy; no soul so dead
But may awaken strong and glorified,
    If something good be said.
And so I charge ye, by the thorny crown,
    And by the cross on which the Saviour bled,
And by your own soul's hope for fair renown,
    Let something good be said!

*From *Home-Folks*, by James Whitcomb Riley. Used by
special permission of the publishers, *The Bobbs-Merrill Company.*

POLONIUS' ADVICE

Give thy thoughts no tongue,
Nor any unproportion'd thought his act.
Be thou familiar, but by no means vulgar.
Those friends thou hast, and their adoption tried,
Grapple them to thy soul with hoops of steel;
But do not dull thy palm with entertainment
Of each new-hatch'd, unfledged comrade. Beware
Of entrance to a quarrel, but being in,
Bear't that the opposed may beware of thee.
Give every man thy ear, but few thy voice;
Take each man's censure, but reserve thy judge-
      ment.
Costly thy habit as thy purse can buy,
But not express'd in fancy; rich, not gaudy;
For the apparel oft proclaims the man,
And they in France of the best rank and station
Are of a most select and generous choice in that.
Neither a borrower nor a lender be;
For loan oft loses both itself and friend,
And borrowing dulls the edge of husbandry.
This above all: to thine own self be true,
And it must follow, as the night the day,
Thou canst not then be false to any man.

SHAKESPEARE *(Hamlet, Act 1, Scene 3)*.

KING ARTHUR

I. ARTHUR MADE KING

UTHER Pendragon was one of the kings who ruled in Britain so long ago that many marvelous legends have sprung up about him and his more famous son, Arthur. They lived in the days when magicians and witches were believed to be common, and the stories of the time are filled with deeds of magic and with miraculous events.

Merlin was the greatest of magicians, and it was only by his power that King Uther won the wife he wanted and that his son was protected and nurtured during his childhood and youth. Many of the knights of King Uther aspired to his throne, and so to protect the baby Arthur, Merlin carried him to the good knight Sir Ector, who brought him up with his own son Kay; but none knew that the boy was Uther's son.

When Arthur had grown to be a tall, manly youth and was skilled in the use of arms, the Archbishop of Canterbury called together all the men-at-arms and the great ladies of the land, for Merlin had declared that at Christmas-tide great wonders should be done. King Uther had been long dead, and there was much wrangling over his successor, although he had declared on his death bed that his son Arthur was living and should reign in his stead.

113

From all sides, barons, knights and ladies, with long retinues of servants, crowded into London and gathered into the greatest church. When the people came forth from the service there was seen in the churchyard a great marble stone, four square, and having in the midst of it a steel anvil a foot high. Through the middle of this anvil a beautiful sword was sticking, with the point projecting beyond. Around the sword in letters of gold was written, "WHOSO PULLETH THIS SWORD OUT OF THIS STONE AND ANVIL IS THE TRUE-BORN KING OF BRITAIN."

The excitement was great and for some time difficult to quell, for every man who hoped to be king wished to be the first to try to draw the sword; but the Archbishop arranged the men in order, and one after another they made their attempts. Not even the strongest man in the kingdom could move the sword the fraction of a single inch.

When it became certain that no one could draw the sword, the Archbishop set ten knights to guard it and decreed that on New Year's Day the people should meet for other attempts; in the meantime, word should be sent abroad that all in the kingdom might know of the marvelous sword and the reward that awaited the successful knight. A great tournament was called and many rich prizes were offered.

Among those who came to the jousts were Sir Ector and his son, Sir Kay, and the young man Arthur, not yet a knight. In the morning when they rode to the field where the multitude were gathered to watch the jousting, Sir Kay discovered that he had left his sword at his lodgings.

"Arthur, I beg you to ride back and bring me my sword," said Sir Kay.

Arthur willingly rode back, but when he came to the lodging he could not enter, because every one

ARTHUR DRAWS THE SWORD

had gone out to see the jousting. Arthur loved Sir Kay dearly, and could not bear to think of his brother being kept out of the tourney because he had no sword. And so, as he rode by the church-yard and saw the magic sword unguarded in the stone, he thought how fine a weapon it would be for Sir Kay.

"How fortunate that the guards have gone to see the tourney. I'll take this sword to Kay," he said.

When Arthur laid his hand on the jewelled hilt the sword came free from its resting place, and the boy bore it joyously to his brother.

As soon as Sir Kay saw the sword he knew it was the one that had been in the magic stone. Hastily riding to Sir Ector he said, "See, here is the sword of the stone. It must be that I am to be king."

Sir Ector answered, "Give me the weapon and come with me to the church."

Together with Arthur they rode to the church, and all three alighted from their horses and saw that the sword was gone from the stone.

"Now, my son, swear by the holy book to tell me honestly how you got the sword."

"My brother Arthur brought it to me—this I swear," said Sir Kay.

"How did you get this sword?" said Sir Ector, turning to Arthur.

"Sir," said Arthur, "when I could not find my brother's sword and returned by this place I saw the sword sticking in the stone. So I came and pulled at it and it yielded easily, and I took it to Sir Kay, for I would not have my brother swordless."

"Were there any knights about the stone?" asked Sir Ector.

"None," said Arthur.

"Now I understand," said Sir Ector; "you, Arthur, are to be king of Britain."

KING ARTHUR

Statue by Peter Vischer, in the Hofkirche, Innsbruck

"Why should I be king of Britain?" asked the boy.

"I know not why, except that God wills it so, for it has been ordained that the man who should draw the sword from the stone is the true-born king of Britain. Now let me see whether you can put the sword where it was and draw it forth again."

"That is not difficult," said Arthur, as he thrust the sword back into the stone.

Sir Ector tried to pull it out again, but he could not move it.

"Now you try," he said to Sir Kay.

Although Sir Kay pulled with all his might the sword remained immovable.

"Now you try it," said Sir Ector to Arthur.

"I will," said Arthur, as he grasped the hilt and drew the sword out without any difficulty.

Then Sir Ector and Sir Kay knelt down before Arthur and said, "Now we know you for our king and swear allegiance to you."

"Now my own dear father, and Kay, my brother, do not kneel to me."

"Arthur," said Sir Ector, "I must now tell you that you are not my son, nor is Sir Kay your brother. I do not know who you are, but I did not think you were of kingly lineage."

Then Arthur wept, for he loved Ector and Kay as though they were father and brother to him.

"When you are king," asked Sir Ector, "will you be kind to me and my family?"

"Indeed I will," said Arthur, "or I shall be much to blame, for I am more deeply in debt to you than to any other man in all the world, and to your wife, whom I have always thought my mother and who has cared for me as for her own son. If it ever is the will of God that I be king of Britain, ask what you desire and it will be my pleasure to accord it."

The three then went to the Archbishop and told him all that had happened. He counseled them to remain quiet till after the tournament, when Arthur should make the trial in public. At that time, after all had struggled madly to pull out the sword and had failed, Arthur drew it out easily before the astonished eyes of the onlookers.

The barons and knights laughed in derision and said, "Shall Britain be ruled over by a boy? Let us have another trial at Twelfth Day."

At Twelfth Day and at Easter were the trials again held with the same results, but the fierce barons would not recognize Arthur until the people grew angry and shouted, "Arthur is our king. We will have no one but Arthur for our king."

Even the fierce knights who aspired to the throne could not resist the call of the people combined with that of the many barons who sided with Sir Ector. When the Archbishop placed the crown upon the head of the young king all there did homage to Arthur though many scowled and threatened the life of the new ruler. Arthur did not forget his promises, but made Sir Kay his seneschal and gave broad lands and rich presents to his foster parents.

II. ARTHUR WEDS GUINEVERE. THE ROUND TABLE

ARTHUR'S reign began with savage wars with his neighbors and with sedition and rebellion in his kingdom. In every conflict he was successful, and every victory made him friends, for he was a noble man and administered his affairs with justice to all.

Moreover, he cut roads through the forests and made it possible for his husbandmen to cultivate the lands without danger from wild beasts or fear of marauders. He established justice everywhere so that even the poor felt sure of his protection. If treachery or oppression appeared among his nobles he punished them severely, but he forgave personal injuries freely.

Many of the rulers of petty kingdoms near Arthur had occasion to bless him for brave assistance, and among them was Leodegrance, king of Cameliard, whom Arthur, in a fierce battle in which ten thousand men were slain, freed from the tyranny of King Rience. After the battle, Leodegrance entertained Arthur and his friends at a great feast, at which Guinevere, the beautiful young daughter of the host, served the table. At the sight of the fair maid Arthur's heart was won, and ever after he loved her faithfully.

Merlin, the great magician, had always been the friend and counselor of Arthur, and to his sound advice and wonderful enchantments the king was indebted for much of his power and renown. Before Arthur proposed to marry Guinevere, he took counsel of Merlin, who looked sorrowful and dismayed at the young king's words.

"If indeed your heart is set on the fair Guinevere, you may not change it. Yet it had been better for you to have loved another."

Delighted at even this guarded advice Arthur went at once to Leodegrance and asked for the hand of his young daughter. Leodegrance consented with joy, for he loved Arthur greatly, and welcomed him as a son-in-law.

In the great cathedral of Canterbury the two were married by the Archbishop, while without, the people reflected in wild celebrations the joys of the king and his fair bride.

Among the gifts which King Arthur received was one from King Leodegrance which pleased him most. "This gift," said Leodegrance, "is the Table Round which King Uther Pendragon gave to me and around which can sit a hundred and fifty knights. This table the great Merlin made, as he made also the hundred and fifty sieges which surround it."

The day of his marriage Arthur chose one hundred and twenty-eight knights to found his famous Order of the Round Table, and to each he gave one of the sieges or carved chairs, upon the back of which, as each knight took his seat, appeared his name in magical letters of gold. Soon all the seats were filled excepting one, the Siege Perilous, in which no man might sit under peril of his life, unless he were blameless and free from all sin. When by death or otherwise any of the other sieges became vacant, a new knight was chosen to occupy it, and the magic letters changed to spell his name.

THE WEDDING OF ARTHUR AND GUINEVERE

Camelot, the lordly castle of Arthur, with its vast halls and beautiful grounds, was all raised by Merlin's magic power without the aid of human hands. Here at Christmas, at Easter and at Pentecost great festivals were held, and Arthur's knights would gather to feast, to joust in tournament and to tell the stories of the wonderful adventures which had befallen them since the last meeting; and great was their knightly pleasure in these gatherings.

III.   ARTHUR AND PELLINORE

ONE day Arthur dressed himself in his best armor, mounted his best horse and rode forth alone to seek adventure. He had started before dawn and had ridden slowly along.

Just at day-break he saw Merlin running toward him in deadly peril, for three fierce vagabonds brandishing huge clubs were close at his heels. Arthur rode toward the robbers, and they turned and fled at the sight of an armed knight.

"O, Merlin," said Arthur, "this time certainly you would have been killed in spite of your magic if I had not appeared to rescue you."

"No," said Merlin, "I could have saved myself if I had wished; but you are nearer death than I am, for now you are certainly traveling toward death unless God befriend you."

Arthur asked the magician what he meant, but the wily man would give no explanation. However, he turned and accompanied Arthur.

As they rode along they came across a beautiful

wayside spring, near which, under a wide-spreading tree, a rich tent was set. In front of it sat a sturdy knight full armed for battle.

"Sir Knight," said Arthur, "why do you sit here in full armor thus watching the road?"

"It is my custom," said the knight, "and no man may pass by unless he fight with me."

"That is a vile custom," said the king, "and I bid you give it up."

"That will I not do," said the knight. "If any man does not like my custom, let him change it."

"I will change it," said Arthur.

"I will defend myself," answered the knight.

Then the knight arose, took shield and spear, mounted the war-horse tethered near and rode at Arthur, who spurred his horse to meet the shock. They came together with such force that their horses were thrown back upon their haunches and their spears were shivered against their shields. Arthur recovered himself and pulled out his sword.

"No, no," said the knight, "I pray you let us fight again with spears. It is the fairer way."

"I would be very willing," assented Arthur, "if I had another spear."

"But I have spears for both," declared the knight, as he called to a squire to bring him two good spears.

When the weapons were brought Arthur selected one and the knight took the other. Drawing apart they again charged together, and again their spears were both broken at the hand. Again Arthur put his hand to his sword, but the knight protested a second time.

"Nay, not so," he said, "for the honor of our knighthood let us joust once more. You are the

strongest knight and the best jouster I have ever
met."

"I am willing," said Arthur, "if you will let me
have another spear."

Two more spears were brought—heavy ones such
as only the best of knights could handle. Again
Arthur chose the one he liked, and again they drew
apart.

This time they ran together with greater force
than ever, and once more Arthur shivered his spear
on the shield of his opponent. But this time the
spear of the unknown knight struck Arthur's shield
full in the center and drove both horse and rider to
the earth.

The king sprang free from his horse, recovered
his shield, drew his sword and cried, "Now will I
fight you on foot, for I have lost the honor on horseback."

"No, I will fight only on horseback," said the
knight.

Then Arthur grew very angry and rushed afoot
at the knight. Seeing how determined the king
was, and thinking it dishonorable to keep his seat
while Arthur fought on foot, the knight alighted
and dressed his shield against his foe.

Long and fierce was the battle, for both were full
of anger and resentment. They charged and fell
back; they hacked and hewed until shields and armor were bent and broken in many places. Both
were sorely wounded, and the blood ran until the
trampled ground was stained with it. Then, out
of breath and weary from the terrible exertion, they
both rested for a few moments, but they soon began the duel again, rushing together like two fierce

wild animals and striking such blows that both were
many times brought to their knees. Every time,
however, they recovered themselves and renewed

MERLIN SAVES ARTHUR

the terrific struggle. At last the swords met full in
the air, and Arthur's was broken at the hilt.

"Now yield," said the strange knight, "for you
are wholly in my power and I can slay or release
you as I will. Yield now to me as a recreant knight
or I will slay you as you stand."

"As for death," said Arthur, "let it come when it will. I would rather die than shame my manhood by yielding."

And then like lightning Arthur leaped upon the knight, clasped him round the middle and threw him to the ground. But the knight was a powerful man, and throwing Arthur off he hurled him to the ground, struck off his helm and raised his sword to behead the king.

All the time Merlin had stood and watched the fray, but when he saw the deadly peril in which Arthur lay, he called out, "Knight, hold your hand! If you slay this knight you put this kingdom in the greatest peril, for this is a more worshipful knight than you dream of."

"Why, who is he?" asked the knight.

"It is King Arthur," Merlin replied.

Then was the knight fearful of the vengeance of the King, if he should survive the encounter. He raised his sword again and would have killed Arthur as he lay, but Merlin cast an enchantment over him and he fell into a deep sleep.

The magician caught up the king and rode forth on the knight's horse.

"Alas!" said Arthur, "what have you done, Merlin? Have you slain this good knight by your crafts? There is no braver knight in the world than he was. I would give half my kingdom if he were alive again."

"Do not trouble yourself," replied Merlin. "He is in less danger than you are, for he lies asleep and will awake whole and refreshed in three hours. I told you how powerful a knight he was, and you would have certainly been slain here if I had not been by to help. This same knight shall live to do you great service."

"Who is the knight?" asked Arthur.

"It is King Pellinore; and he shall have two sons, both of whom shall be good men; and one shall have no equal in strength, courage and goodness."

IV.   ARTHUR GETS EXCALIBUR

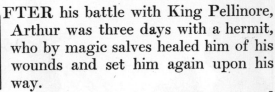

AFTER his battle with King Pellinore, Arthur was three days with a hermit, who by magic salves healed him of his wounds and set him again upon his way.

As they rode along, Arthur turned to Merlin and said, "Behold, I have no sword."

"That does not matter," replied Merlin; "there is a good sword near here that shall be yours if I can get it for you."

They turned aside and rode till they came to a beautiful little lake, now quiet in the afternoon light. As Arthur looked he saw in the middle of the lake an arm clothed in white samite, "mystic, wonderful," stretched up and holding in its hand a flashing sword.

"Lo!" said Merlin. "Yonder is the sword of which I spoke."

As Arthur looked he saw a fair maid coming toward him over the water.

"What damsel is that?" he inquired of Merlin.

"That is the Lady of the Lake," answered the magician. "Speak kindly to her and ask her to give you the sword."

As the beautiful maid came nearer she saluted
Arthur and he returned the courtesy.

"Damsel," said Arthur, "what rich sword is that
which yonder hand holds above the water? I would
it were mine, for I have no sword."

ARTHUR RECEIVES EXCALIBUR

"That is my sword, Excalibur," answered the
maid, "and I will give it to you if you will give me
a gift when I ask it."

"Right willingly will I give you what you ask,
so that I may have the sword."

"Well, take the boat and row yourself out to the sword. When the time comes I will ask the gift."

So Arthur got down from his horse, tied it to a tree and entered the boat. When he had come to the arm Arthur reached up and grasped the sword and scabbard. Immediately both were released, and the white-clothed arm sank back into the waters.

When he returned to the land the maiden had disappeared, and the two rode on their way. Arthur kept looking at his sword, for he admired it very much.

"Which do you prefer," asked Merlin, "the sword or the scabbard?"

"I like the sword the better," replied Arthur.

"That is not wise," rejoined the magician. "The scabbard is worth ten of the swords, because while you have the scabbard on you, you cannot lose a drop of blood no matter how severe your wound. Therefore keep the scabbard always by you."

The number of King Arthur's Knights varies from twelve to several hundred, according to the different poets or romancers. Here is one account:

"The fellowship of the Table Round,
　Soe famous in those dayes;
Whereatt a hundred noble knights
　And thirty sat alwayes;
Who for their deeds and martiall feates,
　As bookes done yett record,
Amongst all other nations
　Wer fearèd through the world."
Legend of King Arthur (Old Ballad)

BALIN AND BALAN

HEN Arthur was at one time in Camelot with his knights, a messenger came to him from Rience, king of North Wales and Ireland, saying, "My Lord, the king Rience has conquered eleven kings, and all of them do homage to him.

Moreover, each gave to the king his beard, shaved clean from his face, and my master has used the eleven beards to trim his mantle. One place on the mantle is still vacant, and Rience demands that you send your beard at once to fill the vacant place or he will come with sword and spear, lay waste your land and take your beard and your head with it."

Then was Arthur terribly enraged, and would have killed the messenger on the spot, but that he remembered the knightly usage and spared the herald.

"Now this is the most insulting message ever sent from one man to another. Return to your king and tell him that my beard is yet too young to trim a mantle with, and that, moreover, neither I nor any of my lieges owe him homage. On the other hand I demand homage from him, and unless he render it, I will assemble my knights and take both his head and his kingdom."

The messenger departed, and soon Arthur heard that Rience had invaded the kingdom with a great

130

host, and had slain large numbers of people. Arthur then hurriedly summoned his barons, knights and men-at-arms to meet him at Camelot for council.

When Arthur and his followers had gathered at Camelot a damsel richly clothed in a robe of fur rode among them, and as she came before the king she let fall the mantle from her shoulders, and lo! there was girt at her side a noble sword.

Arthur wondered, and said, "Why do you come before me in this unseemly manner, girt with a great sword?"

The damsel answered, "I am girt with this great sword against my will and may not remove it until it is drawn from its scabbard, a thing that can be done only by a knight, and that a passing good one, without treachery or villainy of any sort. I have been with King Rience, and many of his knights have tried to draw the sword from its scabbard, but no one succeeded. I have heard that here you have many good knights, and perchance one may be found who can pull the blade."

"This is marvelous," said Arthur. "I will myself make the first attempt, not because I think myself the best knight, but to give my knights an example."

Then Arthur seized the sword by the scabbard and the hilt and pulled at it eagerly, but it would not move.

"Sir," said the damsel, "you need not pull the half so hard, for he who is fit can pull it with little strength."

Then one after another the knights all tried, but none could draw the sword.

"Alas," said the maiden, "I had thought that in this court there would be found at least one man of gentle blood on both his father's and his mother's side, himself without treason or guile."

There was then at the court a poor knight born in Northumberland who had been in prison for slaying the king's cousin, but who had been released at the request of the barons, for he was known to be a good man and well born.

Balin, for that was the knight's name, wished to try the sword, but was afraid to come forward because of his appearance. As the damsel was departing from the court, Balin called to her and said:

"Fair maid, I beg you to let me try to draw the sword, for though I am poorly clad I feel in my heart that I am as good as many who have tried, and I think I can succeed."

The damsel looked at Balin, and though she saw that he was a strong and handsome man, yet she looked at his poor raiment and thought that he could not be a noble knight without treachery and villainy. So she said to him, "Sir, put me to no more trouble, for I cannot think you will succeed where so many others have failed."

"Ah, fair damsel," said Balin, "perchance good deeds are not in a man's clothing, but manliness and bravery are hid within the person, and many a worshipful knight is not known to all the people. Therefore honor and greatness are not in raiment."

"By the Lord," said the damsel, "you speak well and say the truth. Therefore shall you try the sword."

And Balin grasped the scabbard and drew the sword out easily, and when he saw the sword he was greatly pleased, for it was a marvelous weapon of finest steel.

"Certainly," said the damsel, "this is a good knight, the best I have ever found, without treason,

THE DAMSEL LET FALL HER MANTLE

treachery or villainy; and many noble deeds shall he do. Now, gentle and gracious knight, give back the sword to me."

"No," said Balin, "this sword will I keep unless it be taken from me by force."

"Well," said the damsel, "you are unwise to hold the sword from me, for with it you shall slay the best friend that you have, the man you best love in all the world; and the sword shall also be your destruction."

"Nevertheless," replied Balin, "I shall take the event as God gives it me. But the sword you shall not have."

"Within a very short time," said the damsel, "you shall repent it. I ask the sword more on your account than mine, for I am sad for your sake. It is a great pity that you will not believe that the sword will be your destruction."

Speaking thus the damsel departed from the court, sorrowing as she went. As soon as the damsel had gone, Balin sent for his horse and his armor and made ready to depart from the court.

"Do not leave us so lightly," said King Arthur, "for though I have in ignorance misused thee, I know now that thou art a noble knight, and if thou wilt stay, I will advance thee much to thy liking."

"God bless your highness," said Balin. "Though no man may ever value your kindness and bounty more, yet at the present time I must thank you for your kindness and beseech your good grace."

"If you must go," said Arthur, "I pray you not to tarry long, for right welcome will you be on your return, and then I shall take pains to make right what I did amiss before."

"God reward your lordship," said Balin, as he made ready to depart.

Ere he could leave, however, there came riding into the court the Lady of the Lake, from whom King Arthur had received his sword. She was

richly clothed, and as she entered she saluted
Arthur royally and said, "I come now to ask the
gift you promised me when I gave you the sword."

"That is right," said Arthur; "a gift I certainly
promised you, but I have forgotten the name of
the sword you gave me."

"The name of the sword is Excalibur. That is
to say, 'Cut Steel.'"

"That is right," said the king. "Now ask what
you will and you shall have it if it lies in my power
to give it."

"I ask," returned the Lady, "the head of the
knight that to-day has won the other sword, or else
the head of the damsel who brought the sword.
By right I should have the heads of both, for he
slew my brother, a good and true knight, and that
woman caused my father's death."

"Indeed," said Arthur, "I cannot grant such a
request as that with any justice to myself. Therefore, ask what else you will and I will grant it."

"I want nothing else," said the Lady; "I will
ask no other thing."

Now when Balin was leaving the court he saw
this Lady of the Lake. Three years before she
had slain Balin's mother, and all this time he had
been searching for the wicked woman. Then some
one told him that she had asked his head of Arthur.

On hearing this, Balin went straight to the woman and said, "It is unlucky for you that I have
found you to-day. You asked my head of King
Arthur, and therefore you shall lose yours."

With these words Balin drew his sword, and
before any one could interfere struck off her head,
even before the face of King Arthur.

"Alas," said Arthur, "why have you done this deed? You have shamed me and all my court, for this was a lady to whom I was indebted, and she came here under my safe conduct. I shall never forgive you this vile deed."

"Sire," said Balin, "withdraw your displeasure, for this same lady was the falsest lady living, and by enchantment and sorcery she has destroyed many good knights. She it was who through falsehood and treachery caused my mother to be burned."

"No matter what cause you had," replied the king, "you should have waited till she left my presence. You shall certainly repent this deed, for such another insult I never had in my court. Therefore, withdraw from my presence with all the haste you may."

Balin took up the head of the Lady and carried it to his hostelry, where he met his squire.

"Now," said Balin, as the two rode out of the town, "much I regret to have displeased King Arthur. You must, however, take this head and carry it to my friends in Northumberland, and tell them that my most bitter enemy is dead. Tell them, too, that I am out of prison, and how I came to get this sword."

"Alas," said the squire, "you were greatly to blame for so displeasing King Arthur."

"As for that," said Balin, "I will go with all the haste I can to meet King Rience that I may destroy him or die myself. If perchance I may happen to overthrow him, then Arthur will forgive me and be my gracious lord."

"Where shall I meet you?" said the squire.

"In King Arthur's court," answered Balin.

When Balin left King Arthur's court, Lanceor, a proud and arrogant knight who counted himself the best of Arthur's followers, went and offered to ride after Balin and bring him back dead or alive.

"Go," said King Arthur, "for I am wroth with Balin and would have revenge for the insult he has shown me."

So Lanceor departed to arm himself, and in the meantime, Merlin arrived, and hearing of the death of the Lady of the Lake, by the sword of Balin, went in to King Arthur.

"Now," said Merlin, "you should know that this damsel who brought the sword to the court is the falsest woman living. She has a brother whom she hates beyond measure, and it was to compass his death that she came hither, for it had been decreed that whoso drew the sword should slay her brother. This I know to be true. Would to God she had never come to this court, for the knight that drew the sword shall die by that sword, and this shall be a great reproach to you and your court; for no man liveth of greater ability and prowess than this same knight Balin, and much good will he do you. It is a great pity he may not live to serve you with his strength and hardiness."

In the meantime Lanceor, armed at all points, rode at full speed after Balin, and when he caught sight of him he called in a loud voice, "Stop, you false knight, for you shall return with me whether you will or not, and your shield and your sword shall not help you."

When Balin heard the voice he turned his horse fiercely and said, "What is it you will with me? Will you joust with me?"

"Yes," said the Irish knight. "For that reason have I followed you."

"Perchance," said Balin, "it would have been better if you had remained at home, for many a man who strives to overthrow his enemy falls himself in the struggle. From what court do you come?"

"I am from the court of King Arthur," said Lanceor, "and I came to seek revenge for the insult you showed Arthur and his court this day."

"I see," said Balin, "that I must fight with you, but I much regret that I have done wrong before King Arthur and his court. Your quarrel with me is foolish, for the lady that I slew did me, through falsehood and treachery, the greatest harm on earth, else would I have been as loath as any knight that lives to slay a lady."

"Cease talking," said Lanceor, "and face me, for only one of us shall remain alive."

Then they levelled their spears and clashed together as hard as their horses could. The spear of the Irish knight struck Balin on the shield and broke all in pieces, but Balin's spear pierced the shield of Lanceor, passed through his hauberk and body and even into his horse, so that Lanceor fell, a dead man.

Regretting much that he had slain one of Arthur's knights, Balin buried Lanceor and proceeded on his way.

He had not ridden far into the forest when he saw a knight coming towards him whom by his arms he recognized as his brother Balan. When they met they dismounted and kissed each other and wept for pure joy.

When they had calmed themselves a little, Balan said, "I had no thought of meeting you here; I had supposed you were still in prison, for a knight that I met at the castle of Four Stones told me how you had been imprisoned by the king. I came this way hoping to serve you."

Balin in reply told him of his adventures until the time they met, and added, "Truly I am very sad that King Arthur is displeased with me, for he is the most worshipful knight that reigneth on this earth. Now I mean to regain his love or perish in the attempt. King Rience is even now besieging the Castle Terrabil, and thither do I ride to see what I can do against him."

"I will go with you," said Balan, "and we will help each other as true knights and good brethren ought to do."

As they talked they saw coming toward them a misshapen old man. This was Merlin in a strange disguise, though the brothers did not know him.

"Ah, Balin," said the old dwarf, "too ready are you to strike in anger, for here you have slain one of the noblest knights of Arthur's court, and his kinsmen will follow you through the world till they have slain you."

"As for that," said Balin, "I have little fear, but I regret beyond words that I have displeased my lord, King Arthur."

"Be that as it may," answered Merlin, "you have given the saddest blow ever struck; and yet worse is to come, for with that same sword will you slay your brother."

"If I believed that," the sad knight replied, "I should kill myself now to prove you a liar."

At that moment the crippled old man vanished suddenly, and the brothers saw Merlin in his own person riding toward them.

"Where are you going?" inquired Merlin.

"At present we have little to do and ride as we please."

"I can tell you where you are going," said the magician. "You go to meet King Rience, but your journey will be a failure unless you are guided by my counsel."

"Ah, Merlin," said Balin, "we will be ruled by you."

"Come on then; but see that you fight manfully, for you will need all your strength and valor."

"Fear not," they both exclaimed. "We will do all that men can do."

"Then," said the magician, "conceal yourselves here in the woods behind the leaves. Hide your horses and rest in patience, for soon will Rience with sixty of his best knights come this way. You can fall upon them from ambush and easily destroy them."

It happened just as Merlin had predicted, and the brothers soon saw the sixty knights riding down the lane.

"Which is Rience?" asked Balin.

"There," said he, "the knight that rides in the midst—that is Rience."

The brothers waited till Rience was opposite them, and then they rushed upon him and bore him down, wounding him severely. Wheeling from the charge they fell upon the followers of Rience and smote them to right and left, so that many fell dead or wounded and the remainder broke into flight.

Returning to King Rience the brothers would have killed him, but he cried, "Slay me not. By my death you will win nothing, but by my life you may win."

"That is so," the two agreed: and they made a litter, and Balan bore Rience to King Arthur, but Balin would not go to the court till he had done more for Arthur.

The tale of Balin's deeds is too long for recital here, but it may be read in the book of King Arthur's knights. At last, after many days of wandering and many exciting combats, Balin saw by the roadside a cross upon which in letters of gold was written, "No man must ride to this castle alone."

Then, too, an old man came toward him and said, "Balin le Savage, turn now before it is too late. You have already passed the bounds of prudence." With these words the old man vanished, and Balin heard the blast of a horn, like that blown when a huntsman kills an animal.

"That blast," said Balin to himself, "is for me, for I am the prize, yet am I not dead."

As the echoes of the horn died away, Balin saw coming toward him a hundred knights and ladies who rode up to him and smilingly greeted him.

"Come with us to the castle," said they, "and there shall be music and dancing and feasting and much joy."

Balin followed them to the castle and was surprised at the good cheer that awaited him. In the midst of the feast, when joy was at its height, the chief lady of the feast looked at Balin and said, "Knight with the two swords, no man may pass this way unless he fight with a knight who keeps an island near by. Now must you joust with him."

"That is an unhappy custom," said Balin, "that a knight may not pass this way unless he fight."

"You need to fight with but one man," said the lady.

"Well," said Balin, "if I must fight, then must I fight, but a traveling man and his horse are oft-times weary. However, though my horse and my body are weary, my heart is not weary, and I will go where danger awaits me."

"Sir," said one of the knights to Balin, "it seems to me that your shield is not in good condition. Take mine; it is a larger one, and you are quite welcome to it."

So Balin took the strange shield and left his own, with his arms blazoned on it, at the castle, and rode forth to the island. On his way he met a maid who called to him, "O Balin, why have you left your own shield behind? You have now put yourself in the gravest danger, for by the arms upon your shield all men might know you. It is a great pity, indeed, that evil should befall you, for you are the peer of any knight now living."

"I repent exceedingly," said Balin, "that I ever came into this country, but now that I have set foot upon this adventure I may not turn back without shame to myself. Be it life or death, now will I take whatsoever God willeth."

Then he looked carefully at his armor and saw that it was all in good condition and that his shield and spear were in good trim, and then, blessing himself, he mounted his horse. Out of the castle there now came riding toward him a knight on a

powerful charger. Red was the armor of the
knight, red his shield, without any arms or device,
and red were the trappings on his horse. Now this
knight in red was Balan, and when he saw coming
toward him a knight with two swords he thought
it must be his brother Balin, but when he looked at
the shield it was strange, and thus, neither brother
knowing the other, they levelled their spears and
dashed together at full speed.

The spear of each struck fair in the center of the
shield of the other, and their spears were so strong
and their charge so fierce that both horses were
thrown to the ground and the men lay on the
ground unconscious. Balin was sadly bruised by
the fall of his horse, and besides he was weary of
travel, so that Balan was the first to get up and
draw his sword. Balin, however, was little behind
him, and was ready with his weapon to meet the
onset. Balan was first to strike, and though Balin
put up his shield the sword passed through it and
cut through his helm. Balin returned the blow with
that unhappy sword that carried so much misery
with it, and well-nigh killed his brother, but both
recovered themselves and fought together, charging
back and forth until their breath failed them.

As they rested for a moment Balin looked up to
the castle walls and saw that the towers were filled
with ladies. Inspired by the sight, both went into
battle again, and both were wounded many times.
Often they rested and often renewed the combat,
until the ground around them was red with blood.
Both had been wounded seven times or more, and
each wound so serious that it would have been the
death of any less mighty man. Both were weary

and weak from their exertions, but still they fought on. Their helmets were hewed off and their armor fell to pieces till they were almost naked and defenseless.

At last Balan withdrew a little and lay down in utter exhaustion.

"What knight art thou?" said Balin le Savage. "Never have I found a knight that so well matched me."

"My name," he said, "is Balan, brother of the great knight Balin."

"Alas," said Balin, "that ever I should see this day." And with these words he fell back unconscious.

Balan, on his hands and knees, crept to his brother and took the helm from off his head, but even then he did not know him, so bloody and wounded was his face.

When a few minutes later Balin recovered consciousness, he cried, "Oh Balan, my brother, thou hast slain me and I thee. On this account all the world shall speak of us."

"Alas," said Balan, "that I ever saw this day, and shame on me that I knew you not, for I saw your two swords; but because you had a strange shield I thought you were some strange knight."

"There is a false knight in the castle," said Balin, "that got me to leave my own shield and gave me his, and for this reason are we both to die. Would that I might live to destroy the castle and prevent the foul customs that pertain here."

"That, indeed, were the right thing to do," said Balan, "for on the day that I came hither I happened to kill the knight that kept the island, and since then never have I been able to depart but have been compelled to keep this island against all comers. If you had slain me, then must you have

THE FIGHT

kept the island, for no man may leave because of an enchantment."

While they were still talking, the chief lady of the castle, with four knights and six ladies and six yeomen, came to them and listened to their complaining.

"We are two brothers," said they, "born from one mother, and in one grave must we lie, so we pray you to bury us here where the battle was fought."

Weeping at the sad spectacle the lady granted their request and promised that they should be interred with great ceremonies.

"Now," said Balin, "will you send us a priest that we may receive our sacrament, the blessed body of our Lord Jesus Christ?"

"Yes," said the lady, "I will send at once."

When the priest had come and administered the last rite, Balin said, "When we are buried in a single tomb, and when the inscription upon it reads that two brothers in ignorance slew each other, then will every good knight who comes this way see our tomb and pray for the peace of our souls."

Amidst the weeping of the ladies and the gentle-women there, Balan died, but Balin lingered on until after midnight. The lady kept her promise and buried both in one tomb, and placed before it the inscription:

HERE LIE TWO BRETHREN,
EACH SLAIN BY
HIS BROTHER'S HAND.

She knew not their names, but in the morning Merlin came that way, and in letters of gold wrote on the tomb, "Here lieth Balin le Savage, the knight with two swords, and Balan his brother." Then Merlin took the famous sword, unfastened the pommel, and offered the sword to a knight to try; but the knight could not handle it, and Merlin laughed in his face.

"Why do you laugh?" said the knight, angrily.

"For this reason," said Merlin. "No man shall ever handle this sword except Sir Launcelot or else Galahad, his son."

All this Merlin wrote in letters of gold on the pommel of the sword. The scabbard of Balin's sword he left on the side of the island where Sir Galahad would find it.

GERAINT AND ENID[1]

By ALFRED TENNYSON

I

THE brave Geraint, a knight of Arthur's
court,
A tributary prince of Devon, one
Of that great order of the Table
Round,
Had married Enid, Yniol's only
child,
And loved her, as he loved the light of Heaven.
And as the light of Heaven varies, now
At sunrise, now at sunset, now by night
With moon and trembling stars, so loved Geraint
To make her beauty vary day by day,
In crimsons and in purples and in gems.
And Enid, but to please her husband's eye,
Who first had found and loved her in a state
Of broken fortunes, daily fronted him
In some fresh splendor; and the Queen herself,
Loved her, and often with her own white hands
Array'd and deck'd her, as the loveliest,
Next after her own self, in all the court.
And Enid loved the Queen, and with true heart

---

1. Tennyson, in his collection of poems known as the *Idyls of the King*, worked up in beautiful form many of the legends which had grown up around the names of King Arthur and his Knights of the Round Table. *Geraint and Enid* is one of the most popular of these.

ALFRED, LORD TENNYSON
1809–1892

Adored her, as the stateliest and the best
And loveliest of all women upon earth.
At last, forsooth, because his princedom lay
Close on the borders of a territory,
Wherein were bandit earls, and caitiff knights,
Assassins, and all flyers from the hand
Of Justice, and whatever loathes a law:
He craved a fair permission to depart,
And there defend his marches; and the King
Mused for a little on his plea, but, last,
Allowing it, the Prince and Enid rode,
And fifty knights rode with them, to the shores
Of Severn, and they past to their own land;
Where, thinking, that if ever yet was wife
True to her lord, mine shall be so to me,
He compass'd her with sweet observances
And worship, never leaving her, and grew
Forgetful of his promise to the King,
Forgetful of the falcon and the hunt,
Forgetful of the tilt and tournament,
Forgetful of his glory and his name,
Forgetful of his princedom and its cares.
And this forgetfulness was hateful to her.
And by and by the people, when they met
In twos and threes, or fuller companies,
Began to scoff and jeer and babble of him
As of a prince whose manhood was all gone,
And molten down in mere uxoriousness.
And this she gather'd from the people's eyes:
This too the women who attired her head,
To please her, dwelling on his boundless love,
Told Enid, and they sadden'd her the more:
And day by day she thought to tell Geraint,
But could not out of bashful delicacy;

While he that watch'd her sadden, was the more
Suspicious that her nature had a taint.

At last, it chanced that on a summer morn
(They sleeping each by either) the new sun
Beat thro' the blindless casement of the room,
And heated the strong warrior in his dreams;
Who, moving, cast the coverlet aside,
And bared the knotted column of his throat,
The massive square of his heroic breast,
And arms on which the standing muscle sloped,
As slopes a wild brook o'er a little stone,
Running too vehemently to break upon it.
And Enid woke and sat beside the couch,
Admiring him, and thought within herself,
Was ever man so grandly made as he?
Then, like a shadow, past the people's talk
And accusation of uxoriousness
Across her mind, and bowing over him,
Low to her own heart piteously she said:

"O noble breast and all-puissant arms,
Am I the cause, I the poor cause that men
Reproach you, saying all your force is gone?
I *am* the cause, because I dare not speak
And tell him what I think and what they say.
And yet I hate that he should linger here;
I cannot love my lord and not his name.
Far liefer had I gird his harness on him,
And ride with him to battle and stand by,
And watch his mightful hand striking great blows
At caitiffs and at wrongers of the world.
Far better were I laid in the dark earth,
Not hearing any more his noble voice,

Not to be folded more in these dear arms,
And darken'd from the high light in his eyes,
Than that my lord thro' me should suffer shame.
Am I so bold, and could I so stand by,
And see my dear lord wounded in the strife,
Or maybe pierced to death before mine eyes,
And yet not dare to tell him what I think,
And how men slur him, saying all his force
Is melted into mere effeminacy?
O me, I fear that I am no true wife."

Half inwardly, half audibly she spoke,
And the strong passion in her made her weep
True tears upon his broad and naked breast,
And these awoke him, and by great mischance
He heard but fragments of her later words,
And that she fear'd she was not a true wife.
And then he thought, "In spite of all my care,
For all my pains, poor man, for all my pains,
She is not faithful to me, and I see her
Weeping for some gay knight in Arthur's hall."
Right thro' his manful breast darted the pang
That makes a man, in the sweet face of her
Whom he loves most, lonely and miserable.
At this he hurl'd his huge limbs out of bed,
And shook his drowsy squire awake and cried,
"My charger and her palfrey;" then to her
"I will ride forth into the wilderness,
For tho' it seems my spurs are yet to win,
I have not fall'n so low as some would wish.
And thou, put on thy worst and meanest dress
And ride with me." And Enid ask'd, amazed,
"If Enid errs, let Enid learn her fault."
But he, "I charge thee, ask not, but obey."

Then she bethought her of a faded silk,
A faded mantle and a faded veil,
And moving toward a cedarn cabinet,
Wherein she kept them folded reverently
With sprigs of summer laid between the folds,
She took them, and array'd herself therein,
Remembering when first he came on her
Drest in that dress, and how he loved her in it,
And all her foolish fears about the dress,
And all his journey to her, as himself
Had told her, and their coming to the court.

For Arthur on the Whitsuntide before
Held court at old Caerleon upon Usk.
There on a day, he sitting high in hall,
Before him came a forester of Dean,
Wet from the woods, with notice of a hart
Taller than all his fellows, milky-white,
First seen that day: these things he told the King.
Then the good King gave order to let blow
His horns for hunting on the morrow morn.
And when the Queen petition'd for his leave
To see the hunt, allow'd it easily.
So with the morning all the court were gone.
But Guinevere lay late into the morn,
But rose at last, a single maiden with her,
Took horse, and forded Usk, and gain'd the wood;
There, on a little knoll beside it, stay'd
Waiting to hear the hounds; but heard instead
A sudden sound of hoofs, for Prince Geraint,
Late also, wearing neither hunting-dress
Nor weapon, save a golden-hilted brand,
Came quickly flashing thro' the shallow ford
Behind them, and so gallop'd up the knoll.

A purple scarf, at either end whereof
There swung an apple of the purest gold,
Sway'd round about him, as he gallop'd up
To join them, glancing like a dragon-fly
In summer suit and silks of holiday.
Low bow'd the tributary Prince, and she,
Sweetly and statelily, and with all grace
Of womanhood and queenhood, answer'd him:
"Late, late, Sir Prince," she said, "later than we!"
"Yea, noble Queen," he answer'd, "and so late
That I but come like you to see the hunt,
Not join it." "Therefore wait with me," she said;
"For on this little knoll, if anywhere,
There is good chance that we shall hear the hounds:
Here often they break covert at our feet."
And while they listen'd for the distant hunt,
And chiefly for the baying of Cavall,
King Arthur's hound of deepest mouth, there rode
Full slowly by a knight, lady, and dwarf;
Whereof the dwarf lagg'd latest, and the knight
Had vizor up, and show'd a youthful face,
Imperious and of haughtiest lineaments.
And Guinevere, not mindful of his face
In the King's hall, desired his name, and sent
Her maiden to demand it of the dwarf;
Who being vicious, old and irritable,
And doubling all his master's vice of pride,
Made answer sharply that she should not know.
"Then will I ask it of himself," she said.
"Nay, by my faith, thou shalt not," cried the dwarf;
"Thou art not worthy ev'n to speak of him;"
And when she put her horse toward the knight,
Struck at her with his whip, and she return'd
Indignant to the Queen; whereat Geraint

Exclaiming, "Surely I will learn the name,"
Made sharply to the dwarf, and ask'd it of him,
Who answer'd as before; and when the Prince
Had put his horse in motion toward the knight,
Struck at him with his whip, and cut his cheek.
The Prince's blood spurted upon the scarf,
Dyeing it; and his quick, instinctive hand
Caught at the hilt, as to abolish him:
But he, from his exceeding manfulness
And pure nobility of temperament,
Wroth to be wroth at such a worm, refrain'd
From ev'n a word, and so returning said:

"I will avenge this insult, noble Queen,
Done in your maiden's person to yourself:
And I will track this vermin to their earths;
For tho' I ride unarm'd, I do not doubt
To find, at some place I shall come at, arms
On loan, or else for pledge; and, being found,
Then will I fight him, and will break his pride,
And on the third day will again be here,
So that I be not fall'n in fight.   Farewell."

"Farewell, fair Prince," answer'd the stately
      Queen.
"Be prosperous in this journey, as in all;
And may you light on all things that you love,
And live to wed with her whom first you love:
But ere you wed with any, bring your bride,
And I, were she the daughter of a king,
Yea, tho' she were a beggar from the hedge,
Will clothe her for her bridals like the sun."

And Prince Geraint, now thinking that he heard
The noble hart at bay, now the far horn,

A little vext at losing of the hunt,
A little at the vile occasion, rode,
By ups and downs, thro' many a grassy glade
And valley, with fixt eye following the three.
At last they issued from the world of wood,
And climb'd upon a fair and even ridge,
And show'd themselves against the sky, and sank.
And thither came Geraint, and underneath
Beheld the long street of a little town
In a long valley, on one side whereof,
White from the mason's hand, a fortress rose;
And on one side a castle in decay,
Beyond a bridge that spann'd a dry ravine:
And out of town and valley came a noise
As of a broad brook o'er a shingly bed
Brawling, or like a clamor of the rooks
At distance, ere they settle for the night.

And onward to the fortress rode the three,
And enter'd, and were lost behind the walls.
"So," thought Geraint, "I have track'd him to his
    earth."
And down the long street riding wearily,
Found every hostel full, and everywhere
Was hammer laid to hoof, and the hot hiss
And bustling whistle of the youth who scour'd
His master's armor; and of such a one
He ask'd, "What means the tumult in the town?"
Who told him, scouring still, "The sparrow-hawk!"
Then riding close behind an ancient churl,
Who, smitten by the dusty sloping beam,
Went sweating underneath a sack of corn,
Ask'd yet once more what meant the hubbub here?
Who answer'd gruffly, "Ugh! the sparrow-hawk."

Then riding further past an armorer's,
Who, with back turn'd, and bow'd above his work,
Sat riveting a helmet on his knee,
He put the self-same query, but the man
Not turning round, nor looking at him, said:
"Friend, he that labors for the sparrow-hawk
Has little time for idle questioners."
Whereat Geraint flash'd into sudden spleen:
"A thousand pips eat up your sparrow-hawk!
Tits, wrens, and all wing'd nothings peck him dead!
Ye think the rustic cackle of your bourg
The murmur of the world! What is it to me?
O wretched set of sparrows, one and all,
Who pipe of nothing but of sparrow-hawks!
Speak, if ye be not like the rest, hawk-mad,
Where can I get me harborage for the night?
And arms, arms, arms to fight the enemy? Speak!"
Whereat the armorer turning all amazed
And seeing one so gay in purple silks,
Came forward with the helmet yet in hand
And answer'd, "Pardon me, O stranger knight;
We hold a tourney here to-morrow morn,
And there is scantly time for half the work.
Arms? truth! I know not: all are wanted here.
Harborage? truth, good truth, I know not, save,
It may be, at Earl Yniol's, o'er the bridge
Yonder." He spoke and fell to work again.

Then rode Geraint, a little spleenful yet,
Across the bridge that spann'd the dry ravine.
There musing sat the hoary-headed Earl,
(His dress a suit of fray'd magnificence,
Once fit for feasts of ceremony) and said:
"Whither, fair son?" to whom Geraint replied,

"O friend, I seek a harborage for the night."
Then Yniol, "Enter therefore and partake
The slender entertainment of a house
Once rich, now poor, but ever open-door'd."
"Thanks, venerable friend," replied Geraint;
"So that you do not serve me sparrow-hawks
For supper, I will enter, I will eat
With all the passion of a twelve hours' fast."
Then sigh'd and smiled the hoary-headed Earl,
And answer'd, "Graver cause than yours is mine
To curse this hedgerow thief, the sparrow-hawk:
But in, go in; for save yourself desire it,
We will not touch upon him ev'n in jest."

Then rode Geraint into the castle court,
His charger trampling many a prickly star
Of sprouted thistle on the broken stones.
He look'd and saw that all was ruinous.
Here stood a shatter'd archway plumed with fern;
And here had fall'n a great part of a tower,
Whole, like a crag that tumbles from the cliff,
And like a crag was gay with wilding flowers:
And high above a piece of turret stair,
Worn by the feet that now were silent, wound
Bare to the sun, and monstrous ivy-stems
Claspt the gray walls with hairy-fibred arms,
And suck'd the joining of the stones, and look'd
A knot, beneath, of snakes, aloft, a grove.

And while he waited in the castle court,
The voice of Enid, Yniol's daughter, rang
Clear thro' the open casement of the hall,
Singing; and as the sweet voice of a bird,
Heard by the lander in a lonely isle,

Moves him to think what kind of bird it is
That sings so delicately clear, and make
Conjecture of the plumage and the form;
So the sweet voice of Enid moved Geraint;
And made him like a man abroad at morn
When first the liquid note beloved of men
Comes flying over many a windy wave
To Britain, and in April suddenly
Breaks from a coppice gemm'd with green and red,
And he suspends his converse with a friend,
Or it may be the labor of his hands,
To think or say, "There is the nightingale;"
So fared it with Geraint, who thought and said,
"Here, by God's grace, is the one voice for me."

It chanced the song that Enid sang was one
Of Fortune and her wheel, and Enid sang:

"Turn, Fortune, turn thy wheel and lower the
        proud;
Turn thy wild wheel thro' sunshine, storm, and
        cloud;
Thy wheel and thee we neither love nor hate.
"Turn, Fortune, turn thy wheel with smile or
        frown;
With that wild wheel we go not up or down;
Our hoard is little, but our hearts are great.

"Smile and we smile, the lords of many lands;
Frown and we smile, the lords of our own hands;
For man is man and master of his fate.

"Turn, turn thy wheel above the staring crowd;
Thy wheel and thou are shadows in the cloud;
Thy wheel and thee we neither love nor hate."

GERAINT HEARS ENID SINGING

"Hark, by the bird's song ye may learn the nest,"
Said Yniol; "enter quickly." Entering then,
Right o'er a mount of newly-fallen stones,
The dusky-rafter'd many-cobweb'd hall,
He found an ancient dame in dim brocade;
And near her, like a blossom vermeil-white,[2]
That lightly breaks a faded flower-sheath,
Moved the fair Enid, all in faded silk,
Her daughter. In a moment thought Geraint,
"Here by God's rood is the one maid for me."
But none spake word except the hoary Earl:
"Enid, the good knight's horse stands in the court;
Take him to stall, and give him corn, and then
Go to the town and buy us flesh and wine;
And we will make us merry as we may.
Our hoard is little, but our hearts are great."

He spake: the Prince, as Enid past him, fain
To follow, strode a stride, but Yniol caught
His purple scarf, and held, and said, "Forbear!
Rest! the good house, tho' ruin'd, O my son,
Endures not that her guest should serve himself."
And reverencing the custom of the house
Geraint, from utter courtesy, forbore.

So Enid took his charger to the stall;
And after went her way across the bridge,
And reach'd the town, and while the Prince and
      Earl
Yet spoke together, came again with one,
A youth, that following with a costrel[3] bore

2. *Vermeil-white* means *red and white*, or *reddish white*.

3. A *costrel* was a leather, wooden or earthenware bottle, provided with ears, by which it might be hung at the side.

The means of goodly welcome, flesh and wine.
And Enid brought sweet cakes to make them cheer,
And in her veil unfolded, manchet[4] bread.
And then, because their hall must also serve
For kitchen, boil'd the flesh, and spread the board,
And stood behind, and waited on the three.
And seeing her so sweet and serviceable,
Geraint had longing in him evermore
To stoop and kiss the tender little thumb,
That crost the trencher as she laid it down:
But after all had eaten, then Geraint,
For now the wine made summer in his veins,
Let his eye rove in following, or rest
On Enid at her lowly handmaid-work,
Now here, now there, about the dusky hall;
Then suddenly addrest the hoary Earl:

"Fair Host and Earl, I pray your courtesy;
This sparrow-hawk, what is he? tell me of him.
His name? but no, good faith, I will not have it:
For if he be the knight whom late I saw
Ride into that new fortress by your town,
White from the mason's hand, then have I sworn
From his own lips to have it—I am Geraint
Of Devon—for this morning when the Queen
Sent her own maiden to demand the name,
His dwarf, a vicious under-shapen thing,
Struck at her with his whip, and she return'd
Indignant to the Queen; and then I swore
That I would track this caitiff to his hold,
And fight and break his pride, and have it of him.
And all unarm'd I rode, and thought to find
Arms in your town, where all the men are mad;

4. *Manchet bread* is fine white bread.

They take the rustic murmur of their bourg
For the great wave that echoes round the world;
They would not hear me speak: but if ye know
Where I can light on arms, or if yourself
Should have them, tell me, seeing I have sworn
That I will break his pride and learn his name,
Avenging this great insult done the Queen."

Then cried Earl Yniol, "Art thou he indeed,
Geraint, a name far-sounded among men
For noble deeds? and truly I, when first
I saw you moving by me on the bridge,
Felt ye were somewhat, yea, and by your state
And presence might have guess'd you one of those
That eat in Arthur's hall at Camelot.
Nor speak I now from foolish flattery;
For this dear child hath often heard me praise
Your feats of arms, and often when I paused
Hath ask'd again, and ever loved to hear;
So grateful is the noise of noble deeds
To noble hearts who see but acts of wrong:
O never yet had woman such a pair
Of suitors as this maiden; first Limours,
A creature wholly given to brawls and wine,
Drunk even when he woo'd; and be he dead
I know not, but he passed to the wild land.
The second was your foe, the sparrow-hawk,
My curse, my nephew—I will not let his name
Slip from my lips if I can help it—he,
When I that knew him fierce and turbulent
Refused her to him, then his pride awoke;
And since the proud man often is the mean,
He sow'd a slander in the common ear,
Affirming that his father left him gold,

And in my charge, which was not render'd to
      him;
Bribed with large promises the men who served
About my person, the more easily
Because my means were somewhat broken into
Thro' open doors and hospitality;
Raised my own town against me in the night
Before my Enid's birthday, sack'd my house;
From mine own earldom foully ousted me;
Built that new fort to overawe my friends,
For truly there are those who love me yet;
And keeps me in this ruinous castle here,
Where doubtless he would put me soon to death,
But that his pride too much despises me:
And I myself sometimes despise myself;
For I have let men be, and have their way;
Am much too gentle, have not used my power:
Nor know I whether I be very base
Or very manful, whether very wise
Or very foolish; only this I know,
That whatsoever evil happen to me,
I seem to suffer nothing heart or limb,
But can endure it all most patiently."

"Well said, true heart," replied Geraint, "but
      arms,
That if the sparrow-hawk, this nephew, fight
In next day's tourney I may break his pride."

And Yniol answer'd, "Arms, indeed, but old
And rusty, old and rusty, Prince Geraint,
Are mine, and therefore at thine asking, thine.
But in this tournament can no man tilt,
Except the lady he loves best be there.

Two forks are fixt into the meadow ground,
And over these is placed a silver wand.
And over that a golden sparrow-hawk,
The prize of beauty for the fairest there.
And this, what knight soever be in field
Lays claim to for the lady at his side,
And tilts with my good nephew thereupon,
Who being apt at arms and big of bone
Has ever won it for the lady with him,
And toppling over all antagonism
Has earn'd himself the name of sparrow-hawk.
But thou, that hast no lady, canst not fight."

To whom Geraint with eyes all bright replied,
Leaning a little toward him, "Thy leave!
Let *me* lay lance in rest, O noble host,
For this dear child, because I never saw,
Tho' having seen all beauties of our time,
Nor can see elsewhere, anything so fair.
And if I fall her name will yet remain
Untarnish'd as before; but if I live,
So aid me Heaven when at mine uttermost,
As I will make her truly my true wife."

Then, howsoever patient, Yniol's heart
Danced in his bosom, seeing better days,
And looking round he saw not Enid there,
(Who hearing her own name had stol'n away)
But that old dame, to whom full tenderly
And fondling all her hand in his he said,
"Mother, a maiden is a tender thing,
And best by her that bore her understood.
Go thou to rest, but ere thou go to rest
Tell her, and prove her heart toward the Prince."

So spake the kindly-hearted Earl, and she
With frequent smile and nod departing found,
Half disarray'd as to her rest, the girl;
Whom first she kiss'd on either cheek, and then
On either shining shoulder laid a hand,
And kept her off and gazed upon her face,
And told her all their converse in the hall,
Proving her heart: but never light and shade
Coursed one another more on open ground
Beneath a troubled heaven, than red and pale
Across the face of Enid hearing her;
While slowly falling as a scale that falls,
When weight is added only grain by grain,
Sank her sweet head upon her gentle breast;
Nor did she lift an eye nor speak a word,
Rapt in the fear and in the wonder of it;
So moving without answer to her rest
She found no rest, and ever fail'd to draw
The quiet night into her blood, but lay
Contemplating her own unworthiness;
And when the pale and bloodless east began
To quicken to the sun, arose, and raised
Her mother too, and hand in hand they moved
Down to the meadow where the jousts were held,
And waited there for Yniol and Geraint.

And thither came the twain, and when Geraint
Beheld her first in field, awaiting him,
He felt, were she the prize of bodily force,
Himself beyond the rest pushing could move
The chair of Idris.   Yniol's rusted arms
Were on his princely person, but thro' these
Princelike his bearing shone; and errant knights
And ladies came, and by and by the town

Flow'd in, and settling circled all the lists.
And there they fixt the forks into the ground,
And over these they placed the silver wand,
And over that the golden sparrow-hawk.
Then Yniol's nephew, after trumpet blown,
Spake to the lady with him and proclaim'd,
"Advance and take as fairest of the fair,
For I these two years past have won it for thee,
The prize of beauty." Loudly spake the Prince,
"Forbear: there is a worthier," and the knight
With some surprise and thrice as much disdain
Turn'd, and beheld the four, and all his face
Glow'd like the heart of a great fire at Yule,
So burnt he was with passion, crying out,
"Do battle for it then," no more; and thrice
They clash'd together, and thrice they brake their
        spears.
Then each, dishorsed and drawing, lash'd at each
So often and with such blows, that all the crowd
Wonder'd, and now and then from distant walls
There came a clapping as of phantom hands.
So twice they fought, and twice they breathed, and
        still
The dew of their great labor, and the blood
Of their strong bodies, flowing, drain'd their force.
But either's force was match'd till Yniol's cry,
"Remember that great insult done the Queen,"
Increased Geraint's, who heaved his blade aloft,
And crack'd the helmet thro', and bit the bone,
And fell'd him, and set foot upon his breast,
And said, "Thy name?" To whom the fallen man
Made answer, groaning, "Edyrn, son of Nudd!
Ashamed am I that I should tell it thee.
My pride is broken: men have seen my fall."

"Then, Edyrn, son of Nudd," replied Geraint,
"These two things shalt thou do, or else thou diest.
First, thou thyself, with damsel and with dwarf,
Shalt ride to Arthur's court, and coming there,
Crave pardon for that insult done the Queen,
And shalt abide her judgment on it; next,
Thou shalt give back their earldom to thy kin.
These two things shalt thou do, or thou shalt die."
And Edyrn answered, "These things will I do,
For I have never yet been overthrown,
And thou hast overthrown me, and my pride
Is broken down, for Enid sees my fall!"
And rising up, he rode to Arthur's court,
And there the Queen forgave him easily.
And being young, he changed and came to loathe
His crime of traitor, slowly drew himself
Bright from his old dark life, and fell at last
In the great battle fighting for the King.

But when the third day from the hunting-morn
Made a low splendor in the world, and wings
Moved in her ivy, Enid, for she lay
With her fair head in the dim-yellow light,
Among the dancing shadows of the birds,
Woke and bethought her of her promise given
No later than last eve to Prince Geraint—
So bent he seem'd on going the third day,
He would not leave her, till her promise given—
To ride with him this morning to the court,
And there be made known to the stately Queen,
And there be wedded with all ceremony.
At this she cast her eyes upon her dress,
And thought it never yet had look'd so mean.
For as a leaf in mid-November is

To what it was in mid-October, seem'd
The dress that now she look'd on to the dress
She look'd on ere the coming of Geraint.
And still she look'd, and still the terror grew
Of that strange, bright and dreadful thing, a court,
All staring at her in her faded silk:
And softly to her own sweet heart she said:

"This noble prince who won our earldom back,
So splendid in his acts and his attire,
Sweet heaven, how much I shall discredit him!
Would he could tarry with us here awhile,
But being so beholden to the Prince,
It were but little grace in any of us,
Bent as he seem'd on going this third day,
To seek a second favor at his hands.
Yet if he could but tarry a day or two,
Myself would work eye dim, and finger lame,
Far liefer than so much discredit him."

And Enid fell in longing for a dress
All branch'd and flower'd with gold, a costly gift
Of her good mother, given her on the night
Before her birthday, three sad years ago,
That night of fire, when Edyrn sack'd their house,
And scatter'd all they had to all the winds:
For while the mother show'd it, and the two
Were turning and admiring it, the work
To both appear'd so costly, rose a cry
That Edyrn's men were on them, and they fled
With little save the jewels they had on,
Which being sold and sold had bought them bread:
And Edyrn's men had caught them in their flight,
And placed them in this ruin; and she wish'd

The Prince had found her in her ancient home;
Then let her fancy flit across the past,
And roam the goodly places that she knew;
And last bethought her how she used to watch,
Near that old home, a pool of golden carp;
And one was patch'd and blurr'd and lustreless
Among his burnish'd brethren of the pool;
And half asleep she made comparison
Of that and these to her own faded self
And the gay court, and fell asleep again;
And dreamt herself was such a faded form
Among her burnish'd sisters of the pool;
But this was in the garden of a king;
And tho' she lay dark in the pool, she knew
That all was bright; that all about were birds
Of sunny plume in gilded trellis-work;
That all the turf was rich in plots that look'd
Each like a garnet or a turkis in it;
And lords and ladies of the high court went
In silver tissue talking things of state;
And children of the King in cloth of gold
Glanced at the doors or gambol'd down the walks;
And while she thought "They will not see me," came
A stately queen whose name was Guinevere,
And all the children in their cloth of gold
Ran to her, crying, "If we have fish at all
Let them be gold; and charge the gardeners now
To pick the faded creature from the pool,
And cast it on the mixen⁵ that it die."
And therewithal one came and seized on her,
And Enid started waking, with her heart
All overshadow'd by the foolish dream,
And lo! it was her mother grasping her

5. *Mixen* is an old word for *dunghill.*

To get her well awake; and in her hand
A suit of bright apparel, which she laid
Flat on the couch, and spoke exultingly:
　"See here, my child, how fresh the colors look,
How fast they hold like colors of a shell
That keeps the wear and polish of the wave.
Why not? It never yet was worn, I trow:
Look on it, child, and tell me if ye know it."

　And Enid look'd, but all confused at first,
Could scarce divide it from her foolish dream:
Then suddenly she knew it and rejoiced,
And answer'd, "Yea, I know it; your good gift,
So sadly lost on that unhappy night;
Your own good gift!" "Yea, surely," said the dame,
"And gladly given again this happy morn.
For when the jousts were ended yesterday,
Went Yniol thro' the town, and everywhere
He found the sack and plunder of our house
All scatter'd thro' the houses of the town;
And gave command that all which once was ours
Should now be ours again; and yester-eve,
While ye were talking sweetly with your Prince,
Came one with this and laid it in my hand,
For love or fear, or seeking favor of us,
Because we have our earldom back again.
And yester-eve I would not tell you of it,
But kept it for a sweet surprise at morn.
Yea, truly is it not a sweet surprise?
For I myself unwillingly have worn
My faded suit, as you, my child, have yours,
And howsoever patient, Yniol his.
Ah, dear, he took me from a goodly house,
With store of rich apparel, sumptuous fare,

And page, and maid, and squire, and seneschal,
And pastime both of hawk and hound, and all
That appertains to noble maintenance.
Yea, and he brought me to a goodly house;
But since our fortune swerved from sun to shade,
And all thro' that young traitor, cruel need
Constrain'd us, but a better time has come;
So clothe yourself in this, that better fits
Our mended fortunes and a Prince's bride:
For tho' ye won the prize of fairest fair,
And tho' I heard him call you fairest fair,
Let never maiden think, however fair,
She is not fairer in new clothes than old.
And should some great court-lady say, the Prince
Hath pick'd a ragged-robin from the hedge,
And like a madman brought her to the court,
Then were ye shamed, and, worse, might shame the
      Prince
To whom we are beholden; but I know,
When my dear child is set forth at her best,
That neither court nor country, tho' they sought
Thro' all the provinces like those of old
That lighted on Queen Esther, has her match."

Here ceased the kindly mother out of breath;
And Enid listen'd brightening as she lay;
Then, as the white and glittering star of morn
Parts from a bank of snow, and by and by
Slips into golden cloud, the maiden rose,
And left her maiden couch, and robed herself,
Help'd by the mother's careful hand and eye,
Without a mirror, in the gorgeous gown;
Who, after, turn'd her daughter round, and said,
She never yet had seen her half so fair.   *   *   *

"And I can scarcely ride with you to court,
For old am I, and rough the ways and wild;
But Yniol goes, and I full oft shall dream
I see my princess as I see her now,
Clothed with my gift, and gay among the gay."

But while the women thus rejoiced, Geraint
Woke where he slept in the high hall, and call'd
For Enid, and when Yniol made report
Of that good mother making Enid gay
In such apparel as might well beseem
His princess, or indeed the stately Queen,
He answer'd: "Earl, entreat her by my love,
Albeit I give no reason but my wish,
That she ride with me in her faded silk."
Yniol with that hard message went; it fell
Like flaws in summer laying lusty corn:
For Enid, all abash'd she knew not why,
Dared not to glance at her good mother's face,
But silently, in all obedience,
Her mother silent too, nor helping her,
Laid from her limbs the costly-broider'd gift,
And robed them in her ancient suit again,
And so descended. Never man rejoiced
More than Geraint to greet her thus attired;
And glancing all at once as keenly at her
As careful robins eye the delver's toil,
Made her cheek burn and either eyelid fall,
But rested with her sweet face satisfied;
Then seeing cloud upon the mother's brow,
Her by both hands he caught, and sweetly said,

"O my new mother, be not wroth or grieved
At thy new son, for my petition to her.

When late I left Caerleon, our great Queen,
In words whose echo lasts, they were so sweet,
Made promise, that whatever bride I brought,
Herself would clothe her like the sun in Heaven.
Thereafter, when I reach'd this ruin'd hall,
Beholding one so bright in dark estate,
I vow'd that could I gain her, our fair Queen,
No hand but hers, should make your Enid burst
Sunlike from cloud—and likewise thought perhaps,
That service done so graciously would bind
The two together; fain I would the two
Should love each other: how can Enid find
A nobler friend? Another thought was mine;
I came among you here so suddenly,
That tho' her gentle presence at the lists
Might well have served for proof that I was loved,
I doubted whether daughter's tenderness,
Or easy nature, might not let itself
Be moulded by your wishes for her weal;
Or whether some false sense in her own self
Of my contrasting brightness, overbore
Her fancy dwelling in this dusky hall;
And such a sense might make her long for court
And all its perilous glories: and I thought,
That could I someway prove such force in her
Link'd with such love for me, that at a word
(No reason given her) she could cast aside
A splendor dear to women, new to her,
And therefore dearer; or if not so new,
Yet therefore tenfold dearer by the power
Of intermitted usage; then I felt
That I could rest, a rock in ebbs and flows,
Fixt on her faith. Now, therefore, I do rest,
A prophet certain of my prophecy,

That never shadow of mistrust can cross
Between us. Grant me pardon for my thoughts:
And for my strange petition I will make
Amends hereafter by some gaudy-day,
When your fair child shall wear your costly gift
Beside your own warm hearth, with, on her knees,
Who knows? another gift of the high God,
Which, maybe, shall have learn'd to lisp you
      thanks."

He spoke: the mother smiled, but half in tears,
Then brought a mantle down and wrapt her in it,
And claspt and kiss'd her, and they rode away.

Now thrice that morning Guinevere had climb'd
The giant tower, from whose high crest, they say,
Men saw the goodly hills of Somerset,
And white sails flying on the yellow sea;
But not to goodly hill or yellow sea
Look'd the fair Queen, but up the vale of Usk,
By the flat meadow, till she saw them come;
And then descending met them at the gates,
Embraced her with all welcome as a friend,
And did her honor as the Prince's bride,
And clothed her for her bridals like the sun;
And all that week was old Caerleon gay,
For by the hands of Dubric, the high saint,
They twain were wedded with all ceremony.

And this was on the last year's Whitsuntide.
But Enid ever kept the faded silk,
Remembering how first he came on her,
Drest in that dress, and how he loved her in it,
And all her foolish fears about the dress,

And all his journey toward her, as himself
Had told her, and their coming to the court.
　And now this morning when he said to her,
"Put on your worst and meanest dress," she found
And took it, and array'd herself therein.

II

O PURBLIND race of miserable men,
　　How many among us at this very hour
Do forge a life-long trouble for ourselves,
By taking true for false, or false for true;
Here, thro' the feeble twilight of this world
Groping, how many, until we pass and reach
That other, where we see as we are seen!

　So fared it with Geraint, who issuing forth
That morning, when they both had got to horse,
Perhaps because he loved her passionately,
And felt that tempest brooding round his heart,
Which, if he spoke at all, would break perforce
Upon a head so dear in thunder, said:
"Not at my side.　I charge thee ride before,
Ever a good way on before; and this
I charge thee, on thy duty as a wife,
Whatever happens, not to speak to me,
No, not a word!" and Enid was aghast;
And forth they rode, but scarce three paces on,
When crying out, "Effeminate as I am,
I will not fight my way with gilded arms
All shall be iron;" he loosed a mighty purse,
Hung at his belt, and hurl'd it toward the squire.
So the last sight that Enid had of home
Was all the marble threshold flashing, strown

With gold and scatter'd coinage, and the squire
Chafing his shoulder: then he cried again,
"To the wilds!" and Enid leading down the tracks
Thro' which he bade her lead him on, they past
The marches, and by bandit-haunted holds,
Gray swamps and pools, waste places of the hern,
And wildernesses, perilous paths, they rode:
Round was their pace at first, but slacken'd soon:
A stranger meeting them had surely thought
They rode so slowly and they look'd so pale,
That each had suffered some exceeding wrong.
For he was ever saying to himself,
"O I that wasted time to tend upon her,
To compass her with sweet observances,
To dress her beautifully and keep her true"—
And there he broke the sentence in his heart
Abruptly, as a man upon his tongue
May break it, when his passion masters him.
And she was ever praying the sweet heavens
To save her dear lord whole from any wound.
And ever in her mind she cast about
For that unnoticed failing in herself,
Which made him look so cloudy and so cold;
Till the great plover's human whistle amazed
Her heart, and glancing round the waste she fear'd
In every wavering brake an ambuscade.
Then thought again, "If there be such in me,
I might amend it by the grace of Heaven,
If he would only speak and tell me of it."

But when the fourth part of the day was gone,
Then Enid was aware of three tall knights
On horseback, wholly arm'd, behind a rock
In shadow, waiting for them, caitiffs all;

And heard one crying to his fellow, "Look,
Here comes a laggard hanging down his head,
Who seems no bolder than a beaten hound;

ENID LEADS THE WAY

Come, we will slay him and will have his horse
And armor, and his damsel shall be ours."

Then Enid ponder'd in her heart, and said:
"I will go back a little to my lord,
And I will tell him all their caitiff talk;

For, be he wroth even to slaying me,
Far liefer by his dear hand had I die,
Than that my lord should suffer loss or shame."

Then she went back some paces of return,
Met his full frown timidly firm, and said:
"My lord, I saw three bandits by the rock
Waiting to fall on you, and heard them boast
That they would slay you, and possess your horse
And armor, and your damsel should be theirs."

He made a wrathful answer: "Did I wish
Your warning or your silence? one command
I laid upon you, not to speak to me,
And thus ye keep it! Well then, look—for now,
Whether ye wish me victory or defeat,
Long for my life, or hunger for my death,
Yourself shall see my vigor is not lost."

Then Enid waited pale and sorrowful,
And down upon him bare the bandit three.
And at the midmost charging, Prince Geraint
Drave the long spear a cubit thro' his breast
And out beyond; and then against his brace
Of comrades, each of whom had broken on him
A lance that splinter'd like an icicle,
Swung from his brand a windy buffet out
Once, twice, to right, to left, and stunn'd the twain
Or slew them, and dismounting like a man
That skins the wild beast after slaying him,
Stript from the three dead wolves of woman born
The three gay suits of armor which they wore,
And let the bodies lie, but bound the suits

Of armor on their horses, each on each,
And tied the bridle-reins of all the three
Together, and said to her, "Drive them on
Before you;" and she drove them thro' the waste.

He follow'd nearer: ruth began to work
Against his anger in him, while he watch'd
The being he loved best in all the world,
With difficulty in mild obedience
Driving them on: he fain had spoken to her,
And loosed in words of sudden fire the wrath
And smoulder'd wrong that burnt him all within;
But evermore it seem'd an easier thing
At once without remorse to strike her dead,
Than to cry "Halt," and to her own bright face
Accuse her of the least immodesty:
And thus tongue-tied, it made him wroth the more
That she *could* speak whom his own ear had heard
Call herself false: and suffering thus he made
Minutes an age: but in scarce longer time
Than at Caerleon the full-tided Usk,
Before he turn to fall seaward again,
Pauses, did Enid, keeping watch, behold
In the first shallow shade of a deep wood,
Before a gloom of stubborn-shafted oaks,
Three other horsemen waiting, wholly arm'd,
Whereof one seem'd far larger than her lord,
And shook her pulses, crying, "Look, a prize!
Three horses and three goodly suits of arms,
And all in charge of whom? a girl: set on."
"Nay," said the second, "yonder comes a knight."
The third, "A craven; how he hangs his head."
The giant answer'd merrily, "Yea, but one?
Wait here, and when he passes fall upon him."

And Enid ponder'd in her heart and said,
"I will abide the coming of my lord,
And I will tell him all their villany.
My lord is weary with the fight before,
And they will fall upon him unawares.
I needs must disobey him for his good;
How should I dare obey him to his harm?
Needs must I speak, and tho' he kill me for it,
I save a life dearer to me than mine."

And she abode his coming, and said to him
With timid firmness, "Have I leave to speak?"
He said, "Ye take it, speaking," and she spoke.

"There lurk three villains yonder in the wood,
And each of them is wholly arm'd, and one
Is larger-limb'd than you are, and they say
That they will fall upon you while ye pass."

To which he flung a wrathful answer back:
"And if there were an hundred in the wood,
And every man were larger-limb'd than I,
And all at once should sally upon me,
I swear it would not ruffle me so much
As you that not obey me. Stand aside,
And if I fall, cleave to the better man."

And Enid stood aside to wait the event,
Not dare to watch the combat, only breathe
Short fits of prayer, at every stroke a breath.
And he, she dreaded most, bare down upon him.
Aim'd at the helm, his lance err'd; but Geraint's,
A little in the late encounter strain'd,
Struck thro' the bulky bandit's corselet home.

And then brake short, and down his enemy roll'd,
And there lay still; as he that tells the tale
Saw once a great piece of a promontory,
That had a sapling growing on it, slide
From the long shore-cliff's windy walls to the beach,
And there lie still, and yet the sapling grew:
So lay the man transfixt. His craven pair
Of comrades making slowlier at the Prince,
When now they saw their bulwark fallen, stood;
On whom the victor, to confound them more,
Spurr'd with his terrible war-cry; for as one,
That listens near a torrent mountain-brook,
All thro' the crash of the near cataract hears
The drumming thunder of the huger fall
At distance, were the soldiers wont to hear
His voice in battle, and be kindled by it,
And foemen scared, like that false pair who turn'd
Flying, but, overtaken, died the death
Themselves had wrought on many an innocent.

  Thereon Geraint, dismounting, pick'd the lance
That pleased him best, and drew from those dead
       wolves
Their three gay suits of armor, each from each,
And bound them on their horses, each on each.
And tied the bridle-reins of all the three
Together, and said to her, "Drive them on
Before you," and she drove them thro' the wood.

  He follow'd nearer still: the pain she had
To keep them in the wild ways of the wood,
Two sets of three laden with jingling arms,
Together, served a little to disedge
The sharpness of that pain about her heart:

And they themselves, like creatures gently born
But into bad hands fall'n, and now so long
By bandits groom'd, prick'd their light ears, and
      felt
Her low firm voice and tender government.

So thro' the green gloom of the wood they past,
And issuing under open heavens beheld
A little town with towers, upon a rock,
And close beneath, a meadow gemlike chased
In the brown wild, and mowers mowing in it:
And down a rocky pathway from the place
There came a fair-hair'd youth, that in his hand
Bare victual for the mowers: and Geraint
Had ruth again on Enid looking pale:
Then, moving downward to the meadow ground,
He, when the fair-hair'd youth came by him, said,
"Friend, let her eat; the damsel is so faint."
"Yea, willingly," replied the youth; "and thou,
My lord, eat also, tho' the fare is coarse,
And only meet for mowers;" then set down
His basket, and dismounting on the sward
They let the horses graze, and ate themselves.
And Enid took a little delicately,
Less having stomach for it than desire
To close with her lord's pleasure; but Geraint
Ate all the mowers' victuals unawares,
And when he found all empty, was amazed;
And, "Boy," said he, "I have eaten all, but take
A horse and arms for guerdon; choose the best."
He, reddening in extremity of delight,
"My lord, you overpay me fifty-fold."
"Ye will be all the wealthier," cried the Prince.
"I take it as free gift, then," said the boy,

"Not guerdon; for myself can easily,
While your good damsel rests, return, and fetch
Fresh victual for these mowers of our Earl;
For these are his, and all the field is his,
And I myself am his; and I will tell him
How great a man thou art: he loves to know
When men of mark are in his territory:
And he will have thee to his palace here,
And serve thee costlier than with mowers' fare."

Then said Geraint, "I wish no better fare:
I never ate with angrier appetite
Than when I left your mowers dinnerless.
And into no Earl's palace will I go.
I know, God knows, too much of palaces!
And if he want me, let him come to me.
But hire us some fair chamber for the night,
And stalling for the horses, and return
With victual for these men, and let us know."

"Yea, my kind lord," said the glad youth, and
        went,
Held his head high, and thought himself a knight,
And up the rocky pathway disappear'd,
Leading the horse, and they were left alone.

But when the Prince had brought his errant eyes
Home from the rock, sideways he let them glance
At Enid, where she droopt: his own false doom,
That shadow of mistrust should never cross
Betwixt them, came upon him, and he sigh'd;
Then with another humorous ruth remark'd
The lusty mowers laboring dinnerless,
And watched the sun blaze on the turning scythe,

And after nodded sleepily in the heat.
But she, remembering her old ruin'd hall,
And all the windy clamor of the daws
About her hollow turret, pluck'd the grass
There growing longest by the meadow's edge,
And into many a listless annulet,
Now over, now beneath her marriage ring,
Wove and unwove it, till the boy return'd
And told them of a chamber, and they went;
Where, after saying to her, "if ye will,
Call for the woman of the house," to which
She answer'd, "Thanks, my lord;" the two remain'd
Apart by all the chamber's width, and mute
As creatures voiceless thro' the fault of birth,
Or two wild men supporters of a shield,
Painted, who stare at open space, nor glance
The one at other, parted by the shield.

On a sudden, many a voice along the street,
And heel against the pavement echoing, burst
Their drowse; and either started while the door,
Push'd from without, drave backward to the wall,
And midmost of a rout of roisterers,
Femininely fair and dissolutely pale,
Her suitor in old years before Geraint,
Enter'd, the wild lord of the place, Limours.
He moving up with pliant courtliness,
Greeted Geraint full face, but stealthily,
In the mid-warmth of welcome and graspt hand,
Found Enid with the corner of his eye,
And knew her sitting sad and solitary.
Then cried Geraint for wine and goodly cheer
To feed the sudden guest, and sumptuously
According to his fashion, bade the host

Call in what men soever were his friends,
And feast with these in honor of their Earl;
"And care not for the cost; the cost is mine."

And wine and food were brought, and Earl
        Limours
Drank till he jested with all ease, and told
Free tales, and took the word and play'd upon it,
And made it of two colors; for his talk,
When wine and free companions kindled him,
Was wont to glance and sparkle like a gem
Of fifty facets; thus he moved the Prince
To laughter and his comrades to applause.
Then, when the Prince was merry, ask'd Limours
"Your leave, my lord, to cross the room, and speak
To your good damsel there who sits apart,
And seems so lonely?" "My free leave," he said;
"Get her to speak: she doth not speak to me."
Then rose Limours, and looking at his feet,
Like him who tries the bridge he fears may fail,
Crost and came near, lifted adoring eyes,
Bow'd at her side and utter'd whisperingly:

    "Enid, the pilot star of my lone life,
Enid, my early and my only love,
Enid, the loss of whom hath turn'd me wild—
What chance is this? how is it I see you here?
Ye are in my power at last, are in my power.
Yet fear me not: I call mine own self wild,
But keep a touch of sweet civility
Here in the heart of waste and wilderness.
I thought, but that your father came between,
In former days you saw me favorably.
And if it were so do not keep it back:

Make me a little happier: let me know it:
Owe you me nothing for a life half-lost?
Yea, yea, the whole dear debt of all you are.
And, Enid, you and he, I see with joy,
Ye sit apart, you do not speak to him,
You come with no attendance, page or maid,
To serve you—doth he love you as of old?
For, call it lovers' quarrels, yet I know
Tho' men may bicker with the things they love,
They would not make them laughable in all eyes,
Not while they loved them; and your wretched
       dress,
A wretched insult on you, dumbly speaks
Your story, that this man loves you no more.
Your beauty is no beauty to him now:
A common chance—right well I know it—pall'd—
For I know men: nor will ye win him back,
For the man's love once gone never returns.
But here is one who loves you as of old;
With more exceeding passion than of old:

Good, speak the word: my followers ring him
      round:
He sits unarm'd; I hold a finger up;
They understand: nay; I do not mean blood:
Nor need ye look so scared at what I say:
My malice is no deeper than a moat,
No stronger than a wall: there is the keep;
He shall not cross us more; speak but the word:
Or speak it not; but then by him that made me
The one true lover whom you ever own'd,
I will make use of all the power I have.
O pardon me! the madness of that hour,
When first I parted from thee, moves me yet."

At this the tender sound of his own voice
And sweet self-pity, or the fancy of it
Made his eye moist; but Enid fear'd his eyes,
Moist as they were, wine-heated from the feast;
And answered with such craft as women use,
Guilty or guiltless, to stave off a chance
That breaks upon them perilously, and said:

"Earl, if you love me as in former years,
And do not practice on me, come with morn,
And snatch me from him as by violence;
Leave me to-night: I am weary to the death."

Low at leave-taking, with his brandish'd plume
Brushing his instep, bow'd the all-amorous Earl.
And the stout Prince bade him a loud good-night.
He moving homeward babbled to his men,
How Enid never loved a man but him,
Nor cared a broken egg-shell for her lord.

But Enid left alone with Prince Geraint,
Debating his command of silence given,
And that she now perforce must violate it,
Held commune with herself, and while she held
He fell asleep, and Enid had no heart
To wake him, but hung o'er him, wholly pleased
To find him yet unwounded after fight,
And hear him breathing low and equally.
Anon she rose, and stepping lightly, heap'd
The pieces of his armor in one place,
All to be there against a sudden need;
Then dozed awhile herself, but over-toil'd
By that day's grief and travel, evermore
Seem'd catching at a rootless thorn, and then

Went slipping down horrible precipices,
And strongly striking out her limbs awoke;
Then thought she heard the wild Earl at the door,
With all his rout of random followers,
Sound on a dreadful trumpet, summoning her;
Which was the red cock shouting to the light,
As the gray dawn stole o'er the dewy world,
And glimmer'd on his armor in the room.
And once again she rose to look at it,
But touch'd it unawares: jangling, the casque
Fell, and he started up and stared at her.
Then breaking his command of silence given,
She told him all that Earl Limours had said,
Except the passage that he loved her not;
Nor left untold the craft herself had used;
But ended with apology so sweet,
Low-spoken, and of so few words, and seem'd
So justified by that necessity,
That tho' he thought "was it for him she wept
In Devon?" he but gave a wrathful groan,
Saying, "Your sweet faces make good fellows fools
And traitors. Call the host and bid him bring
Charger and palfrey." So she glided out
Among the heavy breathings of the house,
And like a household Spirit at the walls
Beat, till she woke the sleepers, and return'd:
Then tending her rough lord, tho' all unask'd,
In silence, did him service as a squire;
Till issuing arm'd he found the host and cried,
"Thy reckoning, friend?" and ere he learnt it, "Take
Five horses and their armors;" and the host
Suddenly honest, answer'd in amaze,
"My lord, I scarce have spent the worth of one!"
"Ye will be all the wealthier," said the Prince,

And then to Enid, "Forward! and to-day
I charge you, Enid, more especially,
What thing soever ye may hear, or see,
Or fancy (tho' I count it of small use
To charge you) that ye speak not but obey."

And Enid answer'd, "Yea, my lord, I know
Your wish, and would obey; but riding first,
I hear the violent threats you do not hear,
I see the danger which you cannot see:
Then not to give you warning, that seems hard;
Almost beyond me: yet I would obey."

"Yea so," said he, "do it: be not too wise;
Seeing that ye are wedded to a man,
Not all mismated with a yawning clown,
But one with arms to guard his head and yours,
With eyes to find you out however far,
And ears to hear you even in his dreams."

With that he turn'd and look'd as keenly at her
As careful robins eye the delver's toil;
And that within her, which a wanton fool,
Or hasty judger would have call'd her guilt,
Made her cheek burn and either eyelid fall.
And Geraint look'd and was not satisfied.

Then forward by a way which, beaten broad,
Led from the territory of false Limours
To the waste earldom of another earl,
Doorm, whom his shaking vassals call'd the Bull,
Went Enid with her sullen follower on.
Once she look'd back, and when she saw him ride
More near by many a rood than yestermorn,

It wellnigh made her cheerful; till Geraint
Waving an angry hand as who should say
"Ye watch me," sadden'd all her heart again.
But while the sun yet beat a dewy blade,
The sound of many a heavily-galloping hoof
Smote on her ear, and turning round she saw
Dust, and the points of lances bicker in it.
Then not to disobey her lord's behest,
And yet to give him warning, for he rode
As if he heard not, moving back she held
Her finger up, and pointed to the dust.
At which the warrior in his obstinacy,
Because she kept the letter of his word,
Was in a manner pleased, and turning, stood.
And in the moment after, wild Limours,
Borne on a black horse, like a thunder-cloud
Whose skirts are loosen'd by the breaking storm,
Half ridden off with by the thing he rode,
And all in passion uttering a dry shriek,
Dash'd on Geraint, who closed with him, and bore
Down by the length of lance and arm beyond
The crupper, and so left him stunn'd or dead,
And overthrew the next that follow'd him,
And blindly rush'd on all the rout behind.
But at the flash and motion of the man
They vanish'd panic-stricken, like a shoal
Of darting fish, that on a summer morn
Adown the crystal dykes at Camelot
Come slipping o'er their shadows on the sand,
But if a man who stands upon the brink
But lift a shining hand against the sun,
There is not left the twinkle of a fin
Betwixt the cressy islets white in flower;
So, scared but at the motion of the man,

Fled all the boon companions of the Earl,
And left him lying in the public way;
So vanish friendships only made in wine.

Then like a stormy sunlight smiled Geraint,
Who saw the chargers of the two that fell
Start from their fallen lords, and wildly fly,
Mixt with the flyers. "Horse and man," he said,
"All of one mind and all right-honest friends!
Not a hoof left: and I methinks till now
Was honest—paid with horses and with arms;
I cannot steal or plunder, no nor beg:
And so what say ye, shall we strip him there
Your lover? has your palfrey heart enough
To bear his armor? shall we fast, or dine?
No?—then do thou, being right honest, pray
That we may meet the horsemen of Earl Doorm.
I too would still be honest." Thus he said:
And sadly gazing on her bridle-reins,
And answering not a word, she led the way.

But as a man to whom a dreadful loss
Falls in a far land and he knows it not,
But coming back he learns it, and the loss
So pains him that he sickens nigh to death;
So fared it with Geraint, who being prick'd
In combat with the follower of Limours,
Bled underneath his armor secretly,
And so rode on, nor told his gentle wife
What ail'd him, hardly knowing it himself,
Till his eye darken'd and his helmet wagg'd;
And at a sudden swerving of the road,
Tho' happily down on a bank of grass,
The Prince, without a word, from his horse fell.

And Enid heard the clashing of his fall,
Suddenly came, and at his side all pale
Dismounting, loosed the fastenings of his arms,
Nor let her true hand falter, nor blue eye
Moisten, till she had lighted on his wound,
And tearing off her veil of faded silk
Had bared her forehead to the blistering sun,
And swathed the hurt that drain'd her dear lord's
    life.
Then after all was done that hand could do,
She rested, and her desolation came
Upon her, and she wept beside the way.

And many past, but none regarded her,
For in that realm of lawless turbulence,
A woman weeping for her murder'd mate
Was cared as much for as a summer shower:
One took him for a victim of Earl Doorm,
Nor dared to waste a perilous pity on him:
Another hurrying past, a man-at-arms,
Rode on a mission to the bandit Earl;
Half whistling and half singing a coarse song,
He drove the dust against her veilless eyes:
Another, flying from the wrath of Doorm
Before an ever-fancied arrow, made
The long way smoke beneath him in his fear;
At which her palfrey whinnying lifted heel
And scour'd into the coppices and was lost,
While the great charger stood, grieved like a man.

But at the point of noon the huge Earl Doorm,
Broad-faced with under-fringe of russet beard,
Bound on a foray, rolling eyes of prey,
Came riding with a hundred lances up;

But ere he came, like one that hails a ship,
Cried out with a big voice, "What, is he dead?"
"No, no, not dead!" she answer'd in all haste.
"Would some of your kind people take him up,
And bear him hence out of this cruel sun?
Most sure am I, quite sure, he is not dead."

Then said Earl Doorm: "Well, if he be not
        dead,
Why wail ye for him thus? ye seem a child.
And be he dead, I count you for a fool;
Your wailing will not quicken him: dead or not,
Ye mar a comely face with idiot tears.
Yet, since the face is comely—some of you,
Here, take him up, and bear him to our hall:
An if he live, we will have him of our band;
And if he die, why earth has earth enough
To hide him. See ye take the charger too,
A noble one."

He spake, and past away,
But left two brawny spearmen, who advanced,
Each growling like a dog, when his good bone
Seems to be pluck'd at by the village boys
Who love to vex him eating, and he fears
To lose his bone, and lays his foot upon it,
Gnawing and growling: so the ruffians growl'd,
Fearing to lose, and all for a dead man,
Their chance of booty from the morning's raid,
Yet raised and laid him on a litter-bier,
Such as they brought upon their forays out
For those that might be wounded; laid him on it
All in the hollow of his shield, and took
And bore him to the naked hall of Doorm,

(His gentle charger following him unled)
And cast him and the bier in which he lay
Down on an oaken settle in the hall,
And then departed, hot in haste to join
Their luckier mates, but growling as before,
And cursing their lost time, and the dead man,
And their own Earl, and their own souls, and her.
They might as well have blest her: she was deaf
To blessing or to cursing save from one.
  So for long hours sat Enid by her lord,
There in the naked hall, propping his head,
And chafing his pale hands, and calling to him.
Till at the last he waken'd from his swoon,
And found his own dear bride propping his head,
And chafing his faint hands, and calling to him;
And felt the warm tears falling on his face;
And said to his own heart, "She weeps for me:"
And yet lay still, and feign'd himself as dead,
That he might prove her to the uttermost,
And say to his own heart, "She weeps for me."

  But in the falling afternoon return'd
The huge Earl Doorm with plunder to the hall.
His lusty spearmen follow'd him with noise:
Each hurling down a heap of things that rang
Against the pavement, cast his lance aside,
And doff'd his helm: and then there flutter'd in,
Half-bold, half-frighted, with dilated eyes,
A tribe of women, dress'd in many hues,
And mingled with the spearmen: and Earl Doorm
Struck with a knife's haft hard against the board,
And call'd for flesh and wine to feed his spears.
And men brought in whole hogs and quarter beeves,
And all the hall was dim with steam of flesh:

And none spake word, but all sat down at once,
And ate with tumult in the naked hall,
Feeding like horses when you hear them feed;
Till Enid shrank far back into herself,

ENID WATCHING BY GERAINT

To shun the wild ways of the lawless tribe.
But when Earl Doorm had eaten all he would,
He roll'd his eyes about the hall, and found
A damsel drooping in a corner of it.
Then he remember'd her, and how she wept;

And out of her there came a power upon him;
And rising on the sudden he said, "Eat!
I never yet beheld a thing so pale.
God's curse, it makes me mad to see you weep.
Eat! Look yourself. Good luck had your good
　　　man,
For were I dead who is it would weep for me?
Sweet lady, never since I first drew breath
Have I beheld a lily like yourself.
And so there lived some color in your cheek,
There is not one among my gentlewomen
Were fit to wear your slipper for a glove.
But listen to me, and by me be ruled,
And I will do the thing I have not done,
For ye shall share my earldom with me, girl,
And we will live like two birds in one nest,
And I will fetch you forage from all fields,
For I compel all creatures to my will."

　　He spoke: the brawny spearman let his cheek
Bulge with the unswallowed piece, and turning
　　　stared;
While some, whose souls the old serpent long had
　　　drawn
Down, as the worm draws in the wither'd leaf
And makes it earth, hiss'd each at other's ear
What shall not be recorded—women they,
Women, or what had been those gracious things,
But now desired the humbling of their best,
Yea, would have help'd him to it: and all at once
They hated her, who took no thought of them,
But answer'd in low voice, her meek head yet
Drooping, "I pray you of your courtesy,
He being as he is, to let me be."

She spake so low he hardly heard her speak,
But like a mighty patron, satisfied
With what himself had done so graciously,
Assumed that she had thank'd him, adding, "Yea,
Eat and be glad, for I account you mine."

She answer'd meekly, "How should I be glad
Henceforth in all the world at anything,
Until my lord arise and look upon me?"

Here the huge Earl cried out upon her talk,
As all but empty heart and weariness
And sickly nothing; suddenly seized on her,
And bare her by main violence to the board,
And thrust the dish before her, crying, "Eat."
"No, no," said Enid, vext, "I will not eat
Till yonder man upon the bier arise,
And eat with me." "Drink, then," he answer'd.
        "Here!"
(And fill'd a horn with wine and held it to her.)
"Lo! I, myself, when flush'd with fight, or hot,
God's curse, with anger—often I myself,
Before I well have drunken, scarce can eat:
Drink therefore and the wine will change your will."

"Not so," she cried, "By Heaven, I will not drink
Till my dear lord arise and bid me do it,
And drink with me; and if he rise no more,
I will not look at wine until I die."

At this he turned all red and paced his hall,
Now gnaw'd his under, now his upper lip,
And coming up close to her, said at last:
"Girl, for I see ye scorn my courtesies,

Take warning: yonder man is surely dead;
And I compel all creatures to my will.
Not eat nor drink? And wherefore wail for one,
Who put your beauty to this flout and scorn
By dressing it in rags? Amazed am I,
Beholding how ye butt against my wish,
That I forbear you thus: cross me no more.
At least put off to please me this poor gown,
This silken rag, this beggar-woman's weed:
I love that beauty should go beautifully:
For see ye not my gentlewomen here,
How gay, how suited to the house of one
Who loves that beauty should go beautifully?
Rise therefore; robe yourself in this: obey."

He spoke, and one among his gentlewomen
Display'd a splendid silk of foreign loom,
Where like a shoaling sea the lovely blue
Play'd into green, and thicker down the front
With jewels than the sward with drops of dew,
When all night long a cloud clings to the hill,
And with the dawn ascending lets the day
Strike where it clung: so thickly shone the gems.

But Enid answer'd, harder to be moved
Than hardest tyrants in their day of power,
With life-long injuries burning unavenged,
And now their hour has come: and Enid said:

"In this poor gown my dear lord found me first,
And loved me serving in my father's hall:
In this poor gown I rode with him to court,
And there the Queen array'd me like the sun:
In this poor gown he bade me clothe myself,

When now we rode upon this fatal quest
Of honor, where no honor can be gain'd:
And this poor gown I will not cast aside
Until himself arise a living man,
And bid me cast it. I have griefs enough:
Pray you be gentle, pray you let me be:
I never loved, can never love but him:
Yea, God, I pray you of your gentleness,
He being as he is, to let me be."

Then strode the brute Earl up and down his hall,
And took his russet beard between his teeth;
Last, coming up quite close, and in his mood
Crying, "I count it of no more avail,
Dame, to be gentle than ungentle with you;
Take my salute," unknightly with flat hand,
However, lightly, smote her on the cheek.

Then Enid, in her utter helplessness,
And since she thought, "He had not dared to do it,
Except he surely knew my lord was dead,"
Sent forth a sudden sharp and bitter cry,
As of a wild thing taken in the trap,
Which sees the trapper coming thro' the wood.

This heard Geraint, and grasping at his sword,
(It lay beside him in the hollow shield),
Made but a single bound, and with a sweep of it
Shore thro' the swarthy neck, and like a ball
The russet-bearded head roll'd on the floor.
So died Earl Doorm by him he counted dead.
And all the men and women in the hall
Rose when they saw the dead man rise, and fled
Yelling as from a spectre, and the two
Were left alone together, and he said:

"Enid, I have used you worse than that dead
    man;
Done you more wrong: we both have undergone
That trouble which has left me thrice your own:
Henceforward I will rather die than doubt.
And here I lay this penance on myself,
Not, tho' mine own ears heard you yestermorn—
You thought me sleeping, but I heard you say,
I heard you say, that you were no true wife:
I swear I will not ask your meaning in it:
I do believe yourself against yourself,
And will henceforward rather die than doubt."

And Enid could not say one tender word,
She felt so blunt and stupid at the heart:
She only pray'd him, "Fly, they will return
And slay you; fly, your charger is without,
My palfrey lost."   "Then, Enid, shall you ride
Behind me."   "Yea," said Enid, "let us go."
And moving out they found the stately horse,
Who now no more a vassal to the thief,
But free to stretch his limbs in lawful fight,
Neigh'd with all gladness as they came, and stoop'd
With a low whinny toward the pair: and she
Kiss'd the white star upon his noble front,
Glad also; then Geraint upon the horse
Mounted, and reach'd a hand, and on his foot
She set her own and climb'd; he turn'd his face
And kiss'd her climbing, and she cast her arms
About him, and at once they rode away.

And never yet, since high in Paradise
O'er the four rivers the first roses blew,
Came purer pleasure unto mortal kind

Than lived thro' her, who in that perilous hour
Put hand to hand beneath her husband's heart,
And felt him hers again: she did not weep,
But o'er her meek eyes came a happy mist
Like that which kept the heart of Eden green
Before the useful trouble of the rain:
Yet not so misty were her meek blue eyes
As not to see before them on the path,
Right in the gateway of the bandit hold,
A knight of Arthur's court, who laid his lance
In rest, and made as if to fall upon him.
Then, fearing for his hurt and loss of blood,
She, with her mind all full of what had chanced,
Shriek'd to the stranger "Slay not a dead man!"
"The voice of Enid," said the knight; but she,
Beholding it was Edyrn, son of Nudd,
Was moved so much the more, and shriek'd again,
"O cousin, slay not him who gave you life."
And Edyrn moving frankly forward spake:
"My lord Geraint, I greet you with all love;
I took you for a bandit knight of Doorm;
And fear not, Enid, I should fall upon him,
Who love you, Prince, with something of the love
Wherewith we love the Heaven that chastens us.
For once, when I was up so high in pride
That I was half-way down the slope to Hell,
By overthrowing me you threw me higher.
Now, made a knight of Arthur's Table Round,
And since I knew this Earl, when I myself
Was half a bandit in my lawless hour,
I come the mouthpiece of our King to Doorm
(The King is close behind me) bidding him
Disband himself, and scatter all his powers,
Submit, and hear the judgment of the King."

"He hears the judgment of the King of kings,"
Cried the wan Prince; "and lo, the powers of Doorm
Are scatter'd," and he pointed to the field,
Where, huddled here and there on mound and knoll,
Were men and women staring and aghast,
While some yet fled; and then he plainlier told
How the huge Earl lay slain within his hall.
But when the knight besought him, "Follow me,
Prince, to the camp, and in the King's own ear
Speak what has chanced; ye surely have endured
Strange chances here alone;" that other flush'd,
And hung his head, and halted in reply,
Fearing the mild face of the blameless King,
And after madness acted question ask'd:
Till Edyrn crying, "If ye will not go
To Arthur, then will Arthur come to you."
"Enough," he said, "I follow," and they went.
But Enid in their going had two fears,
One from the bandit scatter'd in the field,
And one from Edyrn. Every now and then,
When Edyrn rein'd his charger at her side,
She shrank a little. In a hollow land,
From which old fires have broken, men may fear
Fresh fire and ruin. He, perceiving, said:

"Fair and dear cousin, you that most had cause
To fear me, fear no longer, I am changed.
Once, but for my main purpose in these jousts,
I should have slain your father, seized yourself.
I lived in hope that sometime you would come
To these my lists with him whom best you loved;
And there, poor cousin, with your meek blue eyes,
The truest eyes that ever answer'd Heaven,
Behold me overturn and trample on him.

Then, had you cried, or knelt, or pray'd to me,
I should not less have kill'd him. And you came,—
But once you came,—and with your own true eyes
Beheld the man you loved (I speak as one
Speaks of a service done him) overthrow
My proud self, and my purpose three years old,
And set his foot upon me, and give me life.
There was I broken down; there was I saved:
Tho' thence I rode all-shamed, hating the life
He gave me, meaning to be rid of it.
And all the penance the Queen laid upon me
Was but to rest awhile within her court;
Where first as sullen as a beast new-caged,
And waiting to be treated like a wolf,
Because I knew my deeds were known, I found,
Instead of scornful pity or pure scorn,
Such fine reserve and noble reticence,
Manners so kind, yet stately, such a grace
Of tenderest courtesy, that I began
To glance behind me at my former life,
And find that it had been the wolf's indeed:
And oft I talk'd with Dubric, the high saint,
Who, with mild heat of holy oratory,
Subdued me somewhat to that gentleness,
Which, when it weds with manhood, makes a man.
And you were often there about the Queen,
But saw me not, or mark'd not if you saw;
Nor did I care or dare to speak with you,
But kept myself aloof till I was changed;
And fear not, cousin; I am changed indeed."

    He spoke, and Enid easily believed,
Like simple noble natures, credulous
Of what they long for, good in friend or foe,

There most in those who most have done them ill.
And when they reach'd the camp the King himself
Advanced to greet them, and beholding her
Tho' pale, yet happy, ask'd her not a word,
But went apart with Edyrn, whom he held
In converse for a little, and return'd,
And, gravely smiling, lifted her from horse,
And kiss'd her with all pureness, brother-like,
And show'd an empty tent allotted her,
And glancing for a minute, till he saw her
Pass into it, turn'd to the Prince, and said:

"Prince, when of late ye pray'd me for my leave
To move to your own land, and there defend
Your marches, I was prick'd with some reproof,
As one that let foul wrong stagnate and be,
By having look'd too much thro' alien eyes,
And wrought too long with delegated hands,
Not used mine own: but now behold me come
To cleanse this common sewer of all my realm,
With Edyrn and with others: have ye look'd
At Edyrn? have ye seen how nobly changed?
This work of his is great and wonderful.
His very face with change of heart is changed,
The world will not believe a man repents:
And this wise world of ours is mainly right.
Full seldom doth a man repent, or use
Both grace and will to pick the vicious quitch[6]
Of blood and custom wholly out of him,
And make all clean, and plant himself afresh.
Edyrn has done it, weeding all his heart

6. *Quitch* is another name for couch-grass, a troublesome weed
which spreads rapidly and is eradicated only with the greatest
difficulty.

As I will weed this land before I go.
I, therefore, made him of our Table Round,
Not rashly, but have proved him everyway
One of our noblest, our most valorous,
Sanest and most obedient: and indeed
This work of Edyrn wrought upon himself
After a life of violence, seems to me
A thousand-fold more great and wonderful
Than if some knight of mine, risking his life,
My subject with my subjects under him,
Should make an onslaught single on a realm
Of robbers, tho' he slew them one by one,
And were himself nigh wounded to the death."

    So spake the King; low bow'd the Prince, and
       felt
His work was neither great nor wonderful,
And past to Enid's tent; and thither came
The King's own leech to look into his hurt;
And Enid tended on him there; and there
Her constant motion round him, and the breath
Of her sweet tendance hovering over him,
Fill'd all the genial courses of his blood
With deeper and with ever deeper love,
As the south-west that blowing Bala lake
Fills all the sacred Dee.   So past the days.

Then, when Geraint was whole again, they past
With Arthur to Caerleon upon Usk.
There the great Queen once more embraced her
      friend,
And clothed her in apparel like the day.
Thence after tarrying for a space they rode,
And fifty knights rode with them to the shores

Of Severn, and they past to their own land.
And there he kept the justice of the King
So vigorously yet mildly, that all hearts
Applauded, and the spiteful whisper died:
And being ever foremost in the chase,
And victor at the tilt and tournament,
They called him the great Prince and man of men.
But Enid, whom the ladies loved to call
Enid the Fair, a grateful people named
Enid the Good; and in their halls arose
The cry of children, Enids and Geraints
Of times to be; nor did he doubt her more,
But rested in her fealty, till he crown'd
A happy life with a fair death, and fell
Against the heathen of the Northern Sea
In battle, fighting for the blameless King.

THE HOLY GRAIL

NOTE.—Thomas Malory completed his quaint history of King Arthur in 1469, and sixteen years later the book was printed from the famous old Caxton press. Only one perfect copy of that work is now in existence; but several editions have since been issued with the text modernized, so as to make it easier for us to read, yet with the quaintness and originality of Malory's tale preserved. So charming is it, that the following incidents in the story of the search for the Holy Grail are told nearly as they are now in the Aldine edition of *Le Morte d'Arthur*.

Some rearrangement has been necessary, and a few changes have been made in phraseology. Omissions have been made and paragraphs are indicated and quotation marks used as is now the custom in printing.

Many of the knights joined in the quest for the Grail, and their adventures are told by Malory. Even Launcelot himself failed. We tell the story of the one who succeeded.

THE KNIGHTING OF SIR GALAHAD

T the vigil of Pentecost, when all the fellowship of the Round Table were come unto Camelot and there heard their service, and the tables were set ready to the meat, right so, entered into the hall a full fair gentlewoman on horseback, that had ridden full fast, for her horse was all besweated. Then she there alit and came before the King and saluted him and he said, "Damosel, God thee bless."

"Sir," said she, "for God's sake say me where Sir Launcelot is."

"Yonder ye may see him," said the King.

Then she went unto Launcelot and said, "Sir Launcelot, I require you to come along with me hereby into a forest."

"What will ye with me?" said Sir Launcelot.

"Ye shall know," said she, "when ye come thither."

"Well," said he, "I will gladly go with you."

So Sir Launcelot bade him his squire saddle his horse and bring his arms.

Right so departed Sir Launcelot with the gentlewoman and rode until he came into a forest, and into a great valley, where they saw an abbey of nuns; and there was a squire ready and opened the gates, and so they entered and descended off their horses; and there came a fair fellowship about Sir Launcelot, and welcomed him and were passing glad of his coming.

And they led him into the Abbess's chamber and unarmed him; and therein came twelve nuns that brought with them Galahad, the which was passing fair and well made, that unnethe[1] in the world men might not find his match: and all those ladies wept.

"Sir," said they all, "we bring you here this child the which we have nourished, and we pray you to make him a knight, for of a worthier man's hand may he not receive the order of knighthood."

Then said Sir Launcelot, "Cometh this desire of himself?"

He and all they said, "Yea."

"Then shall he," said Sir Launcelot, "receive the high order of knighthood as to-morn at the reverence of the high feast."

1. This is an old word meaning *with difficulty.*

That night Sir Launcelot had passing good cheer; and on the morn at Galahad's desire, he made him knight and said, "God make him a good man, for of beauty faileth you not as any that liveth."

THE MARVELOUS SWORD

AIR sir," said Sir Launcelot, "will ye come with me unto the court of King Arthur?"

"Nay," said he, "I will not go with you at this time."

Then he departed from them and came to Camelot by the hour of underne[2] on Whitsunday. By that time the King and Queen were gone to the minster to hear their service.

So when the King and all the knights were come from service, the barons espied in the sieges of the Round Table all about, written with golden letters: "Here ought to sit he, and he ought to sit here."[3] And thus they went so long till they came to the Siege Perilous where they found letters newly written of gold which said: "Four hundred winters and four and fifty accomplished after the passion of our Lord Jesus Christ ought this siege to be fulfilled."

Then all they said, "This is a marvelous thing and an adventurous."

"In the name of God," said Sir Launcelot; and then accounted the term of the writing from the

2. *Underne* meant, according to ancient reckoning, nine o'clock in the morning.

3. That is, "Such a one should sit here. and such another one here."

birth of our Lord unto that day. "It seemeth me," said Sir Launcelot, "this siege ought to be fulfilled this same day, for this is the feast of Pentecost after the four hundred and four and fifty years; and if it would please all parties, I would none of these letters were seen this day, till he be come that ought to achieve this adventure."

Then made they to ordain a cloth of silk, for to cover these letters on the Siege Perilous. Then the King bade haste unto dinner.

So as they stood, in came a squire and said unto the King, "Sir, I bring unto you marvelous tidings."

"What be they?" said the King.

"Sir, there is here beneath at the river a great stone which I saw fleet[4] above the water, and therein I saw sticking a sword."

The King said: "I will see that marvel.

So all the knights went with him, and when they came to the river they found there a stone fleeting, as it were of red marble, and therein stuck a fair rich sword, and in the pommel thereof were precious stones wrought with subtle letters of gold. Then the barons read the letters which said in this wise: "Never shall man take me hence, but only he by whose side I ought to hang, and he shall be the best knight in the world."

When the King had seen the letters he said unto Sir Launcelot: "Fair sir, this sword ought to be yours, for I am sure ye be the best knight of the world."

Then Sir Launcelot answered full soberly: "Certes, sir, it is not my sword; also, sir, wit ye well I have no hardiness to set my hand to it, for

4. *Fleet* here means *float.*

it longed not to hang by my side. Also, who that assayeth to take the sword and faileth of it, he shall receive a wound by that sword that he shall not be whole long after. And I will that ye wit that this same day shall the adventures of the Sangreal,[5] that is called the Holy Vessel, begin."

"Now, fair nephew," said the King unto Sir Gawaine, "assay ye, for my love."

"Sir," said Gawaine, "your commandment will I obey."

And therewith he took the sword up by the handles, but he might not stir it.

"I thank you," said the King to Sir Gawaine.

"My lord, Sir Gawaine," said Sir Launcelot, "now wit ye well this sword shall touch you so sore that ye shall will ye had never set your hand thereto for the best castle of this realm."

"Sir," he said, "I might not withsay mine uncle's will and commandment."

But when the King heard this he repented it much, and said unto Sir Percivale, that he should assay for his love.

And he said, "Gladly, for to bear Sir Gawaine fellowship."

And therewith he set his hand on the sword and drew it strongly, but he might not move it. Then

5. The Holy Grail (Graal) was the cup used by Christ at the Last Supper. It is said to have been carved from an emerald, and to have been used by Joseph of Arimathea to catch the last drops of blood from the body of Christ when he was taken down from the cross. The legend continues that Joseph carried the cup to Britain. The grail would not stay in possession of any one unless he were pure and unsullied in character. In the time of King Arthur, one of the descendants of Joseph sinned, and the holy vessel disappeared and was lost. Only the pure could look upon the holy chalice, and so although many of the knights sought it, but one achieved it. *Sangreal* is the old French for *Holy Grail*.

there were more that durst be so hardy to set their hands thereto.

So the King and all went unto the court, and every knight knew his own place, and set him therein, and young men that were knights served them.

GALAHAD IN THE SIEGE PERILOUS

O when they were served and all the sieges fulfilled, save only the Siege Perilous, anon there came in a good old man, and an ancient, clothed all in white, and there was no knight knew from whence he came. And with him he brought a young knight, both on foot, in red arms, without sword or shield, save a scabbard hanging by his side.

And these words he said: "Peace be with you fair lords." Then the old man said unto Arthur: "Sir, I bring here a young knight, the which is of king's lineage, and of the kindred of Joseph of Arimathie, whereby the marvels of this court, and of strange realms, shall be fully accomplished."

The King was right glad of his words, and said unto the good man: "Sir, ye be right welcome, and the young knight with you."

Then the old man made the young knight to unarm him, and he was in a coat of red sandal, and bare a mantle upon his shoulder that was furred with ermine, and put that upon him. And the old knight said unto the young knight: "Sir, follow me."

And anon he led him unto the Siege Perilous, where beside sat Sir Launcelot; and the good man lift up the cloth, and found these letters that said thus: "This is the siege of Sir Galahad, the haut[6] prince."

"Sir," said the old knight, "wit ye well that place is yours." And then he set him down surely in that siege.

And then he said to the old man: "Sir, ye may now go your way, for well have ye done that ye were commanded to do."

So the good man departed. Then all the knights of the Round Table marveled greatly of Sir Galahad, that he durst sit there in that Siege Perilous, and was so tender of age; and wist not from whence he came, but all only by God; and said, "This is he by whom the Sangreal shall be achieved, for there never sat none but he, but he were mischieved."[7]

Then came King Arthur unto Galahad and said: "Sir, ye be welcome, for ye shall move many good knights to the quest of the Sangreal, and ye shall achieve that never knights might bring to an end."

GALAHAD DRAWS THE SWORD OF BALIN

LE SAVAGE

HEN the King took him by the hand, and went down from the palace to shew Galahad the adventures of the stone.

"Sir," said the King unto Sir Galahad, "here is a great marvel as I ever saw, and right good knights have assayed and failed."

"Sir," said Galahad, "that is no marvel, for this adventure is not theirs but mine; and for the surety

6. *Haut* is an old form of *haughty.*   7. That is, *harmed.*

of this sword I brought none with me, for here by my side hangeth the scabbard."

And anon he laid his hand on the sword, and lightly drew it out of the stone, and put it in the sheath, and said unto the King, "Now it goeth better than it did aforehand."

"Sir," said the King, "a shield God shall send you."

"Now have I that sword that was sometime the good knight's, Balin le Savage, and he was a passing good man of his hands; and with this sword he slew his brother Balan, and that was great pity, for he was a good knight, and either slew other through a dolorous stroke."

THE HOLY GRAIL APPEARS

 AM sure," said the King, "at this quest of the Sangreal shall all ye of the Table Round depart, and never shall I see you whole together; therefore, I will see you all whole together in the meadow of Camelot to joust and to tourney, that after your death men may speak of it that such good knights were wholly together such a day."

As unto that counsel and at the King's request they accorded all, and took on their harness that longed unto jousting. But all this moving of the King was for this intent, for to see Galahad proved; for the King deemed he should not lightly come again unto the court after his departing. So were they assembled into the meadow both more and less.[8]

8. That is, the greater and the lesser knights.

Then Sir Galahad began to break spears marvelously, that all men had wonder of him; for he there surmounted all other knights, for within a while he had defouled many good knights of the Table Round save twain, that was Sir Launcelot and Sir Percivale.

And then the King and all estates[9] went home unto Camelot, and so went to evensong to the great minster, and so after upon that to supper, and every knight sat in his own place as they were toforehand. Then anon they heard cracking and crying of thunder, that them thought the place should all to-drive.[10]

In the midst of this blast entered a sunbeam more clearer by seven times than ever they saw day, and all they were alighted of[11] the grace of the Holy Ghost. Then began every knight to behold other, and either saw other, by their seeming, fairer than ever they saw afore. Not for then there was no knight might speak one word a great while, and so they looked every man on other as they had been dumb.

Then there entered into the hall the Holy Grail covered with white samite, but there was none might see it, nor who bare it. And there was all the hall fulfilled[12] with good odours, and every knight had such meats and drinks as he best loved in this world. And when the Holy Grail had been borne through the hall, then the Holy Vessel departed suddenly, that they wist not where it became: then had they

9. *Estate* formerly meant *a person of high rank.*
10. *To-drive* is an old expression meaning *break apart.*
11. *Alighted of* means *lighted by.*
12. *Fulfilled* is here used with its original meaning of *filled full.*

all breath to speak. And then the King yielded thankings to God, of His good grace that he had sent them.

"Now," said Sir Gawaine, "we have been served this day of what meats and drinks we thought on; but one thing beguiled us, we might not see the Holy Grail, it was so preciously covered. Wherefore I will make here avow, that to-morn,[13] without longer abiding, I shall labour in the quest of the Sangreal, that I shall hold me out a twelvemonth and a day, or more if need be, and never shall I return again unto the court till I have seen it more openly than it hath been seen here; and if I may not speed I shall return again as he that may not be against the will of our Lord Jesu Christ."

When they of the Table Round heard Sir Gawaine say so, they arose up the most part and made such avows as Sir Gawaine had made.

And then they went to rest them, and in honor of the highness of Sir Galahad he was led into King Arthur's chamber, and there rested in his own bed. And as soon as it was day the King arose, for he had no rest of all that night for sorrow.

And anon Launcelot and Gawaine commanded their men to bring their arms. And when they all were armed save their shields and their helms, then they came to their fellowship, which were all ready in the same wise, for to go to the minster to hear their service.

Then after the service was done the King would wit how many had undertaken the quest of the Holy Grail; and to account them he prayed them all. Then found they by tale an hundred and fifty, and

13. *To-morn* is an old expression for *to-morrow*.

all were knights of the Round Table. And then they put on their helms and departed, and recommended them all wholly unto the Queen; and there was weeping and great sorrow.

And so they mounted upon their horses and rode through the streets of Camelot; and there was weeping of the rich and poor, and the King turned away and might not speak for weeping.

And on the morrow they were all accorded that they should depart each from other; and then they departed on the morrow with weeping and mourning cheer, and every knight took the way that him best liked.

GALAHAD GETS HIS SHIELD

IDETH Sir Galahad yet without shield, and so he rode four days without any adventure. And at the fourth day after evensong he came to a White Abbey, and there he was received with great reverence, and led to a chamber, and there he was unarmed; and then was he ware of two knights of the Round Table, one was King Bagdemagus, and that other was Sir Uwaine. And when they saw him they went unto him and made of him great solace, and so they went to supper.

"Sirs," said Sir Galahad, "what adventure brought you hither?"

"Sir," said they, "it is told us that within this place is a shield that no man may bear about his neck but if that he be mischieved or dead within three days, or else maimed for ever."

"Ah, sir," said King Bagdemagus, "I shall it bear to-morrow for to assay this strange adventure."

"In the name of God," said Sir Galahad.

"Sir," said Bagdemagus, "an I may not achieve the adventure of this shield ye shall take it upon you, for I am sure ye shall not fail."

"Sir," said Galahad, "I agree right well thereto, for I have no shield."

So on the morn they arose and heard mass. Anon a monk led them behind an altar where the shield hung as white as any snow, but in the middes [14] was a red cross.

"Sir," said the monk, "this shield ought not to be hanged about no knight's neck but he be the worthiest knight of the world, and therefore I counsel you knights to be well advised."

"Well," said King Bagdemagus, "I wot well that I am not the best knight of the world, but yet shall I assay to bear it."

And so he bare it out of the monastery; and then he said unto Sir Galahad: "If it will please you I pray you abide here still, till ye know how I shall speed."

"I shall abide you here," said Galahad. Then King Bagdemagus took with him a squire, the which should bring tidings unto Sir Galahad how he sped.

Then when they had ridden a two mile and came in a fair valley afore an hermitage, then they saw a goodly knight come from that part in white armour, horse and all; and he came as fast as his horse might run, with his spear in the rest, and King Bagdemagus dressed his spear against him and brake it

14. *Middes* is an old word for *midst*.

upon the white knight. But the other struck him so
hard that he brake the mails, and thrust him through
the right shoulder, for the shield covered him not at
that time; and so he bare him from his horse.

GALAHAD GETS HIS SHIELD

And therewith he alighted and took the white
shield from him, saying: "Knight, thou hast done
thyself great folly, for this shield ought not to be
borne but by him that shall have no peer that liveth."
And then he came to King Bagdemagus' squire and
said: "Bear this shield unto the good knight Sir

Galahad, that thou left in the abbey, and greet him well from me, for this shield behoveth[15] unto no man but unto Galahad."

"Sir Galahad," said the squire, when he had come to the White Abbey, "that knight that wounded Bagdemagus sendeth you greeting, and bade that ye should bear this shield, where through great adventures should befall."

"Now blessed be God and fortune," said Galahad. And then he asked his arms, and mounted upon his horse, and hung the white shield about his neck, and commended them unto God.

Then within a while came Galahad thereas[16] the White knight abode him by the hermitage, and every each saluted other courteously.

"Sir," said Galahad, "by this shield be many marvels fallen?"

"Sir," said the knight, "it befell after the passion of our Lord Jesu Christ thirty-two year, that Joseph of Arimathie, the gentle knight, the which took down our Lord off the holy Cross, at that time he departed from Jerusalem with a great party of his kindred with him. And so he laboured till that they came to a city that hight[17] Sarras.

"And at that same hour that Joseph came to Sarras there was a King that hight Evelake, that had great war against the Saracens, and in especial against one Saracen, the which was King Evelake's cousin, a rich king and a mighty, which marched nigh this land. So on a day these two met to do battle. Then Joseph, the son of Joseph of Arim-

15. That is, *belongeth*.
16. *Thereas* is an old word meaning *where*.
17. *Hight* means *was called*.

athie, went to King Evelake and told him he should be discomfit and slain, but if he left his belief of the old law and believed upon the new law. And then there he shewed him the right belief of the Holy Trinity, to the which he agreed unto with all his heart; and there this shield was made for King Evelake, in the name of Him that died upon the Cross.

"And when Evelake was in the battle there was a cloth set afore the shield, and when he was in the greatest peril he let put away the cloth, and then his enemies saw a figure of a man on the Cross, wherethrough they all were discomfit.

"Then soon after there fell a great marvel, that the cross of the shield at one time vanished away that no man wist where it became.

"Not long after that Joseph was laid in his deadly bed. And when King Evelake saw that he made much sorrow, and said: 'For thy love I have left my country, and sith ye shall depart out of this world, leave me some token of yours that I may think on you.' Joseph said: 'That will I do full gladly; now bring me your shield that I took you.' Then Joseph bled sore at the nose, so that he might not by no mean be staunched. And there upon that shield he made a cross of his own blood.

" 'Now may ye see a remembrance that I love you, for ye shall never see this shield but ye shall think on me, and it shall always be as fresh as it is now. And never shall man bear this shield about his neck but he shall repent it, unto the time that Galahad, the good knight, bear it; and he last of my lineage shall have it about his neck, that shall do many marvelous deeds.' "

THE GRAIL ACHIEVED

S O departed Galahad from thence, and he rode five days till that he came to the maimed king. And ever followed Percivale the five days, asking where he had been.

So on a day it befell that they came out of a great forest, and there they met at traverse with Sir Bors, the which rode alone. It is none need to tell if they were glad; and them he saluted, and they yielded him honour and good adventure, and every each told other.

Then rode they a great while till that they came to the castle of Carbonek. And when they entered within the castle King Pelles[18] knew them; then there was great joy, for they wist well by their coming that they had fulfilled the quest of the Sangreal.

Then Eliazar, King Pelles' son, brought tofore them the broken sword wherewith Joseph was stricken through the thigh. Then Bors set his hand thereto, if that he might have soldered it again; but it would not be. Then he took it to Percivale, but he had no more power thereto than he.

"Now have ye it again," said Percivale to Galahad, "for an it be ever achieved by any bodily man ye must do it."

And then he took the pieces and set them together, and they seemed that they had never been broken, and as well as it had been first forged. And when they within espied that the adventure of the sword was achieved, then they gave the sword to

18. King Pelles was the grandfather of Galahad.

Bors; for he was a good knight and a worthy man. And anon alit a voice among them, and said: "They that ought not to sit at the table of Jesu Christ arise, for now shall very knights be fed." So they went thence, all save King Pelles and Eliazar, his son, the which were holy men, and a maid which was his niece; and so these three fellows[19] and they three were there, no more.

Anon they saw knights all armed come in at the hall door, and did off their helms and their arms, and said unto Galahad: "Sir, we have hied right much for to be with you at this table where the holy meat shall be departed."

Then said he: "Ye be welcome, but of whence be ye?"

So three of them said they were of Gaul, and other three said they were of Ireland, and the other three said they were of Denmark.

Therewith a voice said: "There be two among you that be not in the quest of the Sangreal, and therefore depart ye."

Then King Pelles and his son departed. And therewithal beseemed them that there came a man, and four angels from heaven, clothed in likeness of a bishop, and had a cross in his hand; and these four angels bare him in a chair, and set him down before the table of silver whereupon the Sangreal was; and it seemed that he had in middes of his forehead letters the which said: "See ye here Joseph, the first bishop of Christendom, the same which Our Lord succoured in the city of Sarras in the spiritual place."

---

19. *Fellows* had not formerly the rather contemptuous meaning that it has now; it meant simply *comrades*.

Then the knights marveled, for that bishop was dead more than three hundred year tofore. "O knights," said he, "marvel not, for I was sometime an earthly man."

With that they heard the chamber door open, and there they saw angels; and two bare candles of wax, and the third a towel, and the fourth a spear which bled marvelously, that three drops fell within a box which he held with his other hand. And they set the candles upon the table, and the third the towel upon the vessel, and the fourth the holy spear even upright upon the vessel. And then the bishop made semblaunt[20] as though he would have gone to the sacring[21] of the mass. And then he did that longed[22] to a priest to do a mass. And then he went to Galahad and kissed him, and bade him go and kiss his fellows: and so he did anon.

"Now," said he, "servants of Jesu Christ, ye shall be fed afore this table with sweetmeats that never knights tasted."

And when he had said, he vanished away. And they set them at the table in great dread, and made their prayers.

Then looked they and saw a man come out of the Holy Vessel, that had all the signs of the passion of Jesu Christ, bleeding all openly, and said: "My knights, and my servants, and my true children, which be come out of deadly life into spiritual life, I will now no longer hide me from you, but ye shall see now a part of my secrets and of my hidden things: now hold and receive the high meat which

20. *Semblaunt* meant *show, appearance.*
21. *Sacring* is from *sacre,* an old word meaning *consecrate.*
22. That is, *belonged.*

ye have so much desired." Then took he himself the Holy Vessel and came to Galahad; and he kneeled down, and there he received his Saviour, and after him so received all his fellows; and they thought it so sweet that it was marvelous to tell.

Then said he to Galahad: "Son, wottest thou what I hold betwixt my hands?"

"Nay," said he, "but if ye will tell me." "This is," said he, "the holy dish wherein I ate the lamb on Sher-Thursday.[23] And now hast thou seen that thou most desire to see, but yet hast thou not seen it so openly as thou shalt see it in the city of Sarras in the spiritual place. Therefore thou must go hence and bear with thee this Holy Vessel; for this night it shall depart from the realm of Logris, that it shall never be seen more here. And wottest thou wherefor? For he is not served nor worshipped to his right by them of this land, for they be turned to evil living; therefore I shall disinherit them of the honour which I have done them. And therefore go ye three to-morrow unto the sea, where ye shall find your ship ready, and with you take no more but Sir Percivale and Sir Bors." Then gave he them his blessing and vanished away.

That same night about midnight came a voice among them which said: "My sons and not my chief sons, my friends and not my warriors, go ye hence where ye hope best to do and as I bade you."

"Ah, thanked be Thou, Lord, that Thou wilt vouchsafe to call us, Thy sinners. Now may we well prove that we have not lost our pains."

---

23 *Sher Thursday* or *Maundy Thursday* is the name given to Thursday of the Holy Week, the day on which the Last Supper was celebrated.

And anon in all haste they took their harness and departed. But the three knights of Gaul, one of them hight Claudine, King Claudas' son, and the other two were great gentlemen. Then prayed Galahad to every each of them, that if they come to King Arthur's court that they should salute Sir Launcelot, his father, and of them of the Round Table; and prayed them if that they came on that part that they should not forget it.

Right so departed Galahad, Percivale and Bors with him; and so they rode three days, and then they came to a rivage,[24] and found a ship. And when they came to the board they found in the middes the table of silver and the Sangreal which was covered with red samite.

Then were they glad to have such things in their fellowship; and so they entered and made great reverence thereto; and Galahad fell in his prayer long time to Our Lord, that at what time he asked, that he should pass out of this world. So much he prayed till a voice said to him: "Galahad, thou shalt have thy request; and when thou askest the death of thy body thou shalt have it, and then shalt thou find the life of the soul."

Percivale heard this, and prayed him to tell him wherefore he asked such things.

"That shall I tell you," said Galahad; "the other day when we saw a part of the adventures of the Sangreal I was in such joy of heart, that I trow never man was that was earthly. And therefore I wot well, when my body is dead my soul shall be in great joy to see the blessed Trinity every day, and the Majesty of Our Lord, Jesu Christ."

24. *Rivage* is an old word meaning *bank*.

So long were they in the ship that they said to Galahad: "Sir, in this bed ought ye to lie, for so sayeth the scripture."

THE SHIP APPROACHES THE CITY OF SARRAS

And so he laid him down and slept a great while; and when he awaked he looked afore him and saw the city of Sarras. Then took they out of the ship the table of silver, and he took it to Percivale and to Bors, to go tofore, and Galahad came behind. And right so they went to the city, and at the gate of the city they saw an old man crooked. Then Galahad called him and bade him help to bear this heavy thing.

"Truly," said the old man, "it is ten years ago that I might not go but with crutches."

"Care thou not," said Galahad, "and arise up and shew thy good will." And so he assayed, and found himself as whole as ever he was. Then ran he to the table, and took one part against Galahad.

And anon arose there great noise in the city, that a cripple was made whole by knights marvelous that entered into the city. And when the king of the city, which was cleped[25] Estorause, saw the fellowship, he asked them of whence they were, and what thing it was that they had brought upon the table of silver. And they told him the truth of the Sangreal, and the power which that God had set there. Then the king was a tyrant, and was come of the line of paynims,[26] and took them and put them in prison in a deep hole.

But as soon as they were there Our Lord sent them the Sangreal, through whose grace they were alway fulfilled while that they were in prison.

So at the year's end it befell that this King Estorause lay sick, and felt that he should die. Then he sent for the three knights, and they came afore him; and he cried them mercy of that he had done to them, and they forgave it him goodly; and he died anon.

When the king was dead all the city was dismayed, and wist not who might be their king. Right so as they were in counsel there came a voice

25. *Cleped* meant *named.*
26. A *paynim* is an infidel.

among them, and bade them choose the youngest
knight of them three to be their king: "For he shall
well maintain you and all yours." So they made
Galahad king by all the assent of the holy city.

THE LAST APPEARANCE OF THE SANGREAL

Now at the year's end, and the self day after
Galahad had borne the crown of gold, he arose up
early and his fellows, and came to the palace, and
saw tofore them the Holy Vessel, and a man kneeling on his knees in likeness of a bishop, that had

about him a great fellowship of angels as it had
been Jesu Christ himself; and then he arose and
began a mass of Our Lady. And when he came to
the sacrament of the mass, and had done, anon he
called Galahad, and said to him: "Come forth the
servant of Jesu Christ, and thou shalt see that thou
hast much desired to see."

Then Galahad held up his hands toward heaven
and said: "Lord, I thank thee, for now I see that
that hath been my desire many a day. Now, blessed
Lord, would I not longer live, if it might please
thee, Lord."

And therewith the good man took Our Lord's
body betwixt his hands, and proffered it to Galahad, and he received it right gladly and meekly.
"Now wottest thou what I am?" said the good man.

"Nay," said Galahad. "I am Joseph of Arimathie, the which Our Lord hath sent here to thee
to bear thee fellowship; and wottest thou wherefore that he hath sent me more than any other? For
thou hast resembled me in two things; in that thou
hast seen the marvels of the Sangreal, in that thou
hast been a clean maiden, as I have been and am."

And when he had said these words Galahad went
to Percivale and kissed him, and commended him
to God; and so he went to Sir Bors and kissed him,
and commended him to God, and said: "Fair lord,
salute me to my lord, Sir Launcelot, my father, and
as soon as ye see him, bid him remember of this
unstable world."

And therewith he kneeled down tofore the table
and made his prayers, and then suddenly his soul
departed to Jesu Christ, and a great multitude of
angels bare his soul up to heaven, that the two fel-

lows might well behold it. Also the two fellows saw come from heaven an hand, but they saw not the body. And then it came right to the Vessel, and took it and the spear, and so bare it up to heaven. Sithen[27] was there never man so hardy to say that he had seen the Sangreal.

27. *Sithen* is another form of *sith*, and means *since*.

DISSENSIONS AT KING ARTHUR'S COURT

HE quest of the Holy Grail cost King Arthur many of his best knights, and the new ones who joined him by no means took the place of those tried and trusty men who had made his Round Table famous.   Moreover, quarrels and dissensions broke out among them, and many of them forgot their vows and lost the high character they held in the days of Galahad.

The queen and Sir Launcelot incurred the hatred of some of the knights, and there were many complaints made to discredit the queen with Arthur. Finally she was accused of treason, and Arthur, broken-hearted, was compelled to sit in judgment upon his wife as upon any other of his subjects. The punishment for treason in those days was burning at the stake, and the queen was condemned to death in this horrible manner.

In those times all great questions might be settled by trial of battle.   There was a possibility of saving the queen's life if some knight would volunteer to fight her accusers.   For some time she was unable to find any volunteer, and it was only under certain trying conditions that at last Sir Bors agreed to enter the lists.   He bore himself manfully in the fray, but would not have succeeded had not Sir Launcelot appeared in disguise and taken the battle upon himself.   By his mighty prowess, however,

Launcelot established the queen's innocence of treason and restored her to the king.

This was only temporary relief, however, for in the combat some of the best remaining knights were slain; among them were Sir Gareth and Sir Gaheris, both among the closest of Launcelot's friends and both killed by his own hand. Gawaine, their brother, one of the most powerful knights in the court, vowed vengeance for their death and swore to follow Launcelot to the ends of the earth. Launcelot protested that he should never cease to mourn for Sir Gareth and that he would as soon have slain his own nephew as to harm the man whom he made knight and whom he loved as a brother.

"Liar and traitor," cried Sir Gawaine, "you are a traitor both to the king and to me."

Launcelot replied, "I see that never again shall I have your love, though I pray you remember that at one time we were friends, and that once you were indebted to me for your life."

"I care not," said Sir Gawaine, fiercely; "nor do I care for the friendship of the king. As for you, in open combat or by stealth, your life will I have; and as for the king, if he will not aid me now I shall leave his kingdom and fight even against him."

"Cease this brawling before me," said the king. "It is better for us all that Launcelot should depart." Thus was Arthur's greatest knight banished from the kingdom.

This, however, did not terminate the difficulty. Arthur and Gawaine followed Launcelot to France, where in a terrible battle Gawaine was unhorsed and borne to the ground by Sir Launcelot, who, however, declined to kill the valiant knight, although Gawaine still accused him of being a traitor and declared that his enmity should never cease while life lasted. Launcelot had gathered a large following in France, and while Gawaine was being healed of his wounds there was peace between the armies.

In the meantime, Sir Mordred, the traitorous nephew of King Arthur, remained in England and instigated a rebellion against the king. He summoned a parliament and caused himself to be elected king. Queen Guinevere hid herself in the tower of London and could not be induced to leave by threat or entreaty, for she knew that Mordred's purpose was to make her his wife.

This news came to Arthur while he was encamped at Benwick where the battle between his forces and Launcelot's had taken place. Arthur immediately gathered his forces together and set sail for Britain. Mordred learned of his approach and gathered a great army at Dover, where he expected Sir Arthur to arrive, and where he lay in wait in the harbor with a great array of ships of all kinds.

Nothing daunted King Arthur, however, and in a fierce naval battle the forces of Mordred were defeated, while the traitor fled westward, where he gathered his scattered hosts. There were among his men many of King Arthur's favorite knights, men whom he had showed every favor and who were indebted to him for all that they possessed. The desertion of these men made Arthur sorry at heart and left him little joy in his successful battle. As soon as he could he landed and went about among the wounded of his own army and of his enemies, binding up their wounds and giving comfort to those who were dying. The dead he buried with honors of war whether they were his opponents or his friends.

As he went about among the boats he espied Sir Gawaine lying more dead than alive, for in the battle he had received a blow which had reopened the wound Launcelot had given him. When Arthur saw Gawaine he cried to the stricken knight, "My sister's son, here you lie at the point of death, the one man in the world I love most. Now is my joy all gone. Sir Launcelot had all my friendship and you all my love, both of which are gone utterly from me. Now indeed is my earthly joy all departed."

"My uncle, King Arthur," said Gawaine, "you know that this is my death day, and that all has come through my own hastiness; for now am I smitten on an old wound which Sir Launcelot gave me, and I know well I must die. If Sir Launcelot had been with you, this unhappy war had never begun. Now am I the cause of all this, for now I know it was Sir Launcelot that kept his enemies in subjection. I could not join in friendship with him while I lived, but now as I die I pray you give me paper, pen and ink that I may write to Launcelot with mine own hand."

When the writing materials were brought Gawaine sat weakly up and wrote this, "Unto Sir Launcelot, flower of all noble knights that I have heard or saw by my days; I, Sir Gawaine, nephew of King Arthur, send you greeting and let you know that I have been smitten upon the wound that you gave me before the city of Benwick and that I have come to my death day. I wish all the world to know that I, Sir Gawaine, knight of the Round Table, came by my death by my own seeking and not through your fault. So I beseech you, Sir Launcelot, return again to England and sometime see my tomb and say a prayer or two for my soul. Alas, Sir Launcelot, I beseech you by all the love that ever was between us, lose no time but cross the sea in all haste that you may rescue the noble king that made you knight, for he is in peril from that false traitor, my half-brother, Sir Mordred.

"This letter was written but two hours and a half before my death with my own hand and sealed with my heart's blood."

Then King Arthur wept, and sadness fell upon all who stood about. At the hour of noon, after Sir Gawaine had received the sacrament and had begged King Arthur to send for Launcelot, he yielded up the spirit.

After the burial of Sir Gawaine, King Arthur, old before his time, with all his sorrows fresh upon him, made ready to go against Sir Mordred, who had gathered a great army in the west.

THE PASSING OF ARTHUR*

By ALFRED TENNYSON

THAT story which the bold Sir Bedi-
vere,
First made and latest left of all the
knights,
Told, when the man was no more than
a voice
In the white winter of his age, to those
With whom he dwelt, new faces, other minds.

For on their march to westward, Bedivere,
Who slowly paced among the slumbering host,
Heard in his tent the moanings of the King:

"I found Him in the shining of the stars,
I mark'd Him in the flowering of His fields,
But in His ways with men I find Him not.
I waged His wars, and now I pass and die.
O me! for why is all around us here
As if some lesser god had made the world,
But had not force to shape it as he would,
Till the High God behold it from beyond,
And enter it, and make it beautiful?
Or else as if the world were wholly fair,
But that these eyes of men are dense and dim,
And have not power to see it as it is:
Perchance, because we see not to the close;—
For I, being simple, thought to work His will,

*Note.—*The Passing of Arthur* gives us the story of King Arthur
from the time of Sir Gawaine's death.

237

And have but stricken with the sword in vain;
And all whereon I lean'd in wife and friend
Is traitor to my peace, and all my realm
Reels back into the beast, and is no more.
My God, thou hast forgotten me in my death:
Nay—God my Christ—I pass but shall not die."

Then, ere that last weird battle in the west,
There came on Arthur sleeping, Gawain kill'd
In Lancelot's war, the ghost of Gawain blown
Along a wandering wind, and past his ear
Went shrilling, "Hollow, hollow all delight!
Hail, King! to-morrow thou shalt pass away.
Farewell! there is an isle of rest for thee.
And I am blown along a wandering wind,
And hollow, hollow, hollow all delight."
And fainter onward, like wild birds that change
Their season in the night and wail their way
From cloud to cloud, down the long wind the dream
Shrill'd; but in going mingled with dim cries
Far in the moonlit haze among the hills,
As of some lonely city sack'd by night,
When all is lost, and wife and child with wail
Pass to new lords; and Arthur woke and call'd,
"Who spake? A dream. O light upon the wind,
Thine, Gawain, was the voice—are these dim cries
Thine? or doth all that haunts the waste and wild
Mourn, knowing it will go along with me?"

This heard the bold Sir Bedivere and spake:
"O me, my King, let pass whatever will,
Elves, and the harmless glamour of the field;
But in their stead thy name and glory cling
To all high places like a golden cloud

For ever: but as yet thou shalt not pass.
Light was Gawain in life, and light in death
Is Gawain, for the ghost is as the man;
And care not thou for dreams from him, but rise—
I hear the steps of Modred in the west,
And with him many of thy people, and knights
Once thine, whom thou has loved, but grosser grown
Than heathen, spitting at their vows and thee.
Right well in heart they know thee for the King.
Arise, go forth and conquer as of old."

Then spake King Arthur to Sir Bedivere:
"Far other is this battle in the west
Whereto we move, than when we strove in youth,
And brake the petty kings, and fought with Rome,
Or thrust the heathen from the Roman wall,[1]
And shook him thro' the north. Ill doom is mine
To war against my people and my knights.
The king who fights his people fights himself.
And they my knights, who loved me once, the
        stroke
That strikes them dead is as my death to me.
Yet let us hence, and find or feel a way
Thro' this blind haze, which ever since I saw
One lying in the dust at Almesbury,[2]
Hath folded in the passes of the world."

1. Shortly after his accession to the throne, according to the legend, Arthur was called upon to send tribute to Rome. He refused, however, and was successful in the battle against Rome which his refusal caused. The heathen in his own country he also defeated, driving them beyond the "Roman wall"—the wall which had been set up by the Romans at the time of their occupancy of Britain to mark the northern boundary of their territory.

2. Queen Guinevere, after her falseness to Arthur had been proved, had withdrawn to a nunnery at Almesbury. Here Arthur had had an interview with her before setting out on his last campaign.

Then rose the King and moved his host by night,
And ever push'd Sir Modred, league by league,
Back to the sunset bound of Lyonnesse—
A land of old upheaven from the abyss
By fire, to sink into the abyss again;
Where fragments of forgotten peoples dwelt,
And the long mountains ended in a coast
Of ever-shifting sand, and far away
The phantom circle of a moaning sea.
There the pursuer could pursue no more,
And he that fled no further fly the King;
And there, that day when the great light of heaven
Burn'd at his lowest in the rolling year,[3]
On the waste sand by the waste sea they closed.
Nor ever yet had Arthur fought a fight
Like this last, dim, weird battle of the west.
A deathwhite mist slept over sand and sea:
Whereof the chill, to him who breathed it, drew
Down with his blood, till all his heart was cold
With formless fear; and ev'n on Arthur fell
Confusion, since he saw not whom he fought.
For friend and foe were shadows in the mist,
And friend slew friend not knowing whom he slew;
And some had visions out of golden youth,
And some beheld the faces of old ghosts
Look in upon the battle; and in the mist
Was many a noble deed, many a base,
And chance and craft and strength in single fights,
And ever and anon with host to host
Shocks, and the splintering spear, the hard mail
        hewn,
Shield-breakings, and the clash of brands, the crash

3. Can you tell from this on about what day Arthur fought this last battle?

Of battle-axes on shatter'd helms, and shrieks
After the Christ, of those who falling down
Look'd up for heaven, and only saw the mist;
And shouts of heathen and the traitor knights,
Sweat, writhings, anguish, laboring of the lungs
In that close mist, and cryings for the light,
Moans of the dying, and voices of the dead.

Last, as by some one deathbed after wail
Of suffering, silence follows, or thro' death
Or deathlike swoon, thus over all that shore,
Save for some whisper of the seething seas,
A dead hush fell; but when the dolorous day
Grew drearier toward twilight falling, came
A bitter wind, clear from the North, and blew
The mist aside, and with that wind the tide
Rose, and the pale King glanced across the field
Of battle: but no man was moving there;
Nor any cry of Christian heard thereon,
Nor yet of heathen; only the wan wave
Brake in among dead faces, to and fro
Swaying the helpless hands, and up and down
Tumbling the hollow helmets of the fallen,
And shiver'd brands that once had fought with
        Rome,
And rolling far along the gloomy shores
The voice of days of old and days to be.

Then spake King Arthur to Sir Bedivere,
And whiter than the mist that all day long
Had held the field of battle was the King:

"Hearest thou this great voice that shakes the
        world,

And wastes the narrow realm whereon we move,
And beats upon the faces of the dead,
My dead, as tho' they had not died for me?—
O Bedivere, for on my heart hath fall'n
Confusion, till I know not what I am,
Nor whence I am, nor whether I be King.
Behold, I seem but King among the dead."

Then spake the bold Sir Bedivere: "My King,
King everywhere! and so the dead have kings,
There also will I worship thee as King.
Yet still thy life is whole, and still I live
Who love thee; but who hates thee, he that brought
The heathen back among us, yonder stands,
Modred, unharm'd, the traitor of thine house."

Then spake the King: "My house hath been my
            doom.
But call not thou this traitor of my house
Who hath but dwelt beneath one roof with me.
My house are rather they who sware my vows,
Yea, even while they break them, own'd me
            King.
And well for thee, saying in my dark hour,
When all the purport of my throne hath failed,
That quick or dead thou holdest me for King.
King am I, whatsoever be their cry;
And one last act of kinghood shalt thou see
Yet, ere I pass." And uttering this the King
Made at the man: then Modred smote his liege
Hard on that helm which many a heathen sword
Had beaten thin; while Arthur at one blow,
Striking the last stroke with Excalibur,
Slew him, and all but slain himself, he fell.

So all day long the noise of battle roll'd
Among the mountains by the winter sea;
Until King Arthur's Table, man by man,
Had fall'n in Lyonnesse about their lord,
King Arthur. Then, because his wound was deep,
The bold Sir Bedivere uplifted him,
And bore him to a chapel nigh the field,
A broken chancel with a broken cross,
That stood on a dark strait of barren land:
On one side lay the Ocean, and on one
Lay a great water, and the moon was full.

Then spake King Arthur to Sir Bedivere:
"The sequel of to-day unsolders all
The goodliest fellowship of famous knights
Whereof this world holds record. Such a sleep
They sleep—the men I loved. I think that we
Shall never more, at any future time,
Delight our souls with talk of knightly deeds,
Walking about the gardens and the halls
Of Camelot, as in the days that were.
I perish by this people which I made,—
Tho' Merlin sware that I should come again
To rule once more; but, let what will be, be,
I am so deeply smitten thro' the helm
That without help I cannot last till morn.
Thou therefore take my brand Excalibur,
Which was my pride: for thou rememberest how
In those old days, one summer noon, an arm
Rose up from out the bosom of the lake,
Clothed in white samite, mystic, wonderful,
Holding the sword—and how I row'd across
And took it, and have worn it, like a king;
And, wheresoever I am sung or told

In aftertime, this also shall be known:
But now delay not: take Excalibur,
And fling him far into the middle mere:[4]
Watch what thou seëst, and lightly bring me word."

To him replied the bold Sir Bedivere:
"It is not meet, Sir King, to leave thee thus,
Aidless, alone, and smitten thro' the helm—
A little thing may harm a wounded man;
Yet I thy hest will all perform at full,
Watch what I see, and lightly bring thee word."

So saying, from the ruin'd shrine he stept,
And in the moon athwart the place of tombs,
Where lay the mighty bones of ancient men,
Old knights, and over them the sea-wind sang
Shrill, chill, with flakes of foam. He, stepping
                down
By zigzag paths, and juts of pointed rock,
Came on the shining levels of the lake.

There drew he forth the brand Excalibur,
And o'er him, drawing it, the winter moon,
Brightening the skirts of a long cloud, ran forth
And sparkled keen with frost against the hilt:
For all the haft twinkled with diamond sparks,
Myriads of topaz-lights, and jacinth-work
Of subtlest jewelry. He gazed so long
That both his eyes were dazzled as he stood,
This way and that dividing the swift mind,
In act to throw: but at the last it seem'd
Better to leave Excalibur conceal'd
There in the many-knotted waterflags

4. *Mere* is a poetic word for *lake.*

That whistled stiff and dry about the marge.
So strode he back slow to the wounded King.

Then spake King Arthur to Sir Bedivere:
"Hast thou perform'd my mission which I gave?
What is it thou hast seen? or what hast heard?"

And answer made the bold Sir Bedivere:
"I heard the ripple washing in the reeds,
And the wild water lapping on the crag."

To whom replied King Arthur, faint and pale:
"Thou hast betray'd thy nature and thy name,
Not rendering true answer, as beseem'd
Thy fealty, nor like a noble knight:
For surer sign had follow'd, either hand,
Or voice, or else a motion of the mere.
This is a shameful thing for men to lie.
Yet now, I charge thee, quickly go again,
As thou art lief[5] and dear, and do the thing
I bade thee, watch, and lightly bring me word."

Then went Sir Bedivere the second time
Across the bridge, and paced beside the mere,
Counting the dewy pebbles, fix'd in thought;
But when he saw the wonder of the hilt,
How curiously and strangely chased, he smote
His palms together, and he cried aloud:

"And if indeed I cast the brand away,
Surely a precious thing, one worthy note,
Should thus be lost for ever from the earth,
Which might have pleased the eyes of many men.
What good should follow this, if this were done?

5. *Lief* is an old word meaning *beloved*.

What harm, undone? Deep harm to disobey,
Seeing obedience is the bond of rule.
Were it well to obey then, if a king demand
An act unprofitable, against himself?
The King is sick, and knows not what he does.
What record, or what relic of my lord
Should be to aftertime, but empty breath
And rumors of a doubt? But were this kept,
Stored in some treasure-house of mighty kings,
Some one might show it at a joust of arms,
Saying, 'King Arthur's sword, Excalibur,
Wrought by the lonely maiden of the Lake.
Nine years she wrought it, sitting in the deeps
Upon the hidden bases of the hills.'
So might some old man speak in the aftertime
To all the people, winning reverence.
But now much honor and much fame were lost."

So spake he, clouded with his own conceit,[6]
And hid Excalibur the second time,
And so strode back slow to the wounded King.

Then spoke King Arthur, breathing heavily:
"What is it thou hast seen? or what hast heard?"

And answer made the bold Sir Bedivere:
"I heard the water lapping on the crag,
And the long ripple washing in the reeds."

To whom replied King Arthur, much in wrath:
"Ah, miserable and unkind, untrue,
Unknightly, traitor-hearted! Woe is me!
Authority forgets a dying king,

6. *Conceit* here means *fancy*.

Laid widow'd of the power in his eye
That bowed the will. I see thee what thou art,
For thou, the latest-left of all my knights,
In whom should meet the offices of all,
Thou wouldst betray me for the precious hilt;
Either from lust of gold, or like a girl
Valuing the giddy pleasure of the eyes.
Yet, for a man may fail in duty twice,
And the third time may prosper, get thee hence:
But, if thou spare to fling Excalibur,
I will arise and slay thee with my hands."

Then quickly rose Sir Bedivere, and ran,
And, leaping down the ridges lightly, plunged
Among the bulrush beds, and clutch'd the sword,
And strongly wheel'd and threw it. The great
    brand
Made lightnings in the splendor of the moon,
And flashing round and round, and whirl'd in an
    arch,
Shot like a streamer of the northern morn,
Seen where the moving isles of winter shock
By night, with noises of the Northern Sea.
So flash'd and fell the brand Excalibur:
But ere he dipt the surface, rose an arm
Clothed in white samite, mystic, wonderful,
And caught him by the hilt, and brandish'd him
Three times, and drew him under in the mere.
And lightly went the other to the King.

Then spoke King Arthur, drawing thicker
    breath:
"Now see I by thine eyes that this is done.
Speak out: what is it thou hast heard, or seen?"

And answer made the bold Sir Bedivere:
"Sir King, I closed mine eyelids, lest the gems
Should blind my purpose, for I never saw,
Nor shall see, here or elsewhere, till I die,
Not tho' I live three lives of mortal men,
So great a miracle as yonder hilt.
Then with both hands I flung him, wheeling him;
But when I looked again, behold an arm,
Clothed in white samite, mystic, wonderful,
That caught him by the hilt, and brandish'd him
Three times, and drew him under in the mere."

And answer made King Arthur, breathing hard:
"My end draws nigh; 'tis time that I were gone
Make broad thy shoulders to receive my weight,
And bear me to the margin; yet I fear
My wound hath taken cold, and I shall die."

So saying, from the pavement he half rose,
Slowly, with pain, reclining on his arm,
And looking wistfully with wide blue eyes
As in a picture.   Him Sir Bedivere
Remorsefully regarded thro' his tears,
And would have spoken, but he found not words;
Then took with care, and kneeling on one knee,
O'er both his shoulders drew the languid hands,
And rising bore him thro' the place of tombs.

But, as he walk'd, King Arthur panted hard,
Like one that feels a nightmare on his bed
When all the house is mute.   So sigh'd the King,
Muttering and murmuring at his ear, "Quick,
          quick!
I fear it is too late, and I shall die."

But the other swiftly strode from ridge to ridge,
Clothed, with his breath, and looking, as he walk'd,
Larger than human on the frozen hills.
He heard the deep behind him, and a cry
Before. His own thought drove him like a goad.
Dry clash'd his harness in the icy caves
And barren chasms, and all to left and right
The bare black cliff clang'd round him, as he based
His feet on juts of slippery crag that rang
Sharp-smitten with the dint of armed heels—
And on a sudden, lo! the level lake,
And the long glories of the winter moon.[7]

Then saw they how there hove a dusky barge,
Dark as a funeral scarf from stem to stern,
Beneath them; and descending they were ware
That all the decks were dense with stately forms,
Black-stoled, black-hooded, like a dream—by these
Three Queens with crowns of gold: and from them
        rose
A cry that shiver'd to the tingling stars,
And, as it were one voice, an agony
Of lamentation, like a wind that shrills
All night in a waste land, where no one comes,
Or hath come, since the making of the world.

Then murmur'd Arthur, "Place me in the barge."
So to the barge they came. There those three
        Queens

7. This sentence is a striking example of Tennyson's ability to
make the sound of a passage help in conveying the sense. The harsh
e and short a sounds in the earlier part are intended to imitate the
clash of armor and the ring of "armed heels" on the rock; while
the smooth l and o sounds in the last two lines bring to us the
quiet and peacefulness of the scene upon which Bedivere came forth.

Put forth their hands, and took the King, and wept.
But she, that rose the tallest of them all
And fairest, laid his head upon her lap,
And loosed the shatter'd casque, and chafed his
     hands,
And call'd him by his name, complaining loud,
And dropping bitter tears against a brow
Striped with dark blood: for all his face was
     white
And colorless, and like the wither'd moon
Smote by the fresh beam of the springing east;
And all his greaves and cuisses dash'd with drops
Of onset; and the light and lustrous curls—
That made his forehead like a rising sun
High from the daïs-throne—were parch'd with dust,
Or, clotted into points and hanging loose,
Mix'd with the knightly growth that fringed his
     lips.
So like a shatter'd column lay the King;
Not like that Arthur who, with lance in rest,
From spur to plume a star of tournament,
Shot thro' the lists at Camelot, and charged
Before the eyes of ladies and of kings.

    Then loudly cried the bold Sir Bedivere:
"Ah! my Lord Arthur, whither shall I go?
Where shall I hide my forehead and my eyes?
For now I see the true old times are dead,
When every morning brought a noble chance,
And every chance brought out a noble knight.
Such times have been not since the light that led
The holy Elders[8] with the gift of myrrh.

    8. The Elders are the wise men who, with their gifts of myrrh,
came to worship Christ in the manger.

But now the whole Round Table is dissolved
Which was an image of the mighty world,
And I, the last, go forth companionless,
And the days darken round me, and the years,
Among new men, strange faces, other minds."

And slowly answer'd Arthur from the barge:
"The old order changeth, yielding place to new,
And God fulfils himself in many ways,
Lest one good custom should corrupt the world.
Comfort thyself: what comfort is in me?
I have lived my life, and that which I have done
May He within himself make pure! but thou,
If thou shouldst never see my face again,
Pray for my soul. More things are wrought by
    prayer
Than this world dreams of. Wherefore, let thy
    voice
Rise like a fountain for me night and day.
For what are men better than sheep or goats
That nourish a blind life within the brain,
If, knowing God, they lift not hands of prayer
Both for themselves and those who call them friend?
For so the whole round earth is every way
Bound by gold chains about the feet of God.
But now farewell. I am going a long way
With these thou seëst—if indeed I go
(For all my mind is clouded with a doubt)—
To the island-valley of Avilion;
Where falls not hail, or rain, or any snow,
Nor ever wind blows loudly; but it lies
Deep-meadow'd, happy, fair with orchard lawns
And bowery hollows crown'd with summer sea,
Where I will heal me of my grievous wound."

So said he, and the barge with oar and sail
Moved from the brink, like some full-breasted swan
That, fluting a wild carol ere her death,
Ruffles her pure cold plume, and takes the flood
With swarthy webs. Long stood Sir Bedivere
Revolving many memories, till the hull
Look'd one black dot against the verge of
        dawn,
And on the mere the wailing died away.
    But when that moan had past for evermore,
The stillness of the dead world's winter dawn
Amazed him, and he groan'd, "The King is gone."
And therewithal came on him the weird rhyme,
"From the great deep to the great deep he goes."

    Whereat he slowly turn'd and slowly clomb
The last hard footstep of that iron crag;
Thence mark'd the black hull moving yet, and cried,
"He passes to be King among the dead,
And after healing of his grievous wound
He comes again; but—if he come no more—
O me, be yon dark Queens in yon black boat,
Who shriek'd and wail'd, the three whereat we gazed
On that high day, when, clothed with living light,
They stood before his throne in silence, friends
Of Arthur, who should help him at his need?"

    Then from the dawn it seem'd there came, but
        faint
As from beyond the limit of the world,
Like the last echo born of a great cry,
Sounds, as if some fair city were one voice
Around a king returning from his wars.

Thereat once more he moved about, and clomb
Ev'n to the highest he could climb, and saw,
Straining his eyes beneath an arch of hand,
Or thought he saw, the speck that bare the King,

THE BARGE MOVED FROM THE BRINK

Down that long water opening on the deep
Somewhere far off, pass on and on, and go
From less to less and vanish into light.
And the new sun rose bringing the new year.

HENRY HUDSON'S FOURTH VOYAGE [1]

By HENRY R. CLEVELAND

NOTE.—It should be remembered that Hudson had already made three voyages in search of the Northwestern Passage. On his first voyage he tried to sail around the northern part of Greenland, but was driven back by the ice and returned to England, whence he had sailed.

On his second voyage he attempted to find a northeastern passage around the North Cape and north of Europe. He reached Nova Zembla but was unable to get any farther.

On his third voyage he sailed under the management of the Dutch East India Company and left the port of Amsterdam, expecting to go north around the continent of America. In this he was disappointed; but he proceeded west to the Banks of Newfoundland and thence south along the coast of the United States. He visited Penobscot Bay in Maine, sailed around Cape Cod and southward at some distance from the coast, to Virginia, deciding by this time that he could not find a passage westward in that direction. As he knew of the discoveries along the coast of Virginia he returned north, and on his way discovered Delaware Bay and the outlet of the Hudson River. After some delay he explored the river to the present site of Albany, where he again found that his Northwestern Passage was barred by the shallowing waters of the river. This was the extent of the explorations of this voyage, from which he finally returned in safety to London.

China was well known to the people of Hudson's time, but had been reached always by water around the Cape

1. This sketch of Henry Hudson's fourth voyage is taken from the *Life of Henry Hudson* by Henry R. Cleveland, which appears in Jared Sparks's series of books on American biography.

of Good Hope and along the southern shore of Asia, or
by the long and perilous land journey across Europe and
Asia. It was the dream of all these early navigators to
find a water passage much shorter than the one around
the Cape, and for this they naturally looked to the northwest, where they knew the distance must be much shorter.
They little knew that this search was to continue for
hundreds of years—so long, in fact, that no practicable
passage of that sort is even now known.

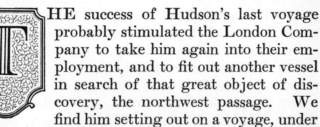

HE success of Hudson's last voyage
probably stimulated the London Company to take him again into their employment, and to fit out another vessel
in search of that great object of discovery, the northwest passage. We
find him setting out on a voyage, under
their auspices, early in the spring of 1610. His
crew numbered several persons, who were destined
to act a conspicuous part in the melancholy events
of this expedition. Among these were Robert Juet,
who had already sailed with him as mate in two of
his voyages; Habakuk Pricket, a man of some intelligence and education, who had been in the service
of Sir Dudley Digges, one of the London Company, and from whose Journal we learn chiefly the
events of the voyage; and Henry Greene, of whose
character and circumstances it is necessary here to
give a brief account.

It appears from the Journal, that Greene was a
young man of good abilities, and education, born
of highly respectable parents, but of such abandoned character, that he had forced his family to cast
him off. Hudson found him in this condition, took
pity upon him, and received him into his house in

London. When it was determined that he should command this expedition, Hudson resolved to take Greene with him, in the hope, that, by exciting his ambition, and by withdrawing him from his accustomed haunts, he might reclaim him. Greene was also a good penman, and would be useful to Hudson in that capacity. With much difficulty Greene's mother was persuaded to advance four pounds, to buy clothes for him; and, at last, the money was placed in the hands of an agent, for fear that it would be wasted if given directly to him. He was not registered in the Company's books, nor did he sail in their pay; but Hudson, to stimulate him to reform, promised to give him wages, and on his return to get him appointed one of the Prince's guards, provided he should behave well on the voyage.

Hudson was also accompanied, as usual, by his son. The crew consisted of twenty-three men, and the vessel was named the *Discovery*. The London Company had insisted upon Hudson's taking in the ship a person, who was to aid him by his knowledge and experience, and in whom they felt great confidence. This arrangement seems to have been very disagreeable to Hudson, as he put the man into another vessel before he reached the mouth of the Thames, and sent him back to London, with a letter to his employers stating his reasons for so doing. What these reasons were, we can form no conjecture, as there is no hint given in the Journal.

He sailed from London on the 17th of April, 1610. Steering north from the mouth of the Thames, and passing in sight of the northern part of Scotland, the Orkney, Shetland, and Faroe Isles, and having, in a little more than a month, sailed along the southern coast of Iceland, where he could see the flames ascending from Mount Hecla, he anchored in a bay on the western side of that island. Here they found a spring so hot, that "it would scald a fowl," in which the crew bathed freely. At this place, Hudson discovered signs of a turbulent and mutinous disposition in his crew. The chief plotter seems to have been Robert Juet, the mate. Before reaching Iceland, Juet had remarked to one of the crew, that there would be bloodshed before the voyage was over; and he was evidently at that time contriving some mischief. While the ship was at anchor in this bay, a circumstance occurred, which gave Juet an opportunity to commence his intrigues. It is thus narrated by Pricket.

"At Iceland, the surgeon and he (Henry Greene) fell out in Dutch, and he beat him ashore in English, which set all the company in a rage, so that we had much ado to get the surgeon aboard. I told the master of it, but he bade me let it alone; for, said he, the surgeon had a tongue that would wrong the best friend he had. But Robert Juet, the master's mate, would needs burn his finger in the embers, and told the carpenter a long tale, when he was drunk, that our master had brought in Greene to crack his credit that should displease him; which words came to the master's ears, who, when he understood it, would have gone back to Iceland, when he was forty leagues from thence, to have sent home his mate, Robert Juet, in a fisherman. But, being otherwise persuaded, all was well. So Henry Greene stood upright, and very inward with the master, and was a serviceable man every way

for manhood; but for religion, he would say, he was
clean paper, whereon he might write what he
would."

He sailed from Iceland on the 1st of June, and
for several days Juet continued to instigate the
crew to mutiny, persuading them to put the ship
about and return to England. This, as we have
seen, came to the knowledge of Hudson, and he
threatened to send Juet back, but was finally paci-
fied. In a few days he made the coast of Greenland, which appeared very mountainous, the hills
rising like sugar loaves, and covered with snow.
But the ice was so thick all along the shore, that it
was found impossible to land. He therefore steered
for the south of Greenland, where he encountered
great numbers of whales. Two of these monsters
passed under the ship, but did no harm; for which
the journalist was devoutly thankful. Having
doubled the southern point of Greenland, he steered
northwest, passed in sight of Desolation Island, in
the neighborhood of which he saw a huge island or
mountain of ice, and continued northwest till the
latter part of June, when he came in sight of land
bearing north, which he supposed to be an island
set down in his chart in the northerly part of Davis's
Strait. His wish was to sail along the western
coast of this island, and thus get to the north of it;
but adverse winds and the quantities of ice which
he encountered every day, prevented him.

Being south of this land, he fell into a current setting westwardly, which he followed, but was in constant danger from the ice. One day, an enormous
mountain of ice turned over near the ship, but fortunately without touching it. This served as a

warning to keep at a distance from these masses, to prevent the ship from being crushed by them. He encountered a severe storm, which brought the ice so thick about the ship, that he judged it best to run her among the largest masses, and there let her lie. In this situation, says the journalist, "some of our men fell sick; I will not say it was of fear, although I saw small sign of other grief." As soon as the storm abated, Hudson endeavoured to extricate himself from the ice. Wherever any open space appeared, he directed his course, sailing in almost every direction; but the longer he contended with the ice, the more completely did he seem to be enclosed, till at last he could go no further. The ship seemed to be hemmed in on every side, and in danger of being soon closely wedged, so as to be immovable. In this perilous situation, even the stout heart of Hudson almost yielded to the feeling of despair; and, as he afterwards confessed to one of the men, he thought he should never escape from the ice, but that he was doomed to perish there.

He did not, however, allow his crew, at the time, to be aware what his apprehensions really were; but, assembling them all around him, he brought out his chart, and showed them that they had advanced in this direction a hundred leagues further than any Englishman had done before; and gave them their choice whether to proceed, or to return home. The men could come to no agreement; some were in favor of returning, others were for pushing forward. This was probably what Hudson expected; the men were mutinous, and yet knew not what they wanted themselves. Having fairly convinced them of this, it was easier to set them at work to extricate the ship from her immediate danger. After much time and labor, they made room to turn the ship round, and then by little and little they worked their way along for a league or two, when they found a clear sea.

The scene which has just been described, seems indeed a subject worthy of the talents of a skilful painter. The fancy of the artist would represent the dreary and frightful appearance of the ice-covered sea, stretching away as far as the eye could reach, a bleak and boundless waste; the dark and broken clouds driving across the fitful sky; the ship motionless amidst the islands and mountains of ice, her shrouds and sails being fringed and stiffened with the frozen spray. On the deck would appear the form of Hudson himself, displaying the chart to his men; his countenance careworn and sad, but still concealing, under the appearance of calmness and indifference, the apprehensions and forebodings, which harrowed his mind. About him would be seen the rude and ruffian-like men; some examining the chart with eager curiosity, some glaring on their commander with eyes of hatred and vengeance, and expressing in their looks those murderous intentions, which they at last so fatally executed.

Having reached a clear sea, Hudson pursued his course northwest, and in a short time saw land bearing southwest, which appeared very mountainous and covered with snow. This he named *Desire Provokes*. He had now entered the Strait which bears his name, and, steering west, he occupied nearly the whole month of July in passing through it. To the various capes, islands, and promontories which he saw, he gave names, either in commemoration of some circumstance, which happened at the time, or in honor of persons and places at home, or else for the reward of the discoverer.

Some islands, near which he anchored, and where his ship was but just saved from the rocks, he called the *Isles of God's Mercies*. On the 19th, he passed a point of land, which he named *Hold with Hope*. To the main land, which he soon after discovered, he gave the name of *Magna Britannia*. On the 2d of September, he saw a headland on the northern shore, which he named *Salisbury's Foreland;* and, running southwest from this point about fourteen leagues, he entered a passage not more than five miles in width, the southern cape at the entrance of which he named *Cape Worsenholme,* and that on the north side, *Cape Digges*.

He now hoped that the passage to the western sea was open before him, and that the great discovery was at length achieved. He therefore sent a number of the men on shore at Cape Digges, to ascend the hills, in the hope that they would see the great ocean open to them beyond the Strait. The exploring party, however, were prevented from making any discovery, by a violent thunder storm, which soon drove them back to the ship. They saw plenty of deer, and soon after espied a number of small piles of stones, which they at first supposed must be the work of some civilized person. On approaching them, and lifting up one of the stones, they found them to be hollow, and filled with fowls, hung by the neck. They endeavored to persuade their commander to wait here, till they could provision the ship from the stores, which were thus remarkably provided for them. But his ardor was so great to find his way into the ocean, which he felt convinced was immediately in the vicinity, that he could suffer no delay, but ordered his men to weigh anchor at once; a precipitancy which he had afterwards reason bitterly to regret. Having advanced about ten leagues through the Strait, he came into the great open Bay or sea which bears his name.

Having entered the Bay, he pursued a southerly course for nearly a month, till he arrived at the bottom of the Bay; when, finding that he was disappointed in his expectation of thus reaching the western seas, he changed his course to the north, in order to retrace his steps. On the 10th of September, he found it necessary to inquire into the conduct of some of the men, whose mutinous disposition had manifested itself a good deal of late. Upon investigation, it appeared, that the mate, Robert Juet, and Francis Clement, the boatswain, had been the most forward in exciting a spirit of insubordination. The conduct of Juet at Iceland was again brought up, and, as it appeared that both he and Clement had been lately plotting against the commander, they were both deposed, and Robert Billet was appointed mate, and William Wilson boatswain.

The remaining part of September and all October were passed in exploring the great Bay. At times the weather was so bad, that they were compelled to run into some bay and anchor; and in one of the storms they were obliged to cut away the cable, and so lost their anchor. At another time they ran upon a sunken ledge of rocks, where the ship stuck fast for twelve hours, but was at last got off without being much injured. The last of October having now arrived, and winter beginning to set in, Hudson ran the vessel into a small bay, and sent a party in search of a good place to intrench themselves till the spring. They soon found a convenient station; and, bringing the ship thither, they hauled her aground. This was on the 1st of November. In ten days they were completely frozen in, and the ship firmly fixed in the sea.

The prospect for Hudson and his men was now dreary and disheartening. In addition to the rigors of a long winter, in a high northern latitude, they had to apprehend the suffering which would arise from a scarcity of provisions. The vessel had been victualled for six months, and that time having now expired, and their stores falling short, while, at the same time, the chance of obtaining supplies from hunting and fishing was very precarious, it was found necessary to put the crew upon an allowance. In order, however, to stimulate the men to greater exertions, Hudson offered a reward or bounty for every beast, fish, or fowl, which they should kill; hoping, that in this way the scanty stock of provisions might be made to hold out till the breaking up of the ice in the spring.

About the middle of November, John Williams, the gunner, died. We are not informed what was his disease, but we are led to suppose from the Journal, that his death was hastened, if not caused, by the unkind treatment he experienced from Hudson. It appears very evident from the simple narration by Pricket, that "the master," as he calls him, had become hasty and irritable in his temper. This is more to be regretted, than wondered at. The continual hardships and disappointments, to which he had been exposed, and especially the last unhappy failure in discovering the northwest passage, when he had believed himself actually within sight of it, must have operated powerfully upon an ardent and enthusiastic mind like his, in which the feeling of regret at failure is always proportionate to the strength and confidence of hope when first formed. In addition to this, the troublesome disposition of the crew, which must have caused ceaseless anxiety, undoubtedly contributed much to disturb his calmness and self-possession, and render him precipitate and irritable in his conduct. Many proofs of this soon occurred.[2]

The death of the gunner was followed by consequences which may be regarded as the beginning of troubles that in the end proved fatal. It appears that it was the custom in those times, when a man died at sea, to sell his clothes to the crew by auction. In one respect, Hudson violated this custom, and probably gained no little ill will thereby. The gunner had a gray cloth gown or wrapper, which Henry Greene had set his heart upon possessing; and Hudson, wishing to gratify his favorite, refused to put it up to public sale, and gave Greene the sole choice of purchasing it.

Not long after this, Hudson ordered the carpenter to go on shore, and build a house, or hut, for the accommodation of the crew. The man replied,

2. In reading the account of this Arctic expedition, we must remember that the author has followed very closely the journal of Pricket and has not tried to determine the truth or falseness of that man's statements. It does not seem probable that a man of Hudson's character should so suddenly become peevish and irritable, nor that his judgment should so suddenly become weak. The journal was probably written to defend Pricket's share in the disgraceful transaction, and so events were colored to suit himself.

that it would now be impossible to do such a piece
of work, from the severity of the weather, and the
quantity of snow. The house ought to have been
erected when they had first fixed their station there,
but now it was too late, and Hudson had refused
to have it done at first. The carpenter's refusal to
perform the work excited the anger of the master
to such a degree, that he drove him violently from
the cabin, using the most opprobrious language, and
finally threatening to hang him.

Greene appeared to take sides with the carpenter,
which made Hudson so angry, that he gave the
gown, which Greene had coveted so much, to Billet,
the mate; telling Greene, with much abusive language, that, as not one of his friends at home would
trust him to the value of twenty shillings, he could
not be expected to trust him for the value of the
gown; and that, as for wages, he should have none
if he did not behave better. These bitter taunts
sunk deep into Greene's heart, and no doubt incited
him to further mutinous conduct.

The sufferings of the men were not less, during
the winter, than they had had reason to apprehend.
Many of them were made lame, probably from chil-
blains and freezing their feet; and Pricket complains
in the Journal, written after the close of the voyage,
that he was still suffering from the effects of this
winter. They were, however, much better supplied
with provisions than they had anticipated. For
three months they had such an abundance of white
partridges about the ship, that they killed a hundred dozen of them; and, on the departure of these,
when spring came, they found a great plenty of
swans, geese, ducks, and other waterfowl.

Hudson was in hopes, when he saw these wild fowl, that they had come to breed in these regions, which would have rendered it much easier to catch them; but he found that they went still further north for this purpose. Before the ice had broken up, these birds too had disappeared, and the horror of starvation began to stare them in the face. They were forced to search the hills, woods, and valleys, for anything that might afford them subsistence; even the moss growing on the ground, and disgusting reptiles, were not spared. Their sufferings were somewhat relieved at last, by the use of a bud, which is described as "full of turpentine matter." Of these buds the surgeon made a decoction, which he gave the men to drink, and also applied them hot to their bodies, wherever any part was affected. This was undoubtedly very effectual in curing the scurvy.

About the time that the ice began to break up, they were visited by a savage, whom Hudson treated so well, that he returned the day after to the ship, bringing several skins, some of which he gave in return for presents he had received the day before. For others Hudson traded with him, but made such hard bargains, that he never visited them again. As soon as the ice would allow of it, some of the men were sent out to fish. The first day they were very successful, catching about five hundred fish; but after this, they never succeeded in taking a quarter part of this number in one day. Being greatly distressed by want of provisions, Hudson took the boat and coasted along the bay to the southwest, in the hope of meeting some of the natives, from whom he might obtain supplies. He saw the woods blazing at a distance, where they had been set on fire by the natives; but he was not able at any time to come within sight of the people themselves. After an absence of several days, he returned unsuccessful to the ship.

The only effect of this little expedition was defeating a conspiracy, formed by Greene, Wilson, and some others, to seize the boat and make off with her. They were prevented from putting this scheme in execution by Hudson's unexpected determination to use the boat himself. Well would it have been for him, if they had been allowed to follow their wishes.

Having returned to the ship, and finding everything now prepared for their departure according to his directions, before weighing anchor he went through the mournful task of distributing to his crew the small remnant of the provisions, about a pound of bread to each man; which he did with tears in his eyes. He also gave them a bill of return, as a sort of certificate for any who might live to reach home. Some of the men were so ravenous, that they devoured in a day or two the whole of their allowance of bread.

They sailed from the bay, in which they had passed the winter, about the middle of June, and, in three or four days, being surrounded with ice, were obliged to anchor. The bread he had given the men, and a few pounds of cheese, which had remained, were consumed. Hudson now intimated to one of the crew, that the chests of all the men would be searched, to find any provisions that might have been concealed there; and ordered him at the same time to bring all that was in his. The man obeyed, and produced thirty cakes in a bag. This indiscretion on the part of Hudson appears to have greatly exasperated his crew, and to have been the immediate cause of open mutiny.

They had been detained at anchor in the ice about a week, when the first signs of this mutiny appeared. Greene, and Wilson, the boatswain, came in the night to Pricket, who was lying in his berth very lame, and told him, that they and several of the crew had resolved to seize Hudson, and set him adrift in the boat, with all on board who were disabled by sickness; that there were but few days' provisions left, and the master appeared entirely irresolute which way to go; that for themselves they had eaten nothing for three days; their only hope, therefore, was in taking command of the ship, and escaping from these regions as quickly as possible; and that they would carry their plot unto execution, or perish in the attempt.

Pricket remonstrated with them in the most earnest manner, entreating them to abandon such a wicked intention, and reminding them of their wives and children, from whom they would be banished forever, if they stained themselves with so great a crime. But all he could say had no effect. He then besought them to delay the execution for three days, for two days, for only twelve hours; but they sternly refused. Pricket then told them, that it was not their safety for which they were anxious, but that they were bent upon shedding blood and revenging themselves, which made them so hasty. Upon this, Greene took up the Bible which lay there, and swore upon it, that he would do no man harm, and that what he did was for the good of the voyage, and for nothing else. Wilson took the same oath, and after him came Juet and the other conspirators separately, and swore in the same words. The words of the oath are recorded by Pricket, because, after his return to England, he was much blamed for administering any oath, as he seemed by so doing to side with the mutineers. The oath, as administered by him, ran as follows:

"You shall swear truth to God, your Prince, and Country; you shall do nothing but to the glory of God and the good of the action in hand, and harm to no man." How little regard was paid to this oath by the mutineers, will shortly appear.

It was decided, that the plot should be put in execution at daylight; and, in the meantime, Greene went into Hudson's cabin to keep him company and prevent his suspicions from being excited. They had determined to put the carpenter and John King into the boat with Hudson and the sick, having some grudge against them for their attachment to the master. King and the carpenter had slept upon deck this night. But about daybreak, King was observed to go down into the hold with the cook, who was going for water. Some of the mutineers ran and shut down the hatch over them, while Greene and another engaged the attention of the carpenter, so that he did not observe what was going on.

Hudson now came up from the cabin, and was immediately seized by Thomas, and Bennet, the cook, who had come up from the hold, while Wilson ran behind and bound his arms. He asked them what they meant, and they told him he would know when he was in the shallop. Hudson called on the

carpenter to help him, telling him that he was
bound; but he could render him no assistance, being
surrounded by mutineers. In the meantime, Juet
had gone down into the hold, where King was; but
the latter, having armed himself with a sword, attacked Juet, and would have killed him, if the
noise had not been heard upon deck by the conspirators, some of whom ran down and overpowered
him. While this was done, two of the sick men,
Lodlo and Bute, boldly reproached their shipmates
for their wickedness, telling them, that their knav-
ery would show itself, and that their actions were
prompted by mere vengeance, not the wish to preserve their lives. But their words had no effect.

The boat was now hauled alongside, and the sick
and lame were called up from their berths. Pricket
crawled upon deck as well as he could, and Hudson,
seeing him, called to him to come to the hatchway
to speak with him. Pricket entreated the men, on
his knees, for the love of God to remember their duty,
and do as they would be done by; but they only
told him to go back to his berth, and would not
allow him to have any communication with Hudson.
When Hudson was in the boat, he called again to
Pricket, who was at the horn window, which lighted
his cabin, and told him that Juet would "overthrow"
them all. "Nay," said Pricket, "it is that villain,
Henry Greene;" and this he said as loud as he could.

After Hudson was put into the boat, the carpenter was set at liberty, but he refused to remain in
the ship unless they forced him; so they told him
he might go in the boat, and allowed him to take
his chest with him. Before he got into the boat,
he went down to take leave of Pricket, who en-

CUT ADRIFT IN HUDSON BAY

treated him to remain in the ship; but the carpenter
said he believed that they would soon be taken on
board again, as there was no one left who knew
enough to bring the ship home; and that he was
determined not to desert the master. He thought
the boat would be kept in tow; but, if they should
be parted, he begged Pricket to leave some token
for them if he should reach Digges's Cape first.
They then took leave of each other with tears in
their eyes, and the carpenter went into the boat,
taking a musket and some powder and shot, an iron
pot, a small quantity of meal, and other provisions.
Hudson's son and six of the men were also put into
the boat. The sails were now hoisted, and they
stood eastward with a fair wind, dragging the shallop from the stern; and in a few hours, being clear
of the ice, they cut the rope by which the boat was
dragged, and soon after lost sight of her forever.

The account here given of the mutiny, is nearly
in the words of Pricket, an eyewitness of the event.
It is difficult at first to perceive the whole enormity
of the crime. The more we reflect upon it, the
blacker it appears. Scarcely a circumstance is
wanting, that could add to the baseness of the villainy, or the horror of the suffering inflicted. The
principal conspirators were men who were bound
to Hudson by long friendship, by lasting obliga-
tions, and by common interests, adventures and
sufferings. Juet had sailed with him on two of his
former voyages, and had shared in the glory of his
discoveries. Greene had been received into his
house, when abandoned even by his own mother;
had been kindly and hospitably entertained, encouraged to reform, and taken, on Hudson's private

responsibility, into a service in which he might gain celebrity and wealth. Wilson had been selected from among the crew, by the approving eye of the commander, and appointed to a place of trust and honor. Yet these men conspired to murder their benefactor, and instigated the crew to join in their execrable scheme.

Not contented with the destruction of their commander, that nothing might be wanting to fill up the measure of their wickedness, they formed the horrible plan of destroying, at the same time, all of their companions whom sickness and suffering had rendered a helpless and unresisting prey to their cruelty. The manner of effecting this massacre was worthy of the authors of such a plot. To have killed their unhappy victims outright would have been comparatively merciful; but a long, lingering, and painful death was chosen for them. The imagination turns with intense and fearful interest to the scene. The form of the commander is before us, bound hand and foot, condescending to no supplication to the mutineers, but calling in vain for assistance from those who would gladly have helped him, but who were overpowered by numbers, or disabled by sickness. The cry of the suffering and dying rings in our ears, as they are dragged from their beds, to be exposed to the inclemencies of the ice-covered sea in an open boat. Among them appears the young son of Hudson, whose tender years can wake no compassion in the cold-blooded murderers.[3]

3. It is impossible to tell very much about this young son of Henry Hudson. In some accounts he is said to be but a lad of seven years old, but as he appears in the journal of the voyage as a sailor, it is probable that he was much older. He had accompanied his father on two of his earlier voyages and possibly on the third.

We refrain from following them, even in fancy, through their sufferings after they are separated from the ship; their days and nights of agony, their cry of distress, and the frenzy of starvation, their hopes of relief defeated, their despair, and their raving as death comes on. Over these awful scenes the hand of God has hung a veil, which hides them from us forever. Let us not seek to penetrate, even in imagination, the terrors which it conceals.

How far Pricket's account, in regard to the course pursued by Hudson, is worthy of confidence, must be left to conjecture. It should be remembered, however, that Pricket was not free from the suspicion of having been in some degree implicated in the conspiracy, and that his narrative was designed in part as a vindication of himself. The indiscreet severity charged upon Hudson, and the hasty temper he is represented to have shown, in embroiling himself with his men, for apparently trifling reasons, are not consistent with the moderation, good sense, and equanimity, with which his conduct had been marked in all his preceding voyages. It is moreover hardly credible, that, knowing as he did the mutinous spirit of some of the crew, he should so rashly inflame this spirit, at a time when he was surrounded by imminent dangers, and when his safety depended on the united support of all the men under his command. Hence, whatever reliance may be placed on the veracity of Pricket, it is due to the memory of Hudson not to overlook the circumstances by which his pen may have been biased.

When Hudson and the men were deposited in the boat, the mutineers busied themselves with breaking open chests and pillaging the ship. They found in the cabin a considerable quantity of biscuit, and a butt of beer; and there were a few pieces of pork, some meal, and a half bushel of peas in the hold. These supplies were enough to save them from immediate starvation; and they expected to find plenty of game at Digges's Cape.

Henry Greene was appointed commander, though evidently too ignorant for the place. It was a full month before they could find their way to the Strait, which leads out of the great Bay in which they had wintered. Part of this time they were detained by the ice; but several days were spent in searching for the passage into Davis's Strait. During this time they landed often, and sometimes succeeded in catching a few fish or wild fowl; but supplied their wants principally by gathering the cockle-grass, which was growing in abundance on every part of the shore. They arrived within sight of Digges's Cape about the last of July, and immediately sent the boat on shore for provisions. The men who landed found considerable quantities of game, as it was a place where the wild fowl breed. There were great numbers of savages about the shore, who appeared very friendly, and testified their joy by lively gestures.

The next day Henry Greene went ashore, accompanied by Wilson, Thomas, Perse, Moter, and Pricket. The last was left in the boat, which was made fast to a large rock, and the others went on shore in search of provisions. While some of the men were busy in gathering sorrel from the rocks, and Greene was surrounded by the natives, with whom he was trading, Pricket, who was lying in the stern of the boat, observed one of the savages coming in at the bows. Pricket made signs to him to keep off; and while he was thus occupied, another savage stole round behind him. Pricket suddenly saw the leg and foot of a man by him, and looking up, perceived a savage with a knife in his hand, aiming a blow at him. He prevented the wound

SAVAGES ON THE SHORE

from being fatal, by raising his arm and warding off the blow; but was still severely cut. Springing up, he grappled with the savage, and drawing his dagger, at length put him to death.

In the meantime, Greene and the others were assaulted by the savages on shore, and with difficulty reached the boat, all of them wounded except Perse and Moter. The latter saved his life by plunging into the water, and catching hold of the stern of the boat. No sooner had they pushed off, than the savages let fly a shower of arrows, which killed Greene outright, and mortally wounded some of the others, among them Perse, who had hitherto escaped. Perse and Moter began to row toward the ship, but Perse soon fainted, and Moter was left to manage the boat alone, as he had escaped unwounded. The body of Greene was thrown immediately into the sea. Wilson and Thomas died that day in great torture, and Perse two days afterwards.

The remainder of the crew were glad to depart from the scene of this fatal combat, and immediately set sail, with the intention of reaching Ireland as soon as possible. While they were in the Strait, they managed to kill a few wild fowl occasionally; but the supply was so small, that they were obliged to limit the crew to half a fowl a day, which they cooked with meal; but this soon failed, and they were forced to devour the candles. The cook fried the bones of the fowls in tallow, and mixed this mess with vinegar, which, says Pricket, was "a great daintie."

Before they reached Ireland, they were so weakened, that they were forced to sit at the helm to steer, as no one among them was able to stand. Just before they came in sight of land, Juet died of want, thus meeting the very fate, to avoid which he had murdered his commander and friend. The men were now in utter despair. Only one fowl was left for the subsistence, and another day would be their last. They abandoned all care of the vessel, and prepared to meet their fate, when the joyful cry of "a sail," was heard. It proved to be a fishing vessel, which took them into a harbor in Ireland, from which they hired a pilot to take them to England; where they all arrived in safety, after an absence of a year and five months.

THE RISE OF ROBERT BRUCE[1]

By Sir Walter Scott[2]

OBERT the Bruce was a remarkably brave and strong man; there was no man in Scotland that was thought a match for him. He was very wise and prudent, and an excellent general; that is, he knew how to conduct an army, and place them in order for battle, as well or better than any great man of his time. He was generous, too, and courteous by nature; but he had some faults, which perhaps belonged as much to the fierce period in which he lived as to his own character. He was rash and passionate, and in his passion he was sometimes relentless and cruel.

Robert the Bruce had fixed his purpose to attempt once again to drive the English out of Scotland, and he desired to prevail upon Sir John the Red Comyn, who was his rival in his pretensions to the throne, to join with him in expelling the foreign

1. Robert Bruce was born in July, 1274. During the early part of his life he was sometimes to be found on the side of the English and sometimes on the side of the Scotch, but as he grew older his patriotic spirit was roused, and he threw himself heart and soul into the cause of his native land. As late as the year 1299, after the Scotch patriot Wallace had been defeated, Bruce was in favor with the English King Edward, but in February, 1306, occurred the event with which Scott's narrative opens.

2. The following interesting account of some of the incidents in the life of Bruce is abridged from Scott's *Tales of a Grandfather*, a series of historical stories which Scott wrote for his little grandson.

enemy by their common efforts. With this purpose, Bruce posted down from London to Dumfries, on the borders of Scotland, and requested an
interview with John Comyn. They met in the
church of the Minorites in that town, before the
high altar. What passed between them is not
known with certainty; but they quarrelled, either
concerning their mutual pretensions to the crown,
or because Comyn refused to join Bruce in the proposed insurrection against the English; or, as many
writers say, because Bruce charged Comyn with
having betrayed to the English his purpose of rising up against King Edward. It is, however, certain that these two haughty barons came to high
and abusive words, until at length Bruce, who I told
you was extremely passionate, forgot the sacred
character of the place in which they stood, and
struck Comyn a blow with his dagger. Having
done this rash deed, he instantly ran out of the
church and called for his horse. Two gentlemen of
the country, Lindesay and Kirkpatrick, friends of
Bruce, were then in attendance on him. Seeing
him pale, bloody, and in much agitation, they
eagerly inquired what was the matter.

"I doubt," said Bruce, "that I have slain the
Red Comyn."

"Do you leave such a matter in doubt?" said
Kirkpatrick. "I will make sicker!"—that is, I will
make certain.

Accordingly, he and his companion Lindesay
rushed into the church, and made the matter certain
with a vengeance, by despatching the wounded
Comyn with their daggers. His uncle, Sir Robert
Comyn, was slain at the same time.

This slaughter of Comyn was a rash and cruel action; and the historian of Bruce observes that it was followed by the displeasure of Heaven; for no man ever went through more misfortunes than Robert Bruce, although he at length rose to great honor.

After the deed was done, Bruce might be called desperate. He had committed an action which was sure to bring down upon him the vengeance of all Comyn's relations, the resentment of the King of England, and the displeasure of the Church, on account of having slain his enemy within consecrated ground. He determined, therefore, to bid them all defiance at once, and to assert his pretensions to the throne of Scotland. He drew his own followers together, summoned to meet him such barons as still entertained hopes of the freedom of the country, and was crowned king at the Abbey of Scone, the usual place where the kings of Scotland assumed their authority.

The commencement of Bruce's undertaking was most disastrous. He was crowned on the twenty-ninth of March, 1306. On the eighteenth of May he was excommunicated by the Pope, on account of the murder of Comyn within consecrated ground, a sentence which excluded him from all benefits of religion, and authorized any one to kill him. Finally, on the nineteenth of June, the new king was completely defeated near Methven by the English Earl of Pembroke. Robert's horse was killed under him in the action, and he was for a moment a prisoner.

But he had fallen into the power of a Scottish knight, who, though he served in the English army, did not choose to be the instrument of putting Bruce into their hands, and allowed him to escape. The conquerors executed their prisoners with their usual cruelty.

BRUCE KILLS COMYN

Bruce, with a few brave adherents, among whom was the young Lord of Douglas, who was afterward called the Good Lord James, retired into the Highland mountains, where they were chased from one place of refuge to another, often in great danger, and suffering many hardships. The Bruce's wife, now Queen of Scotland, with several other ladies, accompanied her husband and his few followers during their wanderings. There was no other way of providing for them save by hunting and fishing. It was remarked that Douglas was the most active and successful in procuring for the unfortunate ladies such supplies as his dexterity in fishing or in killing deer could furnish to them.

Driven from one place in the Highlands to another, starved out of some districts, and forced from others by the opposition of the inhabitants, Bruce attempted to force his way into Lorn; but he was again defeated, through force of numbers, at a place called Dalry. He directed his men to retreat through a narrow pass, and placing himself last of the party, he fought with and slew such of the enemy as attempted to press hard on them. A father and two sons, called M'Androsser, all very strong men, when they saw Bruce thus protecting the retreat of his followers, made a vow that they would either kill this redoubted champion, or make him prisoner. The whole three rushed on the king at once. Bruce was on horseback, in the strait pass we have described, between a precipitous rock and a deep lake. He struck the first man who came up and seized his horse's rein such a blow with his sword, as cut off his hand and freed the bridle. The man bled to death. The other brother had grasped Bruce in the meantime by the leg, and was attempting to throw him from horseback. The king, setting spurs to his horse, made the animal suddenly spring forward, so that the Highlander fell under

the horse's feet, and, as he was endeavoring to rise
again, Bruce cleft his head in two with his sword.
The father, seeing his two sons thus slain, flew des-
perately at the king, and grasped him by the mantle
so close to his body that he could not have room to
wield his long sword. But with the heavy pommel
of that weapon, or, as others say, with an iron hammer which hung at his saddle-bow, the king struck
his third assailant so dreadful a blow, that he dashed
out his brains. Still, however, the Highlander kept
his dying grasp on the king's mantle; so that, to
be freed of the dead body, Bruce was obliged to
undo the brooch, or clasp, by which it was fastened,
and leave that, and the mantle itself, behind him.

At last dangers increased so much around the
brave King Robert, that he was obliged to separate
himself from his queen and her ladies; for the
winter was coming on, and it would be impossible
for the women to endure this wandering life when
the frost and snow should set in. So Bruce left his
queen, with the Countess of Buchan and others, in
the only castle which remained to him, which was
called Kildrummie. The king also left his youngest
brother, Nigel Bruce, to defend the castle against
the English; and he himself, with his second brother
Edward, who was a very brave man, but still more
rash and passionate than Robert himself, went over
to an island on the coast of Ireland, where Bruce
and the few men who followed his fortunes passed
the winter of 1306. In the meantime, ill luck
seemed to pursue all his friends in Scotland. The
castle of Kildrummie was taken by the English,
and Nigel Bruce, a beautiful and brave youth, was
cruelly put to death by the victors. The ladies who

had attended on Robert's queen, as well as the queen herself, and the Countess of Buchan, were thrown into strict confinement, and treated with the utmost severity.

It was about this time that an incident took place, which, although it rests only on tradition in families of the name of Bruce, is rendered probable by the manners of the times. After receiving the last unpleasing intelligence from Scotland, Bruce was lying one morning on his wretched bed, and deliberating with himself whether he had not better resign all thoughts of again attempting to make good his right to the Scottish crown, and, dismissing his followers, transport himself and his brothers to the Holy Land, and spend the rest of his life in fighting against the Saracens; by which he thought, perhaps, he might deserve the forgiveness of Heaven for the great sin of stabbing Comyn in the church at Dumfries. But then, on the other hand, he thought it would be both criminal and cowardly to give up his attempts to restore freedom to Scotland while there yet remained the least chance of his being successful in an undertaking, which, rightly considered, was much more his duty than to drive the infidels out of Palestine, though the superstition of his age might think otherwise.

While he was divided between these reflections, and doubtful of what he should do, Bruce was looking upward to the roof of the cabin in which he lay; and his eye was attracted by a spider, which, hanging at the end of a long thread of its own spinning, was endeavoring, as is the fashion of that creature, to swing itself from one beam in the roof to another, for the purpose of fixing the line on which it meant to stretch its web. The insect made the attempt again and again without success; at length Bruce counted that it had tried to carry its point six times, and been as often unable to do so. It came into his head that he had himself fought just six battles against the English and their allies, and that the poor persevering spider was exactly in the same situation with himself, having made as many trials and been so often disappointed in what it aimed at. "Now," thought Bruce, "as I have no means of knowing what is best to be done, I will be guided by the luck which shall attend this spider. If the insect shall make another effort to fix its thread, and shall be successful, I will venture a seventh time to try my fortune in Scotland; but if the spider shall fail, I will go to the wars in Palestine, and never return to my native country more."

While Bruce was forming this resolution the spider made another exertion with all the force it could muster, and fairly succeeded in fastening its thread to the beam which it had so often in vain attempted to reach. Bruce, seeing the success of the spider, resolved to try his own fortune; and as he had never before gained a victory, so he never afterward sustained any considerable or decisive check or defeat. I have often met with people of the name of Bruce, so completely persuaded of the truth of this story, that they would not on any account kill a spider, because it was that insect which had shown the example of perseverance, and given a signal of good luck, to their great namesake.

Having determined to renew his efforts to obtain possession of Scotland, notwithstanding the smallness of the means which he had for accomplishing so great a purpose, the Bruce removed himself and his followers from Rachrin to the island of Arran, which lies in the mouth of the Clyde. The king landed and inquired of the first woman he met what armed men were in the island. She returned for answer that there had arrived there very lately a body of armed strangers, who had defeated an English officer, the governor of the castle of Brathwick, had killed him and most of his men, and were now amusing themselves with hunting about the island. The king, having caused himself to be guided to the woods which these strangers most frequented, there blew his horn repeatedly.

Now, the chief of the strangers who had taken the castle was James Douglas, one of the best of Bruce's friends, and he was accompanied by some of the bravest of that patriotic band. When he heard Robert Bruce's horn he knew the sound well, and cried out, that yonder was the king, he knew by his manner of blowing. So he and his companions hastened to meet King Robert, and there was great joy on both sides; while at the same time they could not help weeping when they considered their own forlorn condition, and the great loss that had taken place among their friends since they had last parted. But they were stout-hearted men, and looked forward to freeing their country in spite of all that had yet happened.

The Bruce was now within sight of Scotland, and not distant from his own family possessions, where the people were most likely to be attached to him. He began immediately to form plans with Douglas how they might best renew their enterprise against the English. The Douglas resolved to go disguised to his own country, and raise his followers in order to begin their enterprise by taking revenge on an English nobleman called Lord Clifford, upon whom Edward had conferred his estates, and who had taken up his residence in the castle of Douglas.

Bruce, on his part, opened a communication with the opposite coast of Carrick, by means of one of his followers called Cuthbert. This person had directions, that if he should find the countrymen in Carrick disposed to take up arms against the English he was to make a fire on a headland, or lofty cape, called Turnberry, on the coast of Ayrshire, opposite to the island of Arran. The appearance of a fire on this place was to be a signal for Bruce to put to sea with such men as he had, who were not more than three hundred in number, for the purpose of landing in Carrick and joining the insurgents.

Bruce and his men watched eagerly for the signal, but for some time in vain. At length a fire on Turnberry-head became visible, and the king and his followers merrily betook themselves to their ships and galleys, concluding their Carrick friends were all in arms and ready to join with them. They landed on the beach at midnight, where they found their spy Cuthbert alone in waiting for them with very bad news. Lord Percy, he said, was in the country with two or three hundred Englishmen, and had terrified the people so much, both by actions and threats, that none of them dared to think of rebelling against King Edward.

"Traitor!" said Bruce, "why, then, did you make the signal?"

"Alas," replied Cuthbert, "the fire was not made by me, but by some other person, for what purpose I know not; but as soon as I saw it burning, I knew that you would come over, thinking it my signal, and therefore I came down to wait for you on the beach to tell you how the matter stood."

King Robert's first idea was to return to Arran after this disappointment; but his brother Edward refused to go back. He was, as I have told you, a man daring even to rashness. "I will not leave my native land," he said, "now that I am so unexpectedly restored to it. I will give freedom to Scotland, or leave my carcass on the surface of the land which gave me birth."

Bruce, also, after some hesitation, determined that since he had been thus brought to the mainland of Scotland, he would remain there, and take such adventure and fortune as Heaven should send him.

Accordingly, he began to skirmish with the English so successfully, as obliged the Lord Percy to quit Carrick. Bruce then dispersed his men upon various adventures against the enemy, in which they were generally successful. But then, on the other hand, the king, being left with small attendance, or sometimes almost alone, ran great risk of losing his life by treachery or by open violence.

At one time, a near relation of Bruce's, in whom he entirely confided, was induced by the bribes of the English to attempt to put him to death. This villain, with his two sons, watched the king one morning, till he saw him separated from all his men, excepting a little boy, who waited on him as a page. The father had a sword in his hand, one of

the sons had a sword and a spear, and the other
had a sword and a battle-axe. Now, when the king
saw them so well armed, when there were no enemies near, he began to call to mind some hints which
had been given to him, that these men intended to
murder him. He had no weapons excepting his
sword; but his page had a bow and arrow. He
took them both from the little boy, and bade him
stand at a distance; "for," said the king, "if I overcome these traitors, thou shalt have enough of weapons; but if I am slain by them, you may make
your escape, and tell Douglas and my brother to
revenge my death." The boy was very sorry, for he
loved his master; but he was obliged to do as he was
bidden.

In the meantime the traitors came forward upon
Bruce, that they might assault him at once. The
king called out to them, and commanded them to
come no nearer, upon peril of their lives; but the
father answered with flattering words, pretending
great kindness, and still continuing to approach his
person. Then the king again called to them to
stand. "Traitors," said he, "ye have sold my life
for English gold; but you shall die if you come one
foot nearer to me." With that he bent the page's
bow, and as the old conspirator continued to advance, he let the arrow fly at him. Bruce was an
excellent archer; he aimed his arrow so well that it
hit the father in the eye, and penetrated from that
into his brain, so that he fell down dead. Then the
two sons rushed on the king. One of them fetched
a blow at him with an axe, but missed his stroke and
stumbled, so that the king with his great sword cut
him down before he could recover his feet. The

remaining traitor ran on Bruce with his spear; but the king, with a sweep of his sword, cut the steel head off the villain's weapon, and then killed him before he had time to draw his sword. Then the little page came running, very joyful of his master's victory; and the king wiped his bloody sword, and, looking upon the dead bodies, said, "These might have been reputed three gallant men, if they could have resisted the temptation of covetousness."

After the death of these three traitors, Robert the Bruce continued to keep himself concealed in his own earldom of Carrick, and in the neighboring country of Galloway, until he should have matters ready for a general attack upon the English. He was obliged, in the meantime, to keep very few men with him, both for the sake of secrecy, and from the difficulty of finding provisions. Now, many of the people of Galloway were unfriendly to Bruce. They had heard that he was in their country, having no more than sixty men with him; so they resolved to attack him by surprise, and for this purpose they got two hundred men together, and brought with them two or three bloodhounds. These animals were trained to chase a man by the scent of his footsteps, as foxhounds chase a fox, or as beagles and harriers chase a hare. Although the dog does not see the person whose trace he is put upon, he follows him over every step he has taken. At that time these bloodhounds, or sleuthhounds (so called from *slot*, or *sleut*, a word which signifies the scent left by an animal of chase), were used for the purpose of pursuing great criminals. The men of Galloway thought themselves secure, that if they missed taking Bruce, or killing him at the first onset, and if he should escape into the woods, they would find him out by means of these bloodhounds.

The good King Robert Bruce, who was always watchful and vigilant, had received some information of the intention of this party to come upon him suddenly and by night. Accordingly, he quartered his little troop of sixty men on the side of a deep and swift-running river, that had very steep and rocky banks. There was but one ford by which this river could be crossed in that neighborhood, and that ford was deep and narrow, so that two men could scarcely get through abreast; the ground on which they were to land on the side where the king was, was steep, and the path which led upward from the water's edge to the top of the bank, extremely narrow and difficult.

Bruce caused his men to lie down to take some sleep, at a place about half a mile distant from the river, while he himself, with two attendants, went down to watch the ford, through which the enemy must needs pass before they could come to the place where King Robert's men were lying. He stood for some time looking at the ford, and thinking how easily the enemy might be kept from passing there, provided it was bravely defended, when he heard at a distance the baying of a hound, which was always coming nearer and nearer. This was the bloodhound which was tracing the king's steps to the ford where he had crossed, and the two hundred Galloway men were along with the animal, and guided by it. Bruce at first thought of going back to awaken his men; but then he reflected that it might be only some shepherd's dog. "My men," said he, "are sorely tired; I will not disturb their sleep for the yelping of a cur, till I know something more of the matter."

So he stood and listened; and by and by, as the cry of the hound came nearer, he began to hear a trampling of horses, and the voices of men, and the ringing and clattering of armor, and then he was sure the enemy were coming to the river side. Then the king thought, "If I go back to give my men the alarm, these Galloway men will get through the ford without opposition; and that would be a pity, since it is a place so advantageous to make defence against them." So he looked again at the steep path, and the deep river, and he thought that they gave him so much advantage, that he himself could defend the passage with his own hand, until his men came to assist him. His armor was so good and strong, that he had no fear of arrows, and therefore the combat was not so very unequal as it must have otherwise been. He therefore sent his followers to waken his men, and remained alone by the bank of the river.

In the meanwhile, the noise and trampling of the horses increased; and the moon being bright, Bruce beheld the glancing arms of about two hundred men, who came down to the opposite bank of the river. The men of Galloway, on their part, saw but one solitary figure guarding the ford, and the foremost of them plunged into the river without minding him. But as they could only pass the ford one by one, the Bruce, who stood high above them on the bank where they were to land, killed the foremost man with a thrust of his long spear, and with a second thrust stabbed the horse, which fell down, kicking and plunging in his agonies, on the narrow

path, and so prevented the others who were following from getting out of the river. Bruce had thus
an opportunity of dealing his blows at pleasure
among them, while they could not strike at him
again. In the confusion, five or six of the enemy
were slain, or, having been borne down the current,
were drowned in the river. The rest were terrified,
and drew back.

But when the Galloway men looked again, and
saw they were opposed by only one man, they themselves being so many, they cried out that their
honor would be lost forever if they did not force
their way; and encouraged each other, with loud
cries, to plunge through and assault him. But by
this time the king's soldiers came up to his assistance,
and the Galloway men retreated, and gave up their
enterprise.

At another time King Robert and his foster
brother were walking through a wood extremely
weary and hungry. As they proceeded, however,
in the hopes of coming to some habitation, they met
in the midst of the forest with three men who looked
like thieves or ruffians. They were well armed, and
one of them bore a sheep on his back, which it seemed
as if they had just stolen. They saluted the king
civilly; and he, replying to their salutation, asked
them where they were going. The men answered,
they were seeking for Robert Bruce, for that they
intended to join with him. The king answered,
that if they would go with him he would conduct
them where they would find the Scottish king. Then
the man who had spoken changed countenance, and
Bruce, who looked sharply at him, began to suspect
that the ruffian guessed who he was, and that he

and his companions had some design against his person, in order to gain the reward which had been offered for his life.

So he said to them, "My good friends, as we are not well acquainted with each other, you must go before us, and we will follow near to you."

"You have no occasion to suspect any harm from us," answered the man.

"Neither do I suspect any," said Bruce; "but this is the way in which I choose to travel."

The men did as he commanded, and thus they traveled till they came together to a waste and ruinous cottage, where the men proposed to dress some part of the sheep, which their companion was carrying. The king was glad to hear of food; but he insisted that there should be two fires kindled, one for himself and his foster brother at one end of the house, the other at the other end for their three companions. The men did as he desired. They broiled a quarter of mutton for themselves, and gave another to the king and his attendant. They were obliged to eat it without bread or salt; but as they were very hungry, they were glad to get food in any shape, and partook of it very heartily.

Then so heavy a drowsiness fell on King Robert, that, for all the danger he was in, he could not resist an inclination to sleep. But first, he desired his foster brother to watch while he slept, for he had great suspicion of their new acquaintances. His foster brother promised to keep awake, and did his best to keep his word. But the king had not long been asleep ere his foster brother fell into a deep slumber also, for he had undergone as much fatigue as the king. When the three villains saw the king and his attendant asleep, they made signs to each other, and rising up at once, drew their swords with the purpose to kill them both. But the king slept but lightly, and little noise as the traitors made in rising, he was awakened by it, and starting up, drew his sword, and went to meet them. At the same moment he pushed his foster brother with his foot, to awaken him, and he got on his feet; but ere he got his eyes to see clearly, one of the ruffians that were advancing to slay the king, killed him with a stroke of his sword. The king was now alone, one man against three, and in the greatest danger of his life; but his amazing strength, and the good armor which he wore, freed him once more from this great peril, and he killed the three men, one after another. He then left the cottage, very sorrowful for the death of his faithful foster brother, and took his direction toward the place where he had appointed his men to assemble. It was now near night, and the place of meeting being a farmhouse, he went boldly into it, where he found the mistress, an old true-hearted Scotswoman, sitting alone. Upon seeing a stranger enter, she asked him who and what he was. The king answered that he was a traveler journeying through the country.

"All travelers," answered the good woman, "are welcome here, for the sake of one."

"And who is that one," said the king, "for whose sake you make all travelers welcome?"

"It is our rightful king, Robert the Bruce," answered the mistress, "who is the lawful lord of this country; and although he is now pursued and hunted after with hounds and horns, I hope to live to see him king over all Scotland."

"Since you love him so well, dame," said the king, "know that you see him before you. I am Robert the Bruce."

SHE BROUGHT HER TWO SONS

"You!" said the good woman, in great surprise; "and wherefore are you thus alone?—where are all your men?"

"I have none with me at this moment," answered Bruce, "and therefore I must travel alone."

"But that shall not be," said the brave old dame, "for I have two stout sons, gallant and trusty men, who shall be your servants for life and death."

So she brought her two sons, and though she well knew the dangers to which she exposed them, she made them swear fidelity to the king; and they afterward became high officers in his service.

Now, the loyal old woman was getting everything ready for the king's supper, when suddenly there was a great trampling of horses heard round the house. They thought it must be some of the English, and the good wife called upon her sons to fight to the last for King Robert. But shortly after, they heard the voice of the good Lord James of Douglas, and of Edward Bruce, the king's brother, who had come with a hundred and fifty horsemen to this farmhouse, according to the instructions that the king had left with them at parting.

Robert the Bruce was right joyful to meet his brother, and his faithful friend Lord James, and had no sooner found himself once more at the head of such a considerable body of followers, than forgetting hunger and weariness, he began to inquire where the enemy who had pursued them so long had taken up their abode for the night; "For," said he, "as they must suppose us totally scattered and fled, it is likely that they will think themselves quite secure, and disperse themselves into distant quarters, and keep careless watch."

"That is very true,'" answered James of Douglas, "for I passed a village where there are two hundred of them quartered, who had placed no sentinels; and if you have a mind to make haste, we may surprise them this very night, and do them more mischief than they have been able to do us during all this day's chase."

Then there was nothing but mount and ride; and as the Scots came by surprise on the body of English whom Douglas had mentioned, and rushed suddenly into the village where they were quartered, they easily dispersed and cut them to pieces; thus, as Douglas had said, doing their pursuers more injury than they themselves had received during the long and severe pursuit of the preceding day.

The consequence of these successes of King Robert was, that soldiers came to join him on all sides, and that he obtained several victories, until at length the English were afraid to venture into the open country as formerly, unless when they could assemble themselves in considerable bodies. They thought it safer to lie still in the towns and castles which they had garrisoned, and wait till the King of England should once more come to their assistance with a powerful army.

When King Edward the First heard that Scotland was again in arms against him, he marched down to the Borders, with many threats of what he would do to avenge himself on Bruce and his party, whom he called rebels. But he was now old and feeble, and while he was making his preparations, he was taken very ill, and after lingering a long time, at length died on the sixth of July, 1307, at a place in Cumberland called Burgh upon the Sands, in full sight of Scotland, and not three miles from its frontier.

His hatred to that country was so inveterate that his thoughts of revenge seemed to occupy his mind on his death-bed. He made his son promise never to make peace with Scotland until the nation was subdued. He gave also very singular directions concerning the disposal of his dead body. He ordered that it should be boiled in a caldron till the flesh parted from the bones, and that then the bones should be wrapped up in a bull's hide, and carried at the head of the English army, as often as the

Scots attempted to recover their freedom. He thought that he had inflicted such distresses on the Scots, and invaded and defeated them so often, that his very dead bones would terrify them. His son, Edward the Second, did not choose to execute this strange injunction, but caused his father to be buried in Westminster Abbey, where his tomb is still to be seen, bearing for an inscription, *Here Lies the Hammer of the Scottish Nation.*

Edward the Second was neither so brave nor so wise as his father; on the contrary, he was a weak prince, fond of idle amusements and worthless favorites. It was lucky for Scotland that such was his disposition. He marched a little way into Scotland with the large army which Edward the First had collected, and went back again without fighting, which gave great encouragement to Bruce's party.

Several of the Scottish nobility now took arms in different parts of the country, declared for King Robert, and fought against the English troops and garrisons. The most distinguished of these was the good Lord James of Douglas. Other great lords also were now exerting themselves to destroy the English. Among them was Sir Thomas Randolph, whose mother was a sister of King Robert.

While Robert Bruce was gradually getting possession of the country, and driving out the English, Edinburgh, the principal town of Scotland, remained, with its strong castle, in possession of the invaders. Sir Thomas Randolph was extremely desirous to gain this important place; but the castle is situated on a very steep and lofty rock, so that it is difficult or almost impossible even to get up to the foot of the walls, much more to climb over them.

So while Randolph was considering what was to be done, there came to him a Scottish gentleman named Francis, who had joined Bruce's standard, and asked to speak with him in private. He then told Randolph that in his youth he had lived in the Castle of Edinburgh, and that his father had then been keeper of the fortress. It happened at that time that Francis was much in love with a lady who lived in a part of the town beneath the castle, which is called the Grassmarket. Now, as he could not get out of the castle by day to see his mistress, he had practiced a way of clambering by night down the castle rock on the south side, and returning at his pleasure; when he came to the foot of the wall, he made use of a ladder to get over it, as it was not very high at that point, those who built it having trusted to the steepness of the crag; and for the same reason, no watch was placed there. Francis had gone and come so frequently in this dangerous manner, that, though it was now long ago, he told Randolph he knew the road so well that he would undertake to guide a small party of men by night to the bottom of the wall; and as they might bring ladders with them, there would be no difficulty in scaling it. The great risk was, that of their being discovered by the watchmen while in the act of ascending the cliff, in which case every man of them must have perished.

Nevertheless, Randolph did not hesitate to attempt the adventure. He took with him only thirty men (you may be sure they were chosen for activity and courage), and came one dark night to the foot of the rock, which they began to ascend under the guidance of Francis, who went before them, upon his hands and feet, up one cliff, down another, and round another, where there was scarce room to support themselves. All the while, these thirty men were obliged to follow in a line, one after the other, by a path that was fitter for a cat than a man. The noise of a stone falling, or a word spoken from one to another, would have alarmed the watchmen. They were obliged, therefore, to move with the greatest precaution. When they were far up the crag, and near the foundation of the wall, they heard the guards going their rounds, to see that all was safe in and about the castle. Randolph and his party had nothing for it but to lie close and quiet, each man under the crag, as he happened to be placed, and trust that the guards would pass by without noticing them. And while they were waiting in breathless alarm they got a new cause of fright. One of the soldiers of the castle, willing to startle his comrades, suddenly threw a stone from the wall, and cried out, "Aha, I see you well!" The stone came thundering down over the heads of Randolph and his men, who naturally thought themselves discovered. If they had stirred, or made the slightest noise, they would have been entirely destroyed; for the soldiers above might have killed every man of them, merely by rolling down stones. But being courageous and chosen men, they remained quiet, and the English soldiers, who thought their comrade was merely playing them a trick (as, indeed, he had no other meaning in what he said) passed on without further examination.

Then Randolph and his men got up and came in haste to the foot of the wall, which was not above

twice a man's height in that place. They planted
the ladders they had brought, and Francis mounted
first to show them the way; Sir Andrew Grey, a
brave knight, followed him, and Randolph himself
was the third man who got over. Then the rest followed. When once they were within the walls, there
was not so much to do, for the garrison were asleep
and unarmed, excepting the watch, who were speedily destroyed. Thus was Edinburgh Castle taken in
March, 1312.

It was not, however, only by the exertions of
great and powerful barons, like Randolph and
Douglas, that the freedom of Scotland was to be
accomplished. The stout yeomanry and the bold
peasantry of the land, who were as desirous to enjoy
their cottages in honorable independence as the
nobles were to reclaim their castles and estates from
the English, contributed their full share in the efforts
which were made to deliver the country from the
invaders.

While Douglas, Randolph, and other true-
hearted patriots, were taking castles and strong-
holds from the English, King Robert, who now had
a considerable army under his command, marched
through the country, dispersing such bodies of English as he met on the way.

Now when Sir Philip Mowbray, the governor of
Stirling, came to London to tell the king that Stirling, the last Scottish town of importance which
remained in possession of the English, was to be
surrendered if it were not relieved by force of arms
before midsummer, then all the English nobles
called out it would be a sin and shame to permit the
fair conquest which Edward the First had made,

THE ASCENT TO THE CASTLE OF EDINBURGH

to be forfeited to the Scots for want of fighting. It was, therefore, resolved, that the king should go himself to Scotland, with as great forces as he could possibly muster.

King Edward the Second, therefore, assembled one of the greatest armies which a King of England ever commanded. There were troops brought from all his dominions. Many brave soldiers from the French provinces which the King of England possessed in France—many Irish, many Welsh—and all the great English nobles and barons, with their followers, were assembled in one great army. The number was not less than one hundred thousand men.

King Robert the Bruce summoned all his nobles and barons to join him, when he heard of the great preparations which the King of England was making. They were not so numerous as the English by many thousand men. In fact, his whole army did not very much exceed thirty thousand, and they were much worse armed than the wealthy Englishmen; but then, Robert, who was at their head, was one of the most expert generals of the time; and the officers he had under him were his brother Edward, his nephew Randolph, his faithful follower the Douglas, and other brave and experienced leaders, who commanded the same men that had been accustomed to fight and gain victories under every disadvantage of situation and numbers.

The king, on his part, studied how he might supply, by address and stratagem, what he wanted in numbers and strength. He knew the superiority of the English, both in their heavy-armed cavalry, which were much better mounted and armed than

that of the Scots, and in their archers, who were better trained than any others in the world. Both these
advantages he resolved to provide against. With
this purpose, he led his army down into a plain
near Stirling, called the Park, near which, and
beneath it, the English army must needs pass
through a boggy country, broken with water
courses, while the Scots occupied hard, dry ground.
He then caused all the ground upon the front of
his line of battle, where cavalry were likely to act,
to be dug full of holes, about as deep as a man's
knee. They were filled with light brushwood, and
the turf was laid on the top, so that it appeared a
plain field, while in reality it was all full of these
pits as a honeycomb is of holes. He also, it is said,
caused steel spikes, called caltrops, to be scattered
up and down in the plain, where the English cavalry
were most likely to advance, trusting in that manner to lame and destroy their horses.

When the Scottish army was drawn up, the line
stretched north and south. On the south, it was
terminated by the banks of the brook called Bannockburn, which are so rocky, that no troops could
attack them there. On the left, the Scottish line
extended near to the town of Stirling. Bruce
reviewed his troops very carefully; all the useless
servants, drivers of carts, and such like, of whom
there were very many, he ordered to go behind a
great height, afterward, in memory of the event,
called the Gillies' hill, that is, the Servants' hill.
He then spoke to the soldiers, and expressed his
determination to gain the victory, or to lose his life
on the field of battle. He desired that all those who
did not propose to fight to the last, should leave the

field before the battle began, and that none should remain except those who were determined to take the issue of victory or death, as God should send it.

When the main body of his army was thus placed in order, the king posted Randolph, with a body of horse, near to the Church of Saint Ninian's, commanding him to use the utmost diligence to prevent any succors from being thrown into Stirling Castle. He then despatched James of Douglas, and Sir Robert Keith, the Mareschal of the Scottish army, in order that they might survey, as nearly as they could, the English force, which was now approaching from Falkirk. They returned with information, that the approach of that vast host was one of the most beautiful and terrible sights which could be seen—that the whole country seemed covered with men-at-arms on horse and foot, that the number of standards, banners, and pennons (all flags of different kinds) made so gallant a show, that the bravest and most numerous host in Christendom might be alarmed to see King Edward moving against them.

It was upon the twenty-third of June (1314) the King of Scotland heard the news, that the English army were approaching Stirling. He drew out his army, therefore, in the order which he had before resolved on. After a short time, Bruce, who was looking out anxiously for the enemy, saw a body of English cavalry trying to get into Stirling from the eastward. This was the Lord Clifford, who, with a chosen body of eight hundred horse, had been detached to relieve the castle.

"See, Randolph," said the king to his nephew, "there is a rose fallen from your chaplet." By this

he meant, that Randolph had lost some honor, by
suffering the enemy to pass where he had been sta-
tioned to hinder them.   Randolph made no reply,
but rushed against Clifford with little more than half
his number. The Scots were on foot. The English
turned to charge them with their lances, and Randolph drew up his men in close order to receive the
onset.   He seemed to be in so much danger, that
Douglas asked leave of the king to go and assist him.
The king refused him permission.

"Let Randolph," he said, "redeem his own fault;
I cannot break the order of battle for his sake."
Still the danger appeared greater, and the English
horse seemed entirely to encompass the small hand-
ful of Scottish infantry.   "So please you," said
Douglas to the king, "my heart will not suffer me
to stand idle and see Randolph perish—I must go
to his assistance."   He rode off accordingly; but
long before they had reached the place of combat,
they saw the English horses galloping off, many
with empty saddles.

"Halt!" said Douglas to his men, "Randolph has
gained the day; since we were not soon enough to
help him in the battle, do not let us lessen his glory
by approaching the field."   Now, that was nobly
done; especially as Douglas and Randolph were
always contending which should rise highest in the
good opinion of the king and the nation.

The van of the English army now came in sight,
and a number of their bravest knights drew near to
see what the Scots were doing. They saw King
Robert dressed in his armor, and distinguished by
a gold crown, which he wore over his helmet. He
was not mounted on his great war-horse, because

he did not expect to fight that evening. But he rode on a little pony up and down the ranks of his army, putting his men in order, and carried in his hand a sort of battle-axe made of steel. When the king saw the English horsemen draw near, he advanced a little before his own men, that he might look at them more nearly.

There was a knight among the English, called Sir Henry de Bohun, who thought this would be a good opportunity to gain great fame to himself, and put an end to the war, by killing King Robert. The king being poorly mounted, and having no lance, Bohun galloped on him suddenly and furiously, thinking, with his long spear, and his tall powerful horse, easily to bear him down to the ground. King Robert saw him, and permitted him to come very near, then suddenly turned his pony a little to one side, so that Sir Henry missed him with the lance-point, and was in the act of being carried past him by the career of his horse. But as he passed, King Robert rose up in his stirrups, and struck Sir Henry on the head with his battle-axe so terrible a blow, that it broke to pieces his iron helmet as if it had been a nutshell, and hurled him from his saddle. He was dead before he reached the ground. This gallant action was blamed by the Scottish leaders, who thought Bruce ought not to have exposed himself to so much danger, when the safety of the whole army depended on him. The king only kept looking at his weapon, which was injured by the force of the blow, and said, "I have broken my good battle-axe."

The next morning, being the twenty-fourth of June, at break of day, the battle began in terrible

earnest.   The English as they advanced saw the
Scots getting into line.   The Abbot of Inchaffray
walked through their ranks bare-footed, and exhort-

BRUCE SLAYS SIR HENRY DE BOHUN

ed them to fight for their freedom.   They kneeled
down as he passed, and prayed to Heaven for victory.   King Edward, who saw this, called out,
"They kneel down—they are asking forgiveness."

"Yes," said a celebrated English baron, called Ingelram de Umphraville, "but they ask it from God, not from us—these men will conquer, or die upon the field."

The English king ordered his men to begin the battle. The archers then bent their bows, and began to shoot so closely together, that the arrows fell like flakes of snow on a Christmas day. They killed many of the Scots, and might, as at Falkirk, and other places, have decided the victory; but Bruce was prepared for them. He had in readiness a body of men-at-arms, well mounted, who rode at full gallop among the archers, and as they had no weapons save their bows and arrows, which they could not use when they were attacked hand to hand, they were cut down in great numbers by the Scottish horsemen and thrown into total confusion.

The fine English cavalry then advanced to support their archers, and to attack the Scottish line. But coming over the ground which was dug full of pits, the horses fell into these holes, and the riders lay tumbling about, without any means of defence, and unable to rise, from the weight of their armor. The Englishmen began to fall into general disorder; and the Scottish king, bringing up more of his forces, attacked and pressed them still more closely.

On a sudden, while the battle was obstinately maintained on both sides, an event happened which decided the victory. The servants and attendants on the Scottish camp had, as I told you, been sent behind the army to a place afterward called the Gillies' hill. But when they saw that their masters were likely to gain the day, they rushed from their place of concealment with such weapons as they could

get, that they might have their share in the victory
and in the spoil. The English, seeing them come
suddenly over the hill, mistook this disorderly rabble
for a new army coming up to sustain the Scots, and,
losing all heart, began to shift every man for himself. Edward himself left the field as fast as he
could ride. A valiant knight, Sir Giles de Argentine, much renowned in the wars of Palestine,
attended the king till he got him out of the press
of the combat. But he would retreat no further.
"It is not my custom," he said, "to fly." With that
he took leave of the king, set spurs to his horse, and
calling out his war-cry of Argentine! Argentine!
he rushed into the thickest of the Scottish ranks,
and was killed.

Edward first fled to Stirling Castle, and entreated
admittance; but Sir Philip Mowbray, the governor,
reminded the fugitive sovereign that he was obliged
to surrender the castle next day, so Edward was
fain to fly through the Torwood, closely pursued
by Douglas with a body of cavalry. An odd circumstance happened during the chase, which showed
how loosely some of the Scottish barons of that
day held their political opinions: As Douglas was
riding furiously after Edward, he met a Scottish
knight, Sir Laurence Abernethy. with twenty horse.
Sir Laurence had hitherto owned the English interest, and was bringing this band of followers to serve
King Edward's army. But learning from Douglas that the English king was entirely defeated, he
changed sides on the spot, and was easily prevailed
upon to join Douglas in pursuing the unfortunate
Edward, with the very followers whom he had been
leading to join his standard.

Douglas and Abernethy continued the chase, not giving King Edward time to alight from horseback even for an instant, and followed him as far as Dunbar, where the English had still a friend in the governor, Patrick, Earl of March. The earl received Edward in his forlorn condition, and furnished him with a fishing skiff, or small ship, in which he escaped to England, having entirely lost his fine army, and a great number of his bravest nobles.

The English never before or afterward, whether in France or Scotland, lost so dreadful a battle as that of Bannockburn, nor did the Scots ever gain one of the same importance. Many of the best and bravest of the English nobility and gentry lay dead on the field; a great many more were made prisoners; and the whole of King Edward's immense army was dispersed or destroyed.

The English, after this great defeat, were no longer in a condition to support their pretensions to be masters of Scotland, or to continue, as they had done for nearly twenty years, to send armies into that country to overcome it. On the contrary, they became for a time scarce able to defend their own frontiers against King Robert and his soldiers.

Thus did Robert Bruce arise from the condition of an exile, hunted with bloodhounds like a stag or beast of prey, to the rank of an independent sovereign, universally acknowledged to be one of the wisest and bravest kings who then lived. The nation of Scotland was also raised once more from the situation of a distressed and conquered province to that of a free and independent state, governed by its own laws, and subject to its own princes; and although the country was after the Bruce's death often subjected to great loss and distress, both by the hostility of the English, and by the unhappy civil wars among the Scots themselves, yet they never afterward lost the freedom for which Wallace had laid down his life, and which King Robert had recovered, not less by his wisdom than by his weapons. And therefore most just it is, that while the country of Scotland retains any recollection of its history, the memory of those brave warriors and faithful patriots should be remembered with honor and gratitude.[3]

3. Three years after the Battle of Bannockburn, Bruce went over into Ireland to assist in establishing his brother Edward as king of the island. The Irish defended themselves so vigorously that the Scotch were compelled to retire, leaving Edward dead upon the field. For a number of years, Robert the Bruce reigned gloriously over Scotland, but toward the end of his life he fell a victim to leprosy and was compelled to live for two years in his castle at Cardross on the beautiful banks of the River Clyde. During this illness, Edward the Second of England died, and his son Edward the Third, a mere youth, came to the throne. The boy king determined to retrieve the losses that his father had sustained, but was prevented by Douglas, Randolph, and other loyal Scotch leaders, who distinguished themselves by almost incredible deeds of valor.

When the king was dying, he ordered that his heart should be taken from his body, embalmed and given to Douglas to be by him carried to Palestine and buried in Jerusalem. Douglas caused the heart to be enclosed in a silver case, and proud of the distinction the king had shown him, started with a number of followers for Palestine. When he arrived in Spain, however, he was diverted from his original purpose and led to join with King Alphonso in an attempt to drive the Saracens from Granada. In a bitter fight with the Moors, Douglas was killed, and after the battle, his body was found lying across the silver case, as if his last object had been to defend the heart of Bruce. No further attempt was made to carry Robert's heart to Jerusalem, but it was returned to Scotland and buried in the monastery of Melrose.

BRUCE AND THE SPIDER

By BERNARD ARTON

FOR Scotland's and for freedom's right
   The Bruce his part had played,
In five successive fields of fight
   Been conquered and dismayed;
Once more against the English host
His band he led, and once more lost
   The meed for which he fought;
And now from battle, faint and worn,
The homeless fugitive forlorn
   A hut's lone shelter sought.

And cheerless was that resting place
   For him who claimed a throne:
His canopy, devoid of grace,
   The rude, rough beams alone;
The heather couch his only bed,—
Yet well I ween had slumber fled
   From couch of eider down!
Through darksome night till dawn of day,
Absorbed in wakeful thought he lay
   Of Scotland and her crown.

The sun rose brightly, and its gleam
   Fell on that hapless bed,
And tinged with light each shapeless beam
   Which roofed the lowly shed;
When, looking up with wistful eye,
The Bruce beheld a spider try
   His filmy thread to fling

From beam to beam of that rude cot;
And well the insect's toilsome lot
Taught Scotland's future king.

Six times his gossamery thread
The wary spider threw;

BRUCE BEHELD A SPIDER

In vain that filmy line was sped,
For powerless or untrue
Each aim appeared, and back recoiled
The patient insect, six times foiled,
And yet unconquered still;
And soon the Bruce, with eager eye,
Saw him prepare once more to try
His courage, strength, and skill.

One effort more, his seventh and last!
　　The hero hailed the sign!
And on the wished-for beam hung fast
　　That slender, silken line;
Slight as it was, his spirit caught
The more than omen, for his thought
　　The lesson well could trace,
Which even "he who runs may read,"
That Perseverance gains its meed,
　　And Patience wins the race.

THE HEART OF BRUCE

By WILLIAM L. AYTOUN

IT WAS upon an April morn,
　　While yet the frost lay hoar,
We heard Lord James's bugle horn
　　Sound by the rocky shore.

Then down we went, a hundred
　　knights,
All in our dark array,
And flung our armor in the ships
　　That rode within the bay.

We spoke not as the shore grew less,
　　But gazed in silence back,
Where the long billows swept away
　　The foam behind our track.

And aye the purple hues decayed
  Upon the fading hill,
And but one heart in all that ship
  Was tranquil, cold, and still.

The good Lord Douglas paced the deck,
  And O, his face was wan!
Unlike the flush it used to wear
  When in the battle-van.

"Come hither, come hither, my trusty knight,
  Sir Simon of the Lee;
There is a freit lies near my soul
  I fain would tell to thee.

"Thou know'st the words King Robert spoke
  Upon his dying day:
How he bade take his noble heart
  And carry it far away;

"And lay it in the holy soil
  Where once the Saviour trod,
Since he might not bear the blessed Cross,
  Nor strike one blow for God.

"Last night as in my bed I lay,
  I dreamed a dreary dream:—
Methought I saw a Pilgrim stand
  In the moonlight's quivering beam.

"His robe was of the azure dye,
  Snow-white his scattered hairs,
And even such a cross he bore
  As good Saint Andrew bears.

" 'Why go ye forth, Lord James,' he said,
    'With spear and belted brand?
Why do you take its dearest pledge
    From this our Scottish land?

" 'The sultry breeze of Galilee
    Creeps through its groves of palm,
The olives on the Holy Mount
    Stand glittering in the calm.

" 'But 'tis not there that Scotland's heart
    Shall rest by God's decree,
Till the great angel calls the dead
    To rise from earth and sea!

" 'Lord James of Douglas, mark my rede!
    That heart shall pass once more
In fiery fight against the foe,
    As it was wont of yore.

" 'And it shall pass beneath the Cross,
    And save King Robert's vow;
But other hands shall bear it back,
    Not, James of Douglas, thou!'

"Now, by thy knightly faith, I pray,
    Sir Simon of the Lee,—
For truer friend had never man
    Than thou hast been to me,—

"If ne'er upon the Holy Land
    'Tis mine in life to tread,
Bear thou to Scotland's kindly earth
    The relics of her dead."

The tear was in Sir Simon's eye
  As he wrung the warrior's hand,—

I SAW A PILGRIM STAND

"Betide me weal, betide me woe,
  I'll hold by thy command.

"But if in battle-front, Lord James,
  'Tis ours once more to ride,

Nor force of man, nor craft of fiend,
  Shall cleave me from thy side!"

And aye we sailed and aye we sailed
  Across the weary sea,
Until one morn the coast of Spain
  Rose grimly on our lee.

And as we rounded to the port,
  Beneath the watchtower's wall,
We heard the clash of the atabals,
  And the trumpet's wavering call.

"Why sounds yon Eastern music here
  So wantonly and long,
And whose the crowd of armed men
  That round yon standard throng?"

"The Moors have come from Africa
  To spoil and waste and slay,
And King Alonzo of Castile
  Must fight with them to-day."

"Now shame it were," cried good Lord
    James,
  "Shall never be said of me
That I and mine have turned aside
  From the Cross in jeopardie!

"Have down, have down, my merry men
    all,—
  Have down unto the plain;
We'll let the Scottish lion loose
  Within the fields of Spain!"

"Now welcome to me, noble lord,
　Thou and thy stalwart power;
Dear is the sight of a Christian knight,
　Who comes in such an hour!

"Is it for bond or faith you come,
　Or yet for golden fee?
Or bring ye France's lilies here,
　Or the flower of Burgundie?"

"God greet thee well, thou valiant king,
　Thee and thy belted peers,—
Sir James of Douglas am I called,
　And these are Scottish spears.

"We do not fight for bond or plight,
　Nor yet for golden fee;
But for the sake of our blessed Lord,
　Who died upon the tree.

"We bring our great King Robert's heart
　Across the weltering wave.
To lay it in the holy soil
　Hard by the Saviour's grave.

"True pilgrims we, by land and sea,
　Where danger bars the way;
And therefore are we here, Lord King,
　To ride with thee this day!"

The king has bent his stately head,
　And the tears were in his eyne,—
"God's blessing on thee, noble knight,
　For this brave thought of thine!"

"I know thy name full well, Lord James;
   And honored may I be,
That those who fought beside the Bruce
   Should fight this day for me!

"Take thou the leading of the van,
   And charge the Moors amain;
There is not such a lance as thine
   In all the host of Spain!"

The Douglas turned towards us then,
   O, but his glance was high!—
"There is not one of all my men
   But is as bold as I.

"There is not one of my knights
   But bears as true a spear,—
Then onward, Scottish gentlemen,
   And think King Robert's here!"

The trumpets blew, the cross-bolts flew,
   The arrows flashed like flame,
As spur in side, and spear in rest,
   Against the foe we came.

And many a bearded Saracen
   Went down, both horse and man;
For through their ranks we rode like corn,
   So furiously we ran!

But in behind our path they closed,
   Though fain to let us through,
For they were forty thousand men,
   And we were wondrous few.

We might not see a lance's length,
  So dense was their array,
But the long fell sweep of the Scottish blade
  Still held them hard at bay.

"Make in! make in!" Lord Douglas cried,—
  "Make in, my brethren dear!
Sir William of Saint Clair is down;
  We may not leave him here!"

But thicker, thicker grew the swarm,
  And sharper shot the rain,
And the horses reared amid the press,
  But they would not charge again.

"Now Jesu help thee," said Lord James,
  "Thou kind and true Saint Clair!
An' if I may not bring thee off,
  I'll die beside thee there!"

Then in his stirrups up he stood,
  So lionlike and bold,
And held the precious heart aloft
  All in its case of gold.

He flung it from him, far ahead,
  And never spake he more,
But—"Pass thou first, thou dauntless heart,
  As thou wert wont of yore!"

The roar of fight rose fiercer yet,
  And heavier still the stour,
Till the spears of Spain came shivering in,
  And swept away the Moor.

"Now praised be God, the day is won!
    They fly o'er flood and fell,—
Why dost thou draw the rein so hard,
    Good knight, that fought so well?"

"O, ride ye on, Lord King!" he said,
    "And leave the dead to me,
For I must keep the dreariest watch
    That ever I shall dree!

"There lies, above his master's heart,
    The Douglas, stark and grim;
And woe is me I should be here,
    Not side by side with him!

"The world grows cold, my arm is old,
    And thin my lyart hair,
And all that I loved best on earth
    Is stretched before me there.

"O Bothwell banks! that bloom so bright
    Beneath the sun of May,
The heaviest cloud that ever blew
    Is bound for you this day.

"And Scotland! thou mayst veil thy head
    In sorrow and in pain:
The sorest stroke upon thy brow
    Hath fallen this day in Spain!

"We'll bear them back unto our ship,
    We'll bear them o'er the sea,
And lay them in the hallowed earth
    Within our own countrie.

HELD THE HEART ALOFT

"And be thou strong of heart, Lord King,
    For this I tell thee sure,
The sod that drank the Douglas' blood
    Shall never bear the Moor!"

The King he lighted from his horse,
    He flung his brand away,
And took the Douglas by the hand,
    So stately as he lay.

"God give thee rest, thou valiant soul!
    That fought so well for Spain;
I'd rather half my land were gone,
    So that thou wert here again!"

We bore the good Lord James away,
    And the priceless heart we bore,
And heavily we steered our ship
    Towards the Scottish shore.

No welcome greeted our return,
    Nor clang of martial tread,
But all were dumb and hushed as death
    Before the mighty dead.

We laid our chief in Douglas Kirk,
    The heart in fair Melrose;
And woful men were we that day,—
    God grant their souls repose!

THE SKELETON IN ARMOR

By HENRY W. LONGFELLOW

"SPEAK! speak! thou fearful guest!
  Who with thy hollow breast
  Still in rude armor drest,
    Comest to daunt me!
  Wrapt not in Eastern balms,
  But with thy fleshless palms
  Stretched, as if asking alms,
    Why dost thou haunt me?"

Then, from those cavernous eyes
Pale flashes seemed to rise,
As when the northern skies
    Gleam in December;
And, like the water's flow
Under December's snow,
Came a dull voice of woe
    From the heart's chamber.

"I was a Viking[1] old!
My deeds, though manifold,
No Skald[2] in song has told,
    No Saga[3] taught thee!

1. *Vikings* was the name given to the bold Norse seamen who in the eighth, ninth, and tenth centuries infested the northern seas. Tradition maintains that a band of these rovers discovered America centuries before Columbus.

2. A skald was a Norse poet who celebrated in song the deeds of warriors.

3. A saga is an ancient Scandinavian legend or tradition, relating mythical or historical events.

Take heed, that in thy verse
Thou dost the tale rehearse,
Else dread a dead man's curse;
    For this I sought thee.

"Far in the Northern Land,
By the wild Baltic's strand,
I, with my childish hand,
    Tamed the gerfalcon;[4]
And, with my skates fast-bound,
Skimmed the half-frozen Sound,
That the poor whimpering hound
    Trembled to walk on.

"Oft to his frozen lair
Tracked I the grisly bear,
While from my path the hare
    Fled like a shadow;
Oft through the forest dark
Followed the werewolf's[5] bark,
Until the soaring lark
    Sang from the meadow.

"But when I older grew,
Joining a corsair's[6] crew,
O'er the dark sea I flew
    With the marauders.
Wild was the life we led;
Many the souls that sped,

4. A gerfalcon is a large falcon of Northern Europe.

5. According to a popular superstition, a werewolf is a man, who, at times, is transformed into a wolf. Such a wolf is much more savage than a real wolf, and is especially fond of human flesh. This superstition has at some time existed among almost all peoples.

6. *Corsair* is but another name for a pirate.

I WAS A VIKING OLD

Many the hearts that bled,
By our stern orders.

"Many a wassail-bout[7]
Wore the long Winter out;
Often our midnight shout
    Set the cocks crowing,
As we the Berserk's[8] tale
Measured in cups of ale,
Draining the oaken pail,
    Filled to o'erflowing.

"Once as I told in glee
Tales of the stormy sea,
Soft eyes did gaze on me,
    Burning yet tender;
And as the white stars shine
On the dark Norway pine,
On that dark heart of mine
    Fell their soft splendor.

"I wooed the blue-eyed maid,
Yielding, yet half afraid,
And in the forest's shade
    Our vows were plighted.
Under its loosened vest
Fluttered her little breast,
Like birds within their nest
    By the hawk frighted.

7. A wassail-bout is a drinking bout, or carouse.

8. *Berserk*, or *Berserker*, was the name given in heathen times in Scandinavia to a wild warrior or champion. The Berserkers, it is said, had fits of madness, when they foamed at the mouth and howled like beasts, rushing into battle naked and defenseless. It was believed that at such times they were proof against wounds either from fire or from steel.

"Bright in her father's hall
Shields gleamed upon the wall,
Loud sang the minstrels all,
          Chaunting his glory;
When of old Hildebrand
I asked his daughter's hand,
Mute did the minstrels stand
          To hear my story.

"While the brown ale he quaffed,
Loud then the champion laughed.
And as the wind-gusts waft
          The sea-foam brightly,
So the loud laugh of scorn,
Out of those lips unshorn,
From the deep drinking-horn
          Blew the foam lightly.

"She was a Prince's child,
I but a Viking wild,
And though she blushed and smiled,
          I was discarded!
Should not the dove so white
Follow the sea-mew's flight,
Why did they leave that night
          Her nest unguarded?

"Scarce had I put to sea,
Bearing the maid with me,—
Fairest of all was she
          Among the Norsemen!—
When on the white sea-strand,
Waving his arméd hand,
Saw we old Hildebrand,
          With twenty horsemen.

"Then launched they to the blast,
Bent like a reed each mast,
Yet we were gaining fast,
    When the wind failed us;
And with a sudden flaw
Came round the gusty Skaw,[9]
So that our foe we saw
    Laugh as he hailed us.

"And as to catch the gale
Round veered the flapping sail,
Death! was the helmsman's hail,
    Death without quarter!
Mid-ships with iron keel
Struck we her ribs of steel;
Down her black hulk did reel
    Through the black water!

"As with his wings aslant,
Sails the fierce cormorant,
Seeking some rocky haunt,
    With his prey laden,
So toward the open main,
Beating to sea again,
Through the wild hurricane
    Bore I the maiden.

"Three weeks we westward bore,
And when the storm was o'er,
Cloud-like we saw the shore
    Stretching to lee-ward;
There for my lady's bower
Built I the lofty tower,[10]

9. The Skaw is the most northerly point of Denmark

Which, to this very hour,
  Stands looking seaward.

"There lived we many years;
  Time dried the maiden's tears;

THREE WEEKS WE WESTWARD BORE

She had forgot her fears,
  She was a mother;
Death closed her mild blue eyes,
Under that tower she lies;
Ne'er shall the sun arise
  On such another!

"Still grew my bosom then,
  Still as a stagnant fen!

10. At Newport in Rhode Island is an old stone tower, which tradition says was built by the Norsemen when they visited this country. That is the tower to which Longfellow refers here.

Hateful to me were men,
    The sunlight hateful!
In the vast forest here,
Clad in my warlike gear,
Fell I upon my spear,
    O, death was grateful!

"Thus, seamed with many scars
Bursting these prison bars,
Up to its native stars
    My soul ascended!
There from the flowing bowl
Deep drinks the warrior's soul,
Skoal![11] to the Northland! *skoal!*"
    —Thus the tale ended.

11. *Skoal* is the customary salutation in Scandinavia when a health is drunk.

Round Tower at Newport

HOW THEY BROUGHT THE GOOD NEWS FROM GHENT TO AIX

By ROBERT BROWNING

I SPRANG to the stirrup, and Joris
    and he;
I galloped, Dirck galloped, we gal-
    loped all three;
"Good speed!" cried the watch as the
    gate-bolts undrew,
"Speed!" echoed the wall to us gal-
loping through.
Behind shut the postern, the lights sank to rest,
And into the midnight we galloped abreast.

Not a word to each other; we kept the great pace,—
Neck by neck, stride by stride, never changing our
    place;
I turned in my saddle and made its girths tight,
Then shortened each stirrup and set the pique right,
Rebuckled the check-strap, chained slacker the bit,
Nor galloped less steadily Roland a whit.

'T was a moonset at starting; but while we drew
    near
Lokerem, the cocks crew and twilight dawned clear;
At Boom a great yellow star came out to see;
At Düffeld 't was morning as plain as could be;
And from Mecheln church-steeple we heard the
    half-chime,—

So Joris broke silence with "Yet there is time!"
At Aerschot up leaped of a sudden the sun,
And against him the cattle stood black every one,
To stare through the midst at us galloping past;
And I saw my stout galloper Roland at last,
With resolute shoulders, each butting away
The haze, as some blind river headland its spray;
And his low head and crest, just one sharp ear bent
　　back
For my voice, and the other pricked out on his track;
And one eye's black intelligence,—ever that glance
O'er its white edge at me, his own master, askance;
And the thick heavy spume-flakes, which aye and
　　anon
His fierce lips shook upward in galloping on.

By Hasselt Dirck groaned; and cried Joris, "Stay
　　spur!
Your Roos galloped bravely, the fault's not in her;
We'll remember at Aix,"—for one heard the quick
　　wheeze
Of her chest, saw the stretched neck, and staggering
　　knees,
And sunk tail, and horrible heave of the flank,
As down on her haunches she shuddered and sank.

So we were left galloping, Joris and I,
Past Looz and past Tongres, no cloud in the sky;
The broad sun above laughed a pitiless laugh;
'Neath our feet broke the brittle, bright stubble like
　　chaff;
Till over by Dalhem a dome-spire sprang white,
And "Gallop," gasped Joris, "for Aix is in sight!"

"How they'll greet us!"—and all in a moment his
   roan

I CAST LOOSE MY BUFF-COAT

Rolled neck and croup over, lay dead as a stone;
And there was my Roland to bear the whole weight
Of the news which alone could save Aix from her
   fate,
With his nostrils like pits full of blood to the brim,
And with circles of red for his eye-sockets' rim.

Then I cast loose my buff-coat, each holster let fall,
Shook off both my jack-boots, let go belt and all,
Stood up in the stirrup, leaned, patted his ear,
Called my Roland his pet name, my horse without
     peer,—
Clapped my hands, laughed and sang, an noise, bad
     or good,
Till at length into Aix Roland galloped and stood.

And all I remember is friends flocking round.
As I sate with his head 'twixt my knees on the
     ground;
And no voice but was praising this Roland of mine,
As I poured down his throat our last measure of
     wine,
Which (the burgesses voted by common consent)
Was no more than his due who brought good news
     from Ghent.

When we read this poem, the first question that comes
to us is "What *was* the 'good news from Ghent?' " But
we find on looking up the matter that the whole incident is
a fanciful one; Browning simply imagined a very dramatic
situation, and then wrote this stirring poem about it. And
surely he has made it all seem very real to us. We feel the
intense anxiety of the riders to reach Aix on time—for we
are given to understand in the last line of the third stanza
that Aix must learn the news by a certain hour; we feel
the despair of the two who are forced to give up the
attempt, and the increased sense of responsibility of the
only remaining rider; and we fairly hold our breath in
our fear that the gallant Roland will not stand the strain.

The towns mentioned are real places, all of them in
Belgium.

Does the poem seem to you somewhat rough and jerky?
It is a ballad, and that fact accounts in part for its style,
for ballads are not usually smooth and perfect in structure.

But there is another reason for the jerkiness, if we may call it by so strong a name. Read the first two lines aloud, giving them plenty of swing. Do they not remind you of the galloping of a horse, with their regular rise and fall? A little poet might have attempted to write about this wild midnight ride in the same smooth, flowing style in which he would describe a lazy river slipping over the stones; but Browning was a great poet, and knew how to fit sound to sense. Other poets may excel him in writing of quiet, peaceful scenes, but no one who has ever written could put more dash and vigor into a poem than could Browning.

GHENT

REMINISCENCES OF A PIONEER[1]

By EDWIN D. COE

Y father left his old home in Oneida County, New York, in June, 1839, a young man in his twenty-fourth year. The beauty and fertility of the Rock River valley, in Wisconsin, had been widely proclaimed by participants in the Black Hawk War and in the glowing reports of Government engineers. In fact, the latter declared it to be a very Canaan of promise. As a consequence, hundreds of young people, restless and ambitious, and very many older ones whom the panic of the late 30's had separated from their business moorings, turned their thoughts and then their steps toward the new promised land.

When my father was rowed ashore from the steamer at Milwaukee, he could have taken up "government land" within the present limits of that city, but the bluffs and swamps of the future metropolis had no charms for him compared with the vision he had in mind of the Rock River country. So he crossed Milwaukee River on a ferry at the foot of Wisconsin Street, walked out on a sidewalk quavering on stilts until solid ground was reached at Third Street, and then struck the trail for the west.

1. From the Proceedings of the State Historical Society of Wisconsin, 1907.

Along the shore of Pewaukee Lake, the traveler
met a wolf which bristled and snarled but at last
surrendered the right of way before the superior
bluff, which was put up against him, backed by a
"big stick." That night he stayed with a friend
named Terry, who had come West the year before,
and preëmpted a piece of land on the east shore
rock, about seven miles above Watertown. The
next morning he saw on the opposite bank a gently
rising slope covered with stately maples and oaks;
beneath were the grass and flowers of mid June,
and the swift flowing river, clear as a spring brook,
was in front, making the scene one of entrancing
beauty. It was fully equal to his highest expecta-
tions, and he never rested until he had secured title
to that particular block of land.

He at once prepared to build a log house, and,
after a few days, the neighborhood was invited to
the raising. Some men came eight and ten miles,
and a big laugh went around when it was found that
logs a foot and a half and two feet in diameter had
been cut for the house. Four large ones were rolled
together for a foundation, and then the inexperi-
enced young man was told that for a house he
needed to cut logs half as large, and they would
return in a week and raise them. This they did,
showing the kindly, helpful spirit of the early
settlers.

In August my mother came and brought the
household furniture from their Oneida County
home, together with a year's provisions. The trip
from Milwaukee to their log house, nearly forty
miles, took nearly three days by ox team. She was
delighted and happy with the building and its sur-

roundings, and never faltered in her love for that first home in the West. A barrel of pork was among the supplies she had brought, and people came as far as twenty miles to beg a little of it, so tired were they of fresh meat from the woods, and fish from the river; and they never went away empty-handed, as long as it lasted.

They came, as I have said, in 1839, and I the year following. There is a vague, misty period at the beginning of every life, as memory rises from mere nothingness to full strength, when it is not easy to say whether the things remembered may not have been heard from the lips of others. But I distinctly recall some very early events, and particularly the disturbance created by my year-old brother, two years younger than myself, when he screamed with pain one evening and held his bare foot up, twisted to one side.

My mother was ill in bed, and the terrified maid summoned my father from outside, with the story that the baby's ankle was out of joint. He hurried in, gave it one look, and, being a hasty, impetuous man, he declared, "Yes, the child's ankle is out of joint; I must go for a doctor;" and in another moment he would have been off on a seven-mile tramp through the dark to Watertown. But the mother, a level-headed woman, experienced in emergencies, called out from her bed, "Wait a minute; bring me the child and a candle;" and a minute later she had discovered a little sliver which pricked him when he set his foot down, and extricated it between thumb and finger. "There," said she; "I don't think you need walk to Watertown to-night."

Indians were so numerous that I don't remember when they first came out of the haze into my consciousness, but probably in my third year. They were Winnebago and Pottawatomi, the river being a common inheritance of both tribes. In the winter of 1839-40, about thirty families of the former tribe camped for several weeks opposite our home and were very sociable and friendly. Diligent hunters and trappers, they accumulated fully a hundred dollars worth of otter, beaver, bear, deer, and other skins. But a trader came up from Watertown in the spring and got the whole lot in exchange for a four-gallon keg of whisky. That was a wild night that followed. Some of the noisiest came over to our house, and when denied admittance threatened to knock the door down, but my father told them he had two guns ready for them, and they finally left. He afterwards said that he depended more on a heavy hickory club which he had on hand than on the guns—it could be fired faster.

An ugly squaw whose nose had been bitten off years before in a fight, stabbed her brother that night, because he refused her more whisky. He had, according to custom, been left on guard, and was entirely sober. The next day the Indians horrified my mother by declaring that they should cut the squaw into inch pieces if her brother died. They went down to Lake Koshkonong two days later, but he died the first day out. The squaw escaped and lived a lonely life for years after, being known up and down the river as "Old Mag."

At any time of the year we were liable to receive visits from Indians passing to and fro between Lakes Horicon and Koshkonong. They would come into the house without ceremony further than staring into the windows before entering. Being used only to town life in the East, my mother was afraid of them, but she always carried a bold face and would never give them bread, which they always demanded, unless she could readily spare it.

One summer afternoon, when she had finished her housework and had sat down to sew, half a dozen Indians, male and female, suddenly bolted in and clamored for bread. She shook her head and told them she had none for them. When she came West she had brought yeast cakes which, by careful renewal, she kept in succession until the family home was broken up in 1880. Upon the afternoon referred to, she had a large pan of yeast cakes drying before the fireplace. Seeing them, the Indians scowled at her, called her a lying woman, and made a rush for the cakes, each one taking a huge bite. Those familiar with the article know how bitter is the mixture of raw meal, hops, and yeast, and so will not wonder that presently a look of horror came over the Indians' faces and that then they sputtered the unsavory stuff out all over the newly scrubbed floor. My mother used to say that if they had killed her she could not have kept from laughing. They looked very angry at first, but finally concluded that they had not been poisoned and had only "sold" themselves, they huddled together and went out chattering and laughing, leaving my mother a good share of her day's work to do over again.

One day I saw a big Indian shake her by the shoulder because she wouldn't give him bread. She was ironing at the time, and threatened him with a

HALF A DOZEN INDIANS BOLTED IN

hot flat iron till he hurried out. Another came in one warm summer afternoon, shut the door behind him, and leaned against it, glowering at her. For once she was thoroughly frightened. He had with him a tomahawk, having a hollow handle and head, that could be used as a pipe. However, her wits did not desert her. Seeing the cat sleeping peacefully in the corner, she cried, "How did that cat get in here!" and catching up the broom she chased pussy around till she reached the door, when seizing the heavy iron latch she pulled it wide open, sending Mr. Indian into the middle of the room; she then pushed the door back against the wall and set a chair against it. The Indian stood still for a minute, then uttered a grunt and took himself off, probably thinking she was too dangerous a person for him to attempt to bully.

The Indians used to offer for sale venison, fish, and maple sugar, but the line was always drawn on the latter, for it was commonly reported that they strained the sap through their blankets. And you should have seen their blankets! About 1846 a company of civilized Oneidas, some of whom my father had known in the East, camped near by and manufactured a large number of handsome and serviceable baskets. From wild berries they would make dyes that never faded, and print them on the baskets with stamps cut from potatoes. Some of their designs were quite artistic. A small basket and a rattle which they gave my year-old sister showed their good will.

I soon learned to have no fear of the tribesmen, although sometimes a fleet of fifty canoes would be in sight at once, passing down the river to Kosh-

konong; but the first Germans who came to our
parts nearly scared the life out of me. Their heavy
beards, long coats, broad-visored caps, and arm-
long pipes, made me certain that nothing less than
a fat boy of five would satisfy their appetites; and
whenever they appeared I would hunt my mother.
They had bought a considerable tract of land about
five miles from our place, and always wanted to
know of us the road thither. The result was just
such a "jabber match" as could be expected where
neither side knew the other's tongue; but by pointing and motioning my mother was always able to
direct them. Sometimes they wished to come in and
make tea or coffee on our stove, and eat the luncheon
of bread and meat that they had brought across the
water. They would then always urge their food
upon me, so I came to like their black bread very
much and soon revised my first estimate of their
character. All those people cut fine farms out of
the heavy timber and died rich.

The first settlers were mostly Americans, from
New York and New England; but before leaving
the old farm we used to hear of English, Irish,
Dutch, Norwegian, and Welsh settlements. The
latter people enveloped and overflowed our own
particular community and came to form a good
portion of the population.

Besides the numerous nationalities on this front
edge of advancing settlement, there were people of
many and diverse individualities—the uneasy, the
unlucky, the adventurous, the men without money
but full of hope, the natural hunters, the trappers,
the lovers of woods and solitudes, and occasionally
one who had left his country for his country's good;

all these classes were represented. But on the whole the frontier's people were an honest, kindly, generous class, ready to help in trouble or need of any kind.

If there was sickness, watchers by the bedside and harvesters in the field were promptly forthcoming. If a new house or barn was to be raised, every available man came. If a cow was mired, and such was often the case, her owner easily got all the help he wanted. Husking and logging and quilting bees were common, and in the autumn there were bees for candle-dipping, when the family supply of candles would be made for a year; and all such events would of course be followed by a supper, and perhaps a frolic. Visits among the women folk were all-day affairs; if the husbands were invited, it would be of an evening, and the call then would last till midnight with a supper at ten. There was a word of comfort and good cheer in those forest homes. I doubt if any child in modern palaces enjoys happier hours than were mine on winter evenings, when I rested on the broad stone hearth in front of the big fireplace, with its blazing four-foot log, the dog on one side and the cat on the other, while my father told stories that had to be repeated as the stock ran out, and I was gradually lulled to sleep by the soft thunder of my mother's spinning wheel. What could be more luxurious for any youngster?

I remember that when I was about six I saw my first apple. Half of it came to me, and I absorbed it as if to the manor born. What a revelation it was to a lad who could be satisfied with chokecherries and crab apples! In those times, when a visitor called it was common to bring out a dish of well-washed turnips, with plate and case knife, and he could slice them up or scrape them as he chose.

The woods abounded in wild fruits, which the women made the most of for the winter season. Berries, grapes, plums, and crab apples were all utilized. The latter were especially delicious for preserves. The boy who ate them raw off the tree could not get his face back into line the same day; but he would eat them. However, pumpkins were our main reliance for present and future pies and sauce; such pumpkins do not grow now in these latter days. There were two sugar bushes on our place, and a good supply of maple sugar was put up every spring. Many other dainties were added to our regular menu, and a boy with such a cook for a mother as I had, needed no sympathy from any one the whole world round.

The river was three hundred feet wide opposite our house, and about two feet deep, so teams could be driven across at ordinary stages, but foot passengers depended on our boat, a large "dugout." I remember how beautiful it was, when first scooped out from a huge basswood log, clean, white, and sweet-smelling. Strangers and neighbors alike would call across, "Bring over the boat;" and if they were going from our side they would take it over and leave the job of hollering to us. At five years of age I could pole it around very nicely.

One day, when I was first trusted to go in the boat alone, a stranger called over, and as my father was busy, he told me to go after him. The man expressed much wonderment, and some hesitancy to trusting himself to the skill and strength of a bare-footed boy of five; but I assured him I was a veteran at the business. He finally got in very gingerly, and sat down flat on the bottom. All the way over he kept wondering at and praising my work until I was ready to melt with mingled embarrassment and delight. At the shore he asked me unctuously how much he should pay. "Oh, nothing," I said. "But let me pay you. I'd be glad to," said he. "Oh, no, we never take pay," I replied, and dug my toes into the sand, not knowing how to get out of the scrape, yet well pleased at his high estimate of my service. All the time he was plunging down first into one pocket of his barn-door trousers and then the other, till at last he fished out an old "bungtown" cent, which with much graciousness and pomposity he pressed upon me, until my feeble refusals were overcome. I took the coin and scampered away so fast that I must have been invisible in the dust I raised. Showing it to my father, I was told that I ought not to have taken it; but I explained how helpless I had been, and repeated word for word what the man had said, and, unintentionally, somewhat copied his tone and manner. The twinkle in my father's eye showed that he understood. That copper was my first-earned money; if it had only been put out at compound interest, I ought, if the mathematicians are right, to be now living in *otium cum dignitate,*[2] perhaps.

Steve Peck was one of the most notable of the marked characters above hinted at. He was a roistering blade, who captained all the harumscarums of the section. Peck was a surveyor and had

2. *Otium cum dignitate* is a Latin expression meaning *ease with dignity.*

HE FISHED OUT AN OLD BUNGTOWN CENT

helped at the laying out of Milwaukee. Many were the stories told of his escapades, but space will not permit of their rehearsal here. He had selected a choice piece of land and built a good house; then he induced the daughter of an Aberdeen ex-merchant of aristocratic family but broken fortune, who had sought a new chance in the wilds of Wisconsin, to share them with him. But wife and children could not hold him to a settled life, and he sold out one day to a German immigrant, gave his wife a few dollars and disappeared, not to be seen or heard of in those parts again.

Another character was a man named Needham, who also was somewhat of a mystery. The women considered that he had been "crossed in love." He affected a sombre style, rather imitating the manners and habits of the Indians. His cabin was near the river, and he was a constant hunter. Many times when playing by the shore I would become conscious of a strange, noiseless presence, and looking up would see Needham paddling by, swift and silent. It always gave me the shudders and sent me to the house. One day, on coming home from school, I saw a great platter of red meat on the table. I asked who had killed the beef; it was a practice to share the meat with the neighbors, whenever a large animal was killed, taking pay in kind. I was told it was not beef, and being unable to guess was at last informed that it was bear meat, which Mr. Needham had left. As he had killed the animal near where I hunted the cows every night, the news gave me a sensation.

Uncle Ben Piper, the only gray-haired man in the community, kept tavern and was an oracle on nearly all subjects. He was also postmaster, and a wash-stand drawer served as post office. It cost twenty-five cents in those times to pass a letter between Wisconsin and the East. Postage did not have to be prepaid, and I have known my father to go several days before he could raise the requisite cash to redeem a letter which he had heard awaited him in the wash-stand drawer, for Uncle Ben was not allowed to accept farm produce or even bank script for postage.

An Englishman named Pease, who lived near us, had "wheels." He thought the Free Masons and the women were in league to end his life. Every night he ranged his gun and farm tools beside his bed, to help ward off the attack that he constantly expected. Nothing could induce him to eat any food that a woman had prepared. In changing "work" with my father, which often occurred, he would bring his own luncheon and eat it by the fire during mealtime. But after my sister was born, he refused to enter the house; he told the neighbors that "women were getting too thick up at Coe's." Pease had nicknames for all the settlers but one, and while very polite to their faces, he always applied his nicknames in their absence.

A man named Rugg lost caste with his neighbors because he dug and used a potato pit in an Indian mound from which he had thrown out a large number of human bones. Some of the bones were of gigantic size.

There were many good hunters among the settlers; the Smith brothers scorned to shoot a bird or squirrel except through the head. If there were sickness in the family of any neighbor, the Smiths saw that partridges, quail, or pigeons, properly shot, were supplied. Another Smith was a bee hunter, and a very successful one, too. Those were the days when the beautiful passenger pigeons at times seemed to fill the woods and the sky. Deer were very abundant; I have seen them eating hay with my father's cows; and in the spring and fall seasons the river was covered with wild ducks and geese.

Two events in my seventh year left a strong impression upon me. The first was an address by a colored man named Lewis Washington, a runaway slave, who had a natural gift of oratory and made many speeches in this state. I was so curious to see a genuine black man that I got too close to him when he was in the convulsion of putting on his overcoat, and caught a considerable thump. No harm was done, but he apologized very earnestly. I have read that his campaigning of the state was quite effective.

The other occurrence was the visit to Watertown of Herr Dreisbach with his famous menagerie. Our indulgent father took my brother and myself and a neighbor's daughter to see the "great instructive exhibition." It took our ox-team three hours to make the seven miles, and the elephant's footprints by the bridges, and other impedimenta of the great show, which we passed, carried our excitement, which had been cruelly growing for three weeks, well-nigh up to an exploding climax. I was told not to lose my ticket, or I could not get in; and when the ticket taker seized hold of it, I held on until he finally yelled angrily, "Let go, you little cuss!" whereupon my father came to his rescue. The show

on the whole was very satisfactory, except for the
color of Columbus, the fine old elephant, which for
some reason, probably from the show bills on the
barns, I had expected to be of a greenish tint. I
also had supposed that the lion would drag his
chariot at least half a mile, with the driver in heroic
pose, instead of merely two cars' length. Herr
Dreisbach afterwards showed on Rock Prairie, in
the open country, a few miles east of Janesville.
People came from great distances to attend, even
from as far as Baraboo, sometimes camping out two
nights each way.

Our first public edifice was a log schoolhouse
about twenty feet square. It was on the opposite
side of the river, nearly a mile distant, but I began
to attend school before I was fully five years old.
One of the things I remember of one of my early
teachers most distinctly is, that she used to hang a
five-franc piece, tied with blue ribbon, around the
neck of the scholar who had "left off at the head."
I was occasionally favored, but my mother's satisfaction was greatly modified by her fear that I
would lose the coin while taking it back the next day.

The teachers probably could not have passed a
normal school examination, but they could do what
our graduates now cannot do—that is, make and
mend a quill pen. Those were all the pens we had,
and many a time have I chased our geese to get a
new quill. The teachers patiently guided our wob-
bling ideas from the alphabet to cube root. The
lessons over, we were told to "toe the crack," and
"make obeisance," and were then put through our
paces in the field of general knowledge. I still remember, from their drilling, the country, territory,

county, and town in which we lived; that James K.
Polk was president, that George M. Dallas was
vice-president, and that Henry Dodge was governor.   What ancient history that now seems!

Near the school lived a family named Babcock,
with four well-grown boys.   One of them used often
to come over at noon to see one of the teachers.
One noon, on running to the schoolroom after some-

CHASING THE GEESE TO GET A NEW QUILL

thing that I wanted, I was horrified to see my loved
teacher struggling to prevent the young fellow from
kissing her.   I felt very sorry for her, and on going
home promptly reported the outrage to my mother.
She evidently did not approve, but did not make
as much of a demonstration over it as I had expected.   I doubt now, if the teacher was as greatly
in need of my sympathy as I then thought.   The
Babcocks all went to the war, as I am told, and
one of them became colonel of his regiment.   He
came home to be fatally and mysteriously shot one
night on his way to his room in Chicago; the why
and how were never revealed.

The winter after I was six years old I went to
a school taught by a fine young man named Martin

Piper, a relative of Uncle Ben's. The next summer he enlisted in the Mexican War with another of our young neighbors, John Bradshaw. I saw the volunteers from Watertown filling two wagons that carried them to Milwaukee, and I could not keep the tears back, for I feared I should never see John and Martin again. And so it was; they both perished at Vera Cruz.

My last winter's school was taught by my father. I remember that we used to cross the river, which only froze along the edges, on cakes of ice which he would cut out and pole across. The school closed in the spring with an "exhibition," consisting of declamations, dialogues, a little "play," and a spelling contest. The whole countryside was there, and about thirty of us youngsters were put up in the attic, which was floored over with loose boards, to make room for our elders. The only light we had was what percolated up through the cracks, and all that we could see of the exhibition was through them. As we hustled around, sampling them to see where we could see best, we made a good deal of disturbance.

The best place, next the chimney, we were driven back from, for repeated burning had weakened the support. (The beam next to the chimney used to catch fire nearly every day, and we younger ones used to watch it and report to the teacher, who would calmly throw a dipper of water up and put the fire out for the time being.) A fat woman sat under the dangerous place that evening, and made a great outcry if we came near to enjoy the desirable outlook—stout people always seem fearful that something will fall on them. I remember also that her little girl, a pretty creature in curls and a pink dress, spoke "Mary had a little lamb," by having it "lined out" to her.

Our schoolhouse was so set in a noble grove of oaks, elms and maples with a heavy undergrowth, that we could not be seen from the road. Nearly every day droves of cattle went by, and we used to run up through the thicket to see them. It must have been an odd sight to the drovers to see a dozen or more little half-scared faces peering out of the brush, and no building in sight. They would often give us a noisy salute, whereupon we would scamper back, telling of our narrow escape from dangerous beasts and men.

The presidential election in the fall of 1848 aroused a good deal of interest, for Wisconsin had now become a state, and citizens could vote for national candidates. I was in Jonathan Piper's store one evening, with my father, when about a dozen men were present. A political discussion sprang up and grew hot, and finally a division was called for. Two or three voted for Zachary Taylor, the Whig candidate; one for Lewis Cass, the Democrat; and the rest for Martin Van Buren, Free Soiler. The State went with the lone voter, for Cass carried it by a small plurality.

Good health was the rule among the hardworking, plain-living pioneers, but plowing up the soil released the poison which nature seemed to have put there on guard, and every one at one time or another came down with the "shakes." However, the potent influence of sunshine, quinine, and cholagogue speedily won their way, and in a few years malaria had become a mere reminiscence.

In November, 1848, my parents moved to Beaver Dam, and thus our life in the Rock River country came to an end. The splendid primeval forest has now gone, and even before we left much of it had been converted into log heaps and burned. Every night scores of fires would gleam out where the finest hardwood logs, worth now a king's ransom, were turned into smoke and ashes. Even the mills which that grand pioneer, Andrew Hardgrave, had built in 1844, to the great rejoicing of all the people, are gone, and the river flows on over its smooth limestone floor, unvexed as of old. But fine brick buildings have taken the place of the old log structures, and land brings at least twenty times as much per acre as then. Who can argue against that?

THE BUCCANEERS

URING the seventeenth century there were a great number of pirates who committed serious ravages upon the settlements in the West Indies and upon the mainland adjacent, and whose expeditions extended even to the coasts of Chili and Peru. These men were called buccaneers; and the meaning of the word gives some intimation of the origin of the buccaneers themselves.

At an earlier day, many of the settlers in the island of Hispaniola, or Hayti, made their living by hunting cattle and preserving the meat by the *boucan* process. These hunters used to form parties of five or six in number, and arming themselves with musket, bullet bag, powderhorn and knife, they took their way on foot through the tangled forests of the country. When they killed one of the wild cattle, its flesh was cut into long strips and laid upon gratings, constructed of green sticks, where it was exposed to the smoke of a wood fire, which was fed by the fat and waste parts of the animals. The grating upon which the meat was laid was called a *boucan,* and the hunters were called *boucaniers.* Later these hunters were driven from Hayti by the Spaniards and took refuge in some of the neighboring islands, where they revenged themselves for some of the ill-treatment by preying upon the possessions of their oppressors wherever they could find them.

At the same time affairs in Europe brought France and England on the one hand, and Spain on the other, into collision; and as a result, the Spanish possessions in America became the object of French and English attacks. Accordingly, those two nations were inclined to look with a lenient eye upon the depredations committed by the buccaneers, so long as the property of the English and French was respected. As a natural consequence, many of the disreputable and daring characters of both nations joined themselves with the original buccaneers, whom they soon made as corrupt as themselves. Eventually these pirates increased so in number, and grew so daring in their operations that it was necessary for all nations to unite in putting them down; and by that time, the word *buccaneer* had come to mean *pirate* in its worst sense.

From time to time there arose among the buccaneers leaders whose success brought a large following from men of other companies, and in one or two instances a particularly strong man gathered about him almost all the men who were willing to engage in such enterprises. At such times the pirates formed a very powerful organization, and none of the smaller cities were proof against their ravages. Whether the band was large or small, however, the method of operation was always practically the same.

Naturally there were preliminary meetings in which a few men discussed plans and decided upon an expedition of some sort. Then a preliminary meeting was held at which the object of attack was determined, funds were raised, officers were elected, and the smaller details of the expedition were determined. Then articles of agreement were drawn up, signed by the buccaneers, and usually kept with remarkable exactness. In conformity with these agreements, the spoils of the expeditions were distributed among the individuals according to rank, each individual of the ordinary class receiving one share of the plunder, while the officers were given from two to eight, according to their position and influence.

It was customary, however, before any allotment was made to the individuals, to set aside a certain portion of the spoils to be distributed among those who had suffered some injury in the expeditions, and in case any of the members died, that member's share was distributed to his heirs. Besides this, there were special rewards given to the first man who should sight a prize, to the first man to board a ship, and to other men who were noticeably brave and successful.

It was quite customary for two buccaneers to swear brotherhood each to the other, to make written agreements to stand by each other during life, to sign these agreements with their own blood; and then to keep these curious partnerships to the end. There are numerous touching accounts of the devotion with which a friend often followed the fortunes of his sworn brother. In fact, the buccaneers usually dealt honestly and fairly with one another, and in the same way with the Indians, notwithstanding the fact that they were bloodthirsty, cruel and heartless in their treatment of the captives they made on their expeditions.

The usual place of meeting for the buccaneers was upon the west end of the island of Tortuga, which lies off the northern coast of Hayti, although the English pirates after 1654 met on the island of Jamaica. The traders and planters of these islands and of others in the vicinity were not averse to having the buccaneers among them, for no sooner had the latter returned from a successful expedition than they spent, with lavish hand, the money which they had made.

While it is true that between these forays the pirates were given to the wildest excesses, and were anything but a desirable addition to a community, yet there are always plenty of people who are willing to profit by the wastefulness and dissipations of others. Many of the buccaneers, accordingly, had homes which they visited in the intervals of their cruises, where, although their business was well known, they were in a certain sense respected. However, before the pirates were wholly subdued, they had become less and less acceptable residents in any community, and finally were at enmity with every soul not in their own occupation.

That these buccaneers had a large amount of physical bravery, goes without saying; for only a man who feared nothing could undertake such apparently hopeless tasks as these wild plunderers carried to a successful conclusion. In fact many times they were successful for the reason that the vessels or towns they attacked deemed themselves secure from attack by so small a force as the pirates could muster. They were inured to hardship and willing to undergo any amount of pain and suffering, if they could but gather the riches for which they sought. The accounts of their adventures are filled with description of daring deeds, which if undertaken in a better cause would have made the men famous for all time.

The beginning of these expeditions may be placed at about 1625, and the last important cruise of the pirates was made in 1688. After the latter date they gradually dispersed, and the buccaneers appeared no more. In 1664, Mansveldt, who was one of the ablest of the pirate chiefs, conceived the idea of forming an independent government with a flag of its own, and locating his capital at Santa Katalina. His early death prevented him from realizing his purpose; and though his successor, the famous Henry Morgan, attempted to carry out the plan, it met with such opposition from the Governor of Jamaica that it was definitely abandoned. It was under the leadship of this same Morgan that the buccaneers reached the height of their reputation, and executed their most daring and successful raids. Among Morgan's performances was the

capture of the town of Puerto del Principe in
Cuba, and the cities of Porto Bello, Maracaibo and
Gibraltar in South America. His greatest exploit,
however, occurred in 1670, when at the head of
the fleet of thirty-seven ships of all sizes manned
by more than two thousand pirates, he captured
the forts on the Chagres River, marched across the
Isthmus of Panama, and after ten days of incredible hardship and suffering, fighting against a force
of twenty-five hundred men, captured the city of
Panama. After a stay of about three weeks he
returned across the Isthmus.

So unsatisfactory in value were the spoils of this
expedition, that Morgan was accused of embezzling
some portion, and in consequence became very
unpopular with his followers.

However, as this expedition was made against the
Spanish, it received some approval from the English; and Morgan, abandoning his career as a pirate,
accepted the lieutenant-governorship of Jamaica,
and was subsequently made governor of that island,
in which capacity he did much toward suppressing
piracy in the Caribbean Sea.

We have two notable accounts of the deeds of the
early buccaneers. One was published in 1678 in
Amsterdam by John Esquemeling, who wrote from
observation, as he was himself one of the pirates,
and present at many of the conflicts which he
describes. The second account is the journal of
Basil Ringrose, who, as a pirate, took part in
Sharp's voyage around South America, and was
finally killed in a plundering raid.

CAPTAIN MORGAN AT MARACAIBO[1]

APTAIN Morgan had been so long absent from Maracaibo that he knew that the Spaniards had had sufficient time to fortify themselves strongly, and so hinder his departure from the lake. Without waiting to collect the full sum he had required from the inhabitants of Gibraltar, he demanded some of the townsmen as hostages, whom he might carry with him on his return journey, and whom he would release upon the full payment of the tribute he had levied.

Four persons who had been agreed upon were delivered to him as hostages for the sums demanded, and at last Morgan weighed anchor and set sail with great haste, directing his course toward Maracaibo.

Four days later, he arrived in front of the town and found things very much in the same condition as that in which they had been left, yet he was very much disturbed when he learned from an old man, who had been left alone and sick in the village, that three Spanish men-of-war were lying at anchor in the entrance to the lake, waiting patiently for the return of the pirates. Moreover, the great castle that stood at the opening of the channel had been

1. This account of Henry Morgan's deeds at Maracaibo is taken from the narrative of John Esquemeling, but no attempt has been made to give a literal translation of his words. Morgan had passed through the Gulf of Venezuela, captured the town of Maracaibo and made his way through the narrow passage into the lake of the same name, where he captured and despoiled Gibraltar. At the opening of this sketch, he is in Lake Maracaibo, seeking an opportunity to return to the open sea.

again repaired, provided with great guns and garrisoned by a strong force which was well supplied with ammunition.

Morgan was indeed in a dangerous predicament, for the passages leading out of the lake were narrow and tortuous. In order to learn just what force he had to meet, he sent his swiftest boat scouting through the inlet, while his ships remained within the lake.

The next day the boat came back, confirming what the old man had said and assuring Morgan that it had been so close to the Spanish ships that it was in great danger of being sunk by their shells. The biggest ship carried forty guns, the second had thirty and the smallest twenty-four. As Morgan's largest ship did not carry more than fourteen small guns, the Spanish forces appeared much superior. In fact, every one thought that Morgan must lose all hope, considering the difficulty of his passing safely with his little fleet through these winding passages, amidst the great ships and by the strong fort. Moreover, there appeared no way of escape by land, and there was certainly no other outlet into the sea.

Captain Morgan, however, was not a man to be easily discouraged, and these terrible dangers left him wholly undaunted. In a spirit of bravado he boldly sent a Spanish prisoner to the admiral of the ships commanding of him a considerable tribute or ransom, threatening, in case the ransom was not promptly paid, to set the city of Maracaibo in flames and to destroy the whole Spanish fleet. After two days the Spaniard returned, bringing from the admiral a letter which read much as follows:

"To Captain Morgan, Commander of the Pirate
    Fleet:

"Having understood by all our friends and neighbors that you have dared to attempt and commit
hostilities in the countries, cities, towns and villages
belonging to the dominions of his Catholic Majesty,
my Sovereign Lord and Master, I let you understand by these lines that I have come here and have
put into a very good state of defense that castle
which you took out of the hands of a parcel of
cowards; for I have again mounted the artillery
which you spiked and made useless.

"My intent is to dispute with you your passage
out of the lake and to follow and pursue you everywhere. Notwithstanding, if you be content to surrender with humility all that you have taken,
together with the slaves and all other prisoners, I
will let you pass freely and without trouble or
molestation, providing you agree to return to your
own country at once.

"But in case you make any resistance or opposition to my offers, I assure you I will utterly destroy
you and put every man of you to the sword. This
is my last absolute resolution. Be prudent, therefore, and do not abuse my bounty. I have with me
very good soldiers who desire nothing more ardently
than to revenge on you and your people all the
infamous cruelties and brutal acts that you have
committed upon the Spanish nation in America.

"Dated on board the royal ship Magdalena,
lying at anchor at the entry of Lake Maracaibo,
this twenty-fourth day of April, Sixteen Hundred
Sixty-nine.

Don Alonso del Campo y Espinosa."

As soon as Captain Morgan had received this letter, he called all his men together in the market
place at Maracaibo, and after reading the contents
both in French and in English, he requested the
advice of his companions upon the whole matter,
and asked whether they preferred to surrender all
they had gained in order to obtain their liberty, or
if they wished to fight for their possessions. With
one voice they cried: "We will fight and spill the
very last drop of blood in our veins rather than
surrender the booty which we have captured at the
risk of our lives."

Among those who shouted most loudly was one
who pushed his way forward to Captain Morgan
and said: "If you will take care of the rest, I, with
only twelve men, will agree to destroy the biggest
of those ships. I will take that vessel which we captured in the River of Gibraltar and make of her
a fire ship. However, to conceal our purpose from
the enemy, we will fill her decks with logs of wood
standing erect and wearing hats and caps. We
will put more of these logs at the portholes where
they can be made to counterfeit cannon. At the
stern we will hang out the English colors, and so
make the enemy think that she is one of our largest
ships well equipped for battle."

Everybody agreed to the sailor's proposal, but
after all they were not fully satisfied nor fully
relieved of their fears, and on the next day they
tried again to come to some agreement with Don
Alonso. Morgan sent him two messengers bearing
the following propositions:

First, that he would quit Maracaibo without doing
any damage to the town, or taking any ransoms.

Second, that he would set at liberty half of his slaves and all the other prisoners without ransom.

Third, that he would send home freely those four chief inhabitants of Gibraltar whom he held as hostages for the ransoms which had been promised.

Don Alonso rejected these propositions instantly, considering it dishonorable to grant them. In return he sent back a message to the effect that if the pirates did not surrender themselves voluntarily into his hands within two days under the conditions of his letter, he would immediately come and force them to do it.

Deeply angered by this message, Captain Morgan put everything in order for fighting, resolving to get out of the lake by main force without surrendering anything. In the first place he commanded that all the slaves and the prisoners should be tied and guarded very closely. After this his men gathered all the pitch, tar and brimstone they could find in the town, and with them stocked the fire ship, which we have spoken of before. They mixed the powder, the brimstone and the tar with great quantities of palm leaves, and arranged everything so that it would burn quickly and furiously. They set their counterfeit cannon in proper position at the portholes, and under each fastened heaps of powder so that they would explode with great force and noise. In some of the portholes they fastened little native drums, and upon the decks they placed logs of wood dressed as men, wearing hats and coats and carrying swords and muskets.

When the fire ship was fully fitted out in this manner, they prepared to enter the passageway into the lake. The prisoners were all put into the great boat, and in another they placed all the plate, jewels and other rich things which they had acquired. In the same ship were placed the women and the wounded and suffering. The heavy goods and bulky merchandise were distributed among other vessels, each of which was manned by twelve well-armed sailors.

The fire ship was ordered to go ahead of the rest of the vessels, and at the earliest moment to grapple with the largest of the Spanish ships. Before starting, Morgan had exacted from each of his comrades an oath in which he vowed to defend himself and his comrades against the Spaniards, even to the last drop of his blood, and never under any circumstances to beg for quarter. In return for these pledges, Morgan promised his men that all should be very well rewarded if they were successful.

It was on the thirtieth day of April, 1669, that the buccaneers made their courageous start to find the Spanish. It was growing dark when Captain Morgan found the three ships riding at anchor in the middle of the passageway into the lake, and fearing to attack in the darkness, he ordered his vessels to come to anchor, resolved that if the Spanish attacked he would fight them from that position.

All that night the valiant captain and his men kept a careful and vigilant watch, for the Spanish were almost within gunshot. No sooner had daylight come, however, than the buccaneers weighed anchor and again set sail, starting their course for the Spanish vessels. The latter, seeing them come, themselves put on sail and moved to meet the attack. The fire ship in its place at the head of the line soon met the largest ship, and instantly grappled itself firmly

THE FIRE SHIP GRAPPLED THE SPANIARD

to her side. Too late the Spaniards discovered their terrible danger, and although they made strenuous efforts to free themselves, they were unable to do so. The flames from the burning vessel seized upon the timber and rigging of the ship, and in a very short space of time consumed the stern of the vessel, leaving the fore part to sink into the sea, carrying with it the survivors.

The second Spanish ship, seeing that the pirates were successful in destroying the admiral's vessel, fled toward the castle, but being unable to escape, they sunk their vessel, preferring to lose their ship rather than fall into the hands of the bloodthirsty pirates. A portion of the sunken ship extended above the shallow water and was set on fire. The third vessel was captured by the pirates, all of whom now gave their attention to the Spaniards who were swimming toward the shore from the two wrecked vessels. Many were overtaken, but none would ask for quarter, preferring to die rather than be given life by the pirates.

Rejoicing at their wonderful and almost unexpected victory, the buccaneers pushed rapidly to the shore and attacked the castle with great vigor, but the walls were strong and were defended with such skill that the assailants were driven back time and again. The pirates had nothing but small guns with them, and although they advanced close to the castle walls and kept up a constant fire, yet they were able to do very little damage. On the other hand, the Spaniards were well armed, and in the course of the day succeeded in killing and wounding no less than sixty of the pirates. Toward evening the buccaneers retired discouraged to their ships.

All that night the Spaniards labored hard to strengthen their castle and to put things in readiness for the renewal of the attack which they expected on the morrow. However, Captain Morgan did not continue his attack on the second day, but busied himself in taking prisoner such of the sailors as he could find in the water or on the shore, and trying to recover some of the riches that were lost in the two ships.

Among those whom he captured was the pilot of the second vessel. This man was a stranger among the Spanish, and from him Morgan gathered much information. By this means he discovered that the Spanish Council of State had sent six well-equipped men-of-war with instructions to drive the English pirates out of the seas, and to destroy as many of them as possible. This vigorous action was taken at the order of the Spanish monarch, who had frequently complained to the English of the depredations their subjects were committing on the Spanish possessions, but had never been given the least satisfaction. When, however, the ships arrived at Cartagena, two of the six were found to be too large for cruising along the shallow waters of the coast, and were returned to Spain. The remaining four sailed toward Campeche to seek out the English, but in the port of that city one of the ships was lost in a fierce gale, and only the three which Morgan had now captured remained to act against the pirates. The night before Morgan arrived, the admiral had given a banquet to all his people, and on that occasion he persuaded them neither to take nor to give quarter; and this was the reason why the sailors fought even in the presence of death by

drowning. It seems that Don Alonso had been
warned by a deserting negro that the buccaneers
were building a fire ship, but he deemed it impossible that they should construct one that would
menace the safety of his vessels.

More important information which the pilot gave,
however, was that in the vessel which had been sunk
by the fire ship, was a great quantity of gold and
silver plate, together with other riches to the value
of forty thousand pieces of eight.[2]

Morgan directed one of his ships to remain near
the sunken vessel, drive away the native boats which
prowled around in that vicinity, and try to recover
the treasures. As for himself, the pirate returned
to Gibraltar, where he transferred himself and his
sailors to the larger and stronger ship which he had
captured from the Spaniards.

When he was well established in this new ship, he
sent word to the Spanish admiral, who had escaped
on shore and who was assisting in the defense of the
castle, that a large ransom must be paid or the town
would be burned to the ground. The admiral flatly
refused to pay a single dollar to Morgan; but the
garrison, remembering how successful Morgan had
always been and how fierce was his revenge, concluded to pay the ransom freely. Accordingly, after
some discussion, it was agreed that the Spaniards
should pay twenty thousand pieces of eight and
deliver five hundred beeves on the following day.
This was done, and the pirates salted the flesh of
the cattle and stored it away for their voyage.

Notwithstanding Captain Morgan had promised to deliver the prisoners if the ransom was paid,

2. The piece of eight was equivalent to about $1.25 of our money.

he was so much in fear of destruction by shells from the castle as he was passing out of the lake that he told them he would release none of them until he was entirely out of range and safe in the open sea. In the meantime his men had recovered from the sunken ship fifteen thousand pieces of eight, besides much plate and valuable goods, such as the hilts of swords, and a great quantity of pieces of eight that had melted and run together from the heat of the burning vessel.

After thinking the matter over more fully, Morgan decided that it would not be safe even yet for him to attempt to pass the castle, and accordingly he called before him his prisoners and told them that unless the admiral and the garrison of the castle should promise him free passage out of the lake, he would hang every prisoner on the yards of his ship. Accordingly, the prisoners sent a deputation to Don Alonso beseeching and supplicating him to have pity on the prisoners, who with their wives and children were still on board the ship with Captain Morgan, and to give his word of honor to permit the buccaneers to pass freely; for if such a promise were not given, every one of those in captivity would surely be killed by the sword or hanged.

The reply of Don Alonso was characteristic of the brave leader: "If you had been as loyal to your king in hindering the entry of these pirates as I shall be in preventing their going out, you had never brought this trouble upon yourselves nor upon our nation, which has now suffered so much through your cowardice. In a word, I shall never grant your request, but shall endeavor to maintain to its fullest the respect which is due to my king."

In deep despair over the result of their interview, the Spaniards returned to their fellow-prisoners, and delivered to Captain Morgan the admiral's answer. Morgan replied simply—"If Don Alonso will not give me permission to pass, I must find a way of going without his consent."

In preparation for his dangerous voyage, Morgan gathered his men on shore, and required them to bring to him all the spoils, of whatever nature, they had taken on the cruise. When these were assembled, it was found that besides a huge quantity of merchandise and a large number of slaves, the buccaneers had acquired plate, jewels and money to the value of two hundred fifty thousand pieces of eight. All of this magnificent prize was divided among the buccaneers according to the agreements which had been made before they began the expedition. Each man was permitted to take his share with him upon his own vessel. Morgan made the distribution of his spoils at this time in order not to risk the loss of the entire treasure by the sinking of one ship, and in order that no one faction of his party might succeed in carrying off all the plunder.

After everything was in readiness for the voyage, Morgan perfected a little stratagem by which he hoped to make his escape more safely. He announced to all his men that on a certain night they would sail through the narrow channel, his own ship leading the way. On the day preceding that night the Spaniards in the castle observed great activity in the pirate fleet. Canoes and boats loaded with men left the ships and pulled to the shore some distance away from the castle and on the side away from the channel. Here, overhanging trees hid the boats from the onlookers in the castle so that the latter were not aware that when the boats returned from the shore the men, with the exception of one or two who rowed, were lying concealed in the bottoms of the boats.   Not a one was landed on shore, although it appeared that Morgan was preparing to attack the castle from the land side.

All day long the boats plied back and forth, apparently leaving men and returning empty to the ships.   Expecting a heavy assault, the Spaniards moved their best guns and a greater part of their garrison to that side of the castle which faced the land, and thus left the water side comparatively harmless.

As soon as night came on, the pirates weighed anchor, and by the light of the moon, without setting their sails, they glided slowly out with the ebbing tide, which brought them down almost in sight of the castle.   They then spread their sails as quietly and with as great haste as possible.   The Spaniards saw them and opened fire, hastily moving their guns back to the water side; but a favorable wind blew the vessels past the danger point before the men in the castle could put their guns into position to do any great damage.

When Morgan was safely out of reach of the guns of the castle, he gave his prisoners a boat and sent them ashore, retaining, however, the hostages which he had demanded from the city of Gibraltar, because that place had not yet paid its ransom. Just as he was sailing away, Morgan fired seven great shells against the castle as a farewell message, but the Spaniards did not reply even with so much as a musket shot.

The day after their departure, the buccaneers were overtaken by a terrible tempest which forced them at first to cast anchor, but as the wind increased in force they were compelled to draw their anchor and to put out to sea. Here they were indeed in great danger, for if they were cast on shore, they certainly would receive no mercy from either the Spaniards or the Indians. Once more, however, fortune smiled on Captain Morgan, and after a day or two the wind ceased and the buccaneers went on their way rejoicing.

BRADDOCK'S DEFEAT

By Benjamin Franklin

NOTE.—When it became evident that the conflicting land-claims of the French and English in America would admit of no peaceable settlement, a convention of representatives from the colonies was called to consider a union of the colonies and to find ways of establishing friendly relations with the Indians, especially with the redoubtable Five Nations. This convention met at Albany in 1754, and adopted a plan of union which had been drawn up by Franklin. However, the plan, when submitted to the colonies and to the British government, pleased no one. The colonies rejected it because it gave too much power to the king, the king because it gave too much power to the colonies. Franklin's own account of what followed is here given:

THE British government, not choosing to permit the union of the colonies as proposed at Albany, and to trust that union with their defence, lest they should thereby grow too military and feel their own strength, suspicions and jealousies at this time being entertained of them, sent over General Braddock with two regiments of regular English troops for that purpose. He landed at Alexandria, in Virginia, and thence marched to Fredericktown, in Maryland, where he halted for carriages. Our Assembly apprehending, from some information, that he had conceived violent prejudices against them, as averse

379

to the service, wished me to wait upon him, not as from them, but as postmaster-general, under the guise of proposing to settle with him the mode of conducting with most celerity and certainty the despatches between him and the governors of the several provinces, with whom he must necessarily have continual correspondence, and of which they proposed to pay the expense. My son accompanied me on this journey.

We found the general at Fredericktown, waiting impatiently for the return of those he had sent through the back parts of Maryland and Virginia to collect wagons. I stayed with him several days, dined with him daily, and had full opportunity of removing all his prejudices, by the information of what the Assembly had before his arrival actually done, and were still willing to do, to facilitate his operations. When I was about to depart, the returns of wagons to be obtained were brought in, by which it appeared that they amounted only to twenty-five, and not all of those were in serviceable condition. The general and all the officers were surprised, declared the expedition was then at an end, being impossible, and exclaimed against the ministers for ignorantly landing them in a country destitute of the means of conveying their stores, baggage, etc., not less than one hundred and fifty wagons being necessary.

I happened to say I thought it was a pity they had not been landed rather in Pennsylvania, as in that country almost every farmer had his wagon. The general eagerly laid hold of my words, and said, "Then you, sir, who are a man of interest there, can probably procure them for us; and I beg

BENJAMIN FRANKLIN
1706–1790

you will undertake it." I asked what terms were
to be offered the owners of the wagons; and I was
desired to put on paper the terms that appeared to
me necessary. This I did, and they were agreed to,
and a commission and instructions accordingly prepared immediately. What those terms were will
appear in the advertisement I published as soon as
I arrived at Lancaster, which being, from the great
and sudden effect it produced, a piece of some curiosity, I shall insert it at length, as follows:

"ADVERTISEMENT
"LANCASTER, April 26, 1755.

"Whereas, one hundred and fifty wagons, with
four horses to each wagon, and fifteen hundred saddle or pack horses, are wanted for the service of his
Majesty's forces now about to rendezvous at Will's
Creek, and his excellency General Braddock having
been pleased to empower me to contract for the hire
of the same, I hereby give notice that I shall attend
for that purpose at Lancaster from this day to next
Wednesday evening, and at York from next Thursday morning till Friday evening, where I shall be
ready to agree for wagons and teams, or single
horses, on the following terms, viz.: 1. That there
shall be paid for each wagon, with four good horses
and a driver, fifteen shillings per diem; and for each
able horse with a pack-saddle or other saddle and
furniture, two shillings per diem; and for each able
horse without a saddle, eighteen pence per diem.
2. That pay commence from the time of their joining the forces at Will's Creek, which must be on or
before the 20th of May ensuing, and that a reasonable allowance be paid over and above for the time

necessary for their travelling to Will's Creek and home again after their discharge. 3. Each wagon and team, and every saddle or pack horse, is to be valued by indifferent persons chosen between me and the owner; and in case of the loss of any wagon, team, or other horse in the service, the price according to such valuation is to be allowed and paid. 4. Seven days' pay is to be advanced and paid in hand by me to the owner of each wagon and team or horse, at the time of contracting, if required, and the remainder to be paid by General Braddock, or by the paymaster of the army, at the time of their discharge, or from time to time, as it shall be demanded. 5. No drivers of wagons, or persons taking care of the hired horses, are on any account to be called upon to do the duty of soldiers, or be otherwise employed than in conducting or taking care of their carriages or horses. 6. All oats, Indian corn, or other forage that wagons or horses bring to the camp, more than is necessary for the subsistence of the horses, is to be taken for the use of the army, and a reasonable price paid for the same.

"Note.—My son, William Franklin, is empowered to enter into like contracts with any person in Cumberland County.   B. FRANKLIN."

"To the Inhabitants of the Counties of Lancaster, York, and Cumberland

"FRIENDS AND COUNTRYMEN—Being occasionally at the camp at Frederick a few days since, I found the general and officers extremely exasperated on account of their not being supplied with horses and carriages, which had been expected from this province, as most able to furnish them; but, through the dissensions between our governor and Assembly, money had not been provided, nor any steps taken for that purpose.

"It was proposed to send an armed force immediately into these counties, to seize as many of the best carriages and horses as should be wanted, and compel as many persons into the service as would be necessary to drive and take care of them.

"I apprehend that the progress of British soldiers through these counties on such an occasion, especially considering the temper they are in, and their resentment against us, would be attended with many and great inconveniences to the inhabitants, and therefore more willingly took the trouble of trying first what might be done by fair and equitable means.

The people of these back counties have lately complained to the Assembly that a sufficient currency was wanting; you have an opportunity of receiving and dividing among you a very considerable sum; for, if the service of this expedition should continue, as it is more than probable it will, for one hundred and twenty days, the hire of these wagons and horses will amount to upward of thirty thousand pounds, which will be paid you in silver and gold of the king's money.

"The service will be light and easy, for the army will scarce march above twelve miles per day, and the wagons and baggage horses, as they carry those things that are absolutely necessary to the welfare of the army, must march with the army, and no faster; and are, for the army's sake, always placed where they can be most secure, whether in a march or in a camp.

"If you are really, as I believe you are, good and loyal subjects to his majesty, you may now do a most acceptable service, and make it easy to yourselves; for three or four of such as can not separately spare from the business of their plantations a wagon and four horses and a driver, may do it together, one furnishing the wagon, another one or two horses, and another the driver, and divide the pay proportionately between you; but if you do not this service to your king and country voluntarily, when such good pay and reasonable terms are offered to you, your loyalty will be strongly suspected.

The king's business must be done; so many brave troops, come so far for your defence, must not stand idle through your backwardness to do what may be reasonably expected from you; wagons and horses must be had; violent measures will probably be used, and you will be left to seek a recompense where you can find it, and your case, perhaps, be little pitied or regarded.

"I have no particular interest in this affair, as, except the satisfaction of endeavoring to do good, I shall have only my labor for my pains.

If this method of obtaining the wagons and horses is not likely to succeed, I am obliged to send word to the general in fourteen days; and I suppose Sir John St. Clair, the hussar, with a body of soldiers, will immediately enter the province for the purpose, which I shall be sorry to hear, because I am very sincerely and truly

Your friend and well-wisher,
"B. FRANKLIN."

I received of the general about eight hundred pounds to be disbursed in advance-money to the wagon owners, etc.; but that sum being insufficient, I advanced upward of two hundred pounds more, and in two weeks the one hundred and fifty wagons, with two hundred and fifty-nine carrying horses, were on their march for the camp. The advertisement promised payment according to the valuation, in case any wagon or horse should be lost. The owners, however, alleging they did not know General Braddock, or what dependence might be had on his promise, insisted on my bond for the performance, which I accordingly gave them.

While I was at the camp, supping one evening with the officers of Colonel Dunbar's regiment, he represented to me his concern for the subalterns, who, he said, were generally not in affluence, and could ill afford, in this dear country, to lay in the stores that might be necessary in so long a march, through a wilderness, where nothing was to be purchased.

I commiserated their case, and resolved to endeavor procuring them some relief. I said nothing, however, to him of my intention, but wrote the next morning to the committee of the Assembly, who had the disposition of some public money, warmly recommending the case of these officers to their consideration, and proposing that a present should be sent them of necessaries and refreshments. My son, who had some experience of a camp life, and of its wants, drew up a list for me, which I enclosed in my letter. The committee approved, and used such diligence that, conducted by my son, the stores arrived at the camp as soon as the wagons. They consisted of twenty parcels, each containing—

6 lbs. loaf sugar.

6 lbs. good Muscovado ditto.

1 lb. good green tea.

1 lb. good bohea ditto.

6 lbs. good ground coffee.

6 lbs. chocolate.

1-2 lb. pepper.

1-2 cwt. best white biscuit.

1 quart best white wine vinegar.

1 Gloucester cheese.

1 keg containing 20 lbs. good butter.

2 doz. old Madeira wine.

2 gallons Jamaica spirits.

1 bottle flour of mustard.

2 well-cured hams.

1-2 dozen dried tongues.

6 lbs. rice.

6 lbs. raisins.

These twenty parcels, well packed, were placed on as many horses, each parcel, with the horse, being intended as a present for one officer. They were very thankfully received, and the kindness acknowledged by letters to me from the colonels of both regiments, in the most grateful terms. The general, too, was highly satisfied with my conduct in procuring him the wagons, etc., and readily paid my account of disbursements, thanking me repeatedly, and requesting my further assistance in sending provisions after him. I undertook this also, and was busily employed in it till we heard of his defeat, advancing for the service of my own money upward of one thousand pounds sterling, of which I sent him an account. It came to his hands, luckily for me, a few days before the battle, and he returned me immediately an order on the paymaster for the round sum of one thousand pounds, leaving the remainder to the next account. I consider this payment as good luck, having never been able to obtain that remainder, of which more hereafter.

This general was, I think, a brave man, and might probably have made a figure as a good officer in some European war. But he had too much self-confidence, too high an opinion of the validity of regular troops, and too mean a one of both Americans and Indians. George Croghan, our Indian interpreter, joined him on his march with one hundred of those people, who might have been of great use to his army as guides, scouts, etc., if he had treated them kindly; but he slighted and neglected them, and they gradually left him.

In conversation with him one day, he was giving me some account of his intended progress. "After taking Fort Duquesne," says he, "I am to proceed to Niagara; and, having taken that, to Frontenac, if the season will allow time; and I suppose it will, for Duquesne can hardly detain me above three or four days; and then I see nothing that can obstruct my march to Niagara." Having before resolved in my mind the long line his army must make in their march by a very narrow road, to be cut for them through the woods and bushes, and also what I had read of a former defeat of fifteen hundred French, who invaded the Iroquois country, I had conceived some doubts and some fears for the event of the campaign. But I ventured only to say, "To be sure, sir, if you arrive well before Duquesne, with these fine troops, so well provided with artillery, that place not yet completely fortified, and as we hear with no very strong garrison, can probably make but a short resistance. The only danger I apprehend of obstruction to your march is from ambuscades of Indians, who, by constant practice, are dexterous in laying and executing them; and the slender line, near four miles long, which your army must make, may expose it to be attacked by surprise in its flanks, and to be cut like a thread into several

ON THE MARCH

pieces, which, from their distance, cannot come up in time to support each other."

He smiled at my ignorance, and replied, "These savages may, indeed, be a formidable enemy to your raw American militia, but upon the king's regular and disciplined troops, sir, it is impossible they should make any impression." I was conscious of an impropriety in my disputing with a military man in matters of his profession, and said no more. The enemy, however, did not take the advantage of his

army which I apprehended its long line of march
exposed it to, but let it advance without interruption
till within nine miles of the place; and then,
when more in a body (for it had just passed a river,
where the front had halted till all were come over),

THE AMBUSH

and in a more open part of the woods than any it
had passed, attacked its advanced guard by a heavy
fire from behind trees and bushes, which was the
first intelligence the general had of an enemy's being
near him. This guard being disordered, the general
hurried the troops up to their assistance, which was
done in great confusion, through wagons, baggage,
and cattle; and presently the fire came upon their
flank; the officers, being on horseback, were more
easily distinguished, picked out as marks, and fell

very fast; and the soldiers were crowded together in a huddle, having or hearing no orders, and standing to be shot at till two-thirds of them were killed; and then, being seized with a panic, the whole fled with precipitation.

The wagoners took each a horse out of his team and scampered; their example was immediately followed by others; so that all the wagons, provisions, artillery, and stores were left to the enemy. The general, being wounded, was brought off with difficulty; his secretary, Mr. Shirley, was killed by his side; and out of eighty-six officers, sixty-three were killed or wounded, and seven hundred and fourteen men killed out of eleven hundred. These eleven hundred had been picked men from the whole army; the rest had been left behind with Colonel Dunbar, who was to follow with the heavier part of the stores, provisions, and baggage. The flyers, not being pursued, arrived at Dunbar's camp, and the panic they brought with them instantly seized him and all his people; and, though he had now above one thousand men, and the enemy who had beaten Braddock did not at most exceed four hundred Indians and French together, instead of proceeding, and endeavoring to recover some of the lost honor, he ordered all the stores, ammunition, etc., to be destroyed, that he might have more horses to assist his flight toward the settlements, and less lumber to remove. He was there met with requests from the governors of Virginia, Maryland, and Pennsylvania, that he would post his troops on the frontiers, so as to afford some protection to the inhabitants; but he continued his hasty march through all the country, not thinking himself safe till he arrived at Phila-

delphia, where the inhabitants could protect him.
This whole transaction gave us Americans the first
suspicion that our exalted ideas of the prowess of
British regulars had not been well founded.

In their first march, too, from their landing till
they got beyond the settlements, they had plundered and stripped the inhabitants, totally ruining
some poor families, besides insulting, abusing, and
confining the people if they remonstrated. This
was enough to put us out of conceit of such defend-
ers, if we had really wanted any. How different
was the conduct of our French friends in 1781, who,
during a march through the most inhabited part of
our country from Rhode Island to Virginia, near
seven hundred miles, occasioned not the smallest
complaint for the loss of a pig, a chicken, or even an
apple.

Captain Orme, who was one of the general's aides-
de-camp, and, being grievously wounded, was
brought off with him, and continued with him to
his death, which happened in a few days, told me
that he was totally silent all day, and at night only
said, *"Who would have thought it?"* That he was
silent again the following day, saying only at last,
*"We shall better know how to deal with them
another time;"* and died in a few minutes after.

The secretary's papers, with all the general's
orders, instructions, and correspondence, falling
into the enemy's hands, they selected and translated into French a number of the articles, which
they printed, to prove the hostile intentions of the
British court before the declaration of war. Among
these I saw some letters of the general to the ministry, speaking highly of the great service I had

rendered the army, and recommending me to their notice. David Hume, too, who was some years after secretary to Lord Hertford, when minister in France, and afterward to General Conway, when secretary of state, told me he had seen among the papers in that office, letters from Braddock highly recommending me. But the expedition having been unfortunate, my service, it seems, was not thought of much value, for these recommendations were never of any use to me.

As to rewards from himself, I asked only one, which was that he would give orders to his officers not to enlist any more of our bought servants, and that he would discharge such as had been already enlisted. This he readily granted, and several were accordingly returned to their masters, on my application. Dunbar, when the command devolved on him, was not so generous. He being at Philadelphia, on his retreat, or rather flight, I applied to him for the discharge of the servants of three poor farmers of Lancaster county that he had enlisted, reminding him of the late general's orders on that head. He promised me that, if the masters would come to him at Trenton, where he should be in a few days on his march to New York, he would there deliver their men to them. They accordingly were at the expense and trouble of going to Trenton, and there he refused to perform his promise, to their great loss and disappointment.

As soon as the loss of the wagons and horses was generally known, all the owners came upon me for the valuation which I had given bond to pay. Their demands gave me a great deal of trouble, my acquainting them that the money was ready in the paymaster's hands, but that orders for paying it must first be obtained from General Shirley, and my assuring them that I had applied to that general by letter, but he being at a distance, an answer could not soon be received, and they must have patience; all this was not sufficient to satisfy, and some began to sue me. General Shirley at length relieved me from this terrible situation by appointing commissioners to examine the claims, and ordering payment. They amounted to nearly twenty thousand pounds, which to pay would have ruined me.

Before we had the news of this defeat, the two Doctors Bond came to me with a subscription paper for raising money to defray the expense of a grand firework, which it was intended to exhibit at a rejoicing on receipt of the news of our taking Fort Duquesne. I looked grave, and said it would, I thought, be time enough to prepare for the rejoicing when we knew we should have occasion to rejoice. They seemed surprised that I did not immediately comply with their proposal. "Why . . . !" says one of them, "you surely don't suppose that the fort will not be taken?" "I don't know that it will not be taken, but I know that the events of war are subject to great uncertainty." I gave them the reasons of my doubting; the subscription was dropped, and the projectors thereby missed the mortification they would have undergone if the firework had been prepared. Dr. Bond, on some other occasion afterward, said that he did not like Franklin's forebodings.

READING HISTORY

IVELY or exciting stories are so interesting that we are inclined to read too many of them, and to read them too carelessly. By so doing, we fail to get the highest pleasure reading can give, and never receive the great benefit that is ours for the taking. If we let our arms rest idle for a long time, they become weak and useless; if a boy takes no exercise he cannot expect to be a strong man. So, if he reads nothing that makes him exert his mind, he becomes a weakling in intellect and never feels the pure delight that the man has who can read in a masterful way a masterly selection.

As a matter of fact, history when well written is as fascinating as any story that ever was penned, and it has the merit of being true. Sometimes it is a little harder to read than the light things that are so numerously given us by magazines and story books, but no one shuns hard work where it yields pleasure. A boy will play football or tramp all day with a gun over his shoulder, and not think twice about the hard work he is doing. Reading history bears about the same relation to reading mild love stories and overdrawn adventures that football or skating bears to stringing beads.

Not all history is hard to read; in some of it the interest lies so close to the surface that it grips us with the first glance. Such is the kind we read in the beginning. The adventures of King Arthur, the Cid, Robin Hood, and other half mythical heroes are history in the making—the history that grew up when the world was young, and its great men were something like overgrown boys. That is why we who have boyish hearts like to read about them. Then Robert the Bruce, Cæsar and Alexander are more like the men of to-day and appeal a little more strongly as we get more mature. And finally we have Washington, Lincoln, Lee and Grant as men nearer our own time, whose lives and deeds require our careful thought and our serious study, because they had to contend with the same things and overcome the same obstacles that confront us.

There is really no use in trying to tell just how and in what way history becomes interesting, and nobody cares to read a long article about history. What we older people would wish is merely this: that our young friends should begin to read history and so find out for themselves just how fascinating it is. We can perhaps give a word or two of warning that may save much hard work and many discouragements. Macaulay, Gibbon, Hume and others are great men, and in the tomes they have written are pages of exciting, stimulating narrative; yet one must read so many pages of heavy matter to find the interesting things that it is not worth the time and exertion a young person would need to give. On the other hand, there are writers like Parkman and Prescott who are always readable and entertaining.

The best way to learn to like history is to begin with such readable things as are put into these volumes, and then follow any line of interest that is discovered.

Franklin's description of Braddock's defeat is interesting in itself, and it calls attention to the French and Indian War and to the wonderful career of Franklin himself. These are lines of interest that you may follow out in histories or in works of reference.

THE AMERICAN FLAG

By JOSEPH RODMAN DRAKE

WHEN Freedom, from her mountain height,
  Unfurled her standard to the air,
She tore the azure robe of night,
  And set the stars of glory there!
She mingled with its gorgeous dyes
The milky baldric of the skies,
And striped its pure, celestial white
With streakings of the morning light,
Then, from his mansion in the sun,
She called her eagle bearer down,
And gave into his mighty hand
The symbol of her chosen land!

Majestic monarch of the cloud!
  Who rear'st aloft thy regal form,
To hear the tempest-trumpings loud,
And see the lightning lances driven,
  When strive the warriors of the storm,
And rolls the thunder-drum of heaven,—
Child of the Sun! to thee 't is given
  To guard the banner of the free,
To hover in the sulphur smoke,
To ward away the battle-stroke,

And bid its blendings shine afar,
Like rainbows on the cloud of war,
  The harbingers of victory!

Flag of the brave! thy folds shall fly,
The sign of hope and triumph high!
When speaks the signal-trumpet tone,
And the long line comes gleaming on,
Ere yet the life-blood, warm and wet,
Has dimmed the glistening bayonet,
Each soldier's eye shall brightly turn
To where thy sky-born glories burn,
And, as his springing steps advance,
Catch war and vengeance from the glance.
And when the cannon-mouthings loud
Heave in wild wreaths the battle shroud,
And gory sabres rise and fall
Like shoots of flame on midnight's pall,
Then shall thy meteor glances glow,
  And cowering foes shall shrink beneath
Each gallant arm that strikes below
  That lovely messenger of death.

Flag of the seas! on ocean wave
Thy stars shall glitter o'er the brave;
When death, careering on the gale,
Sweeps darkly round the bellied sail,
And frighted waves rush wildly back
Before the broadside's reeling rack,
Each dying wanderer of the sea
Shall look at once to heaven and thee,
And smile to see thy splendors fly
In triumph o'er his closing eye.

Flag of the free heart's hope and home,
  By angel hands to valor given,
Thy stars have lit the welkin dome,
  And all thy hues were born in heaven.
Forever float that standard sheet!
  Where breathes the foe but falls before us
With Freedom's soil beneath our feet,
  And Freedom's banner streaming o'er us?

This is a poem that may need a little explanation if every one is to appreciate it.

How fancifully the poet tells of the origin of the flag in the first stanza! The blue field and the stars are taken from the sky, and the white from the milky way which stretches like a broad scarf or baldric across the heavens. The red is from the first red streaks that in the morning flash across the eastern skies to herald the rising sun. The eagle, our national bird who supports the shield in our coat of arms, had by the old legends the power to fly full in the face of the sun, and to shield its eyes from the blaze was gifted with a third eyelid. In the talons of this lordly bird Freedom placed our chosen banner.

The second stanza continues the tribute to the eagle. To this regal bird it is given to fling high among the clouds and smoke of battle our brilliant banner, whose bright colors like the rainbow signify victory and peace—the flag of victory, the bow of promise.

The remainder of the lines are so clear in their meaning and so smooth in their structure that they stir our blood with patriotic fire.

BATTLE HYMN OF THE REPUBLIC

By Julia Ward Howe

MINE eyes have seen the glory of the coming of
      the Lord:
He is trampling out the vintage where the grapes
      of wrath are stored;
He hath loosed the fateful lightning of his terrible
      swift sword.
      His truth is marching on.

I have seen him in the watch-fires of a hundred
      circling camps;
They have builded him an altar in the evening
      dews and damps;
I have read his righteous sentence by the dim and
      flaring lamps.
      His day is marching on.

I have read a fiery gospel, writ in burnished rows
      of steel:
"As ye deal with my contemners, so with you my
      grace shall deal;
Let the Hero, born of woman, crush the serpent
      with his heel,
      Since God is marching on."

He has sounded forth the trumpet that shall never
      call retreat;
He is sifting out the hearts of men before his judg-
      ment-seat:
O, be swift, my soul, to answer him! be jubilant,
      my feet!
      Our God is marching on.

In the beauty of the lilies Christ was born across
    the sea,
With a glory in his bosom that transfigures you and
    me;
As he died to make men holy, let us die to make
    men free,
    While God is marching on.

" 'STONEWALL' JACKSON'S WAY"

By J. W. Palmer

Note.—Thomas J. Jackson, the great Confederate general, better known as "Stonewall" Jackson, was loved and admired by his men not only for his military ability, but for his personal virtues, and even for his personal peculiarities as well. He was a deeply religious man, and never began a battle without prayer or failed to give public thanks to God for a victory.

While he believed that the people through whose land he was passing, and indeed all non-combatants, should be guarded as far as possible from the evil results of war, he showed no compassion for the enemies sent against him, and pushed the battle against them with all his might. His death in 1863 was a great loss to the Confederate cause.

COME, stack arms, men! Pile on the rails,
    Stir up the camp-fire bright;
No matter if the canteen fails,
    We'll make a roaring night.
Here Shenandoah brawls along,
There burly Blue Ridge echoes strong,

THOMAS J. ("STONEWALL") JACKSON
1821 1863

To swell the brigade's rousing song
  Of " 'Stonewall' Jackson's way."

We see him now—the old slouched hat
  Cocked o'er his eye askew,
The shrewd, dry smile, the speech so pat,
  So calm, so blunt, so true.
The "Blue-Light Elder" knows 'em well;
Says he, "That's Banks[1]—he's fond of shell,
Lord save his soul! We'll give him"—well,
  That's " 'Stonewall' Jackson's way."

Silence! ground arms! kneel all! caps off!
  "Old Blue-Light's" going to pray.
Strangle the fool that dares to scoff!
  Attention! it's his way.
Appealing from his native sod,
In forma pauperis[2] to God—
"Lay bare thine arm, stretch forth thy rod!
  Amen!" That's " 'Stonewall's' way."

He's in the saddle now—Fall in!
  Steady! the whole brigade!
Hill's[3] at the ford, cut off—we'll win
  His way out, ball and blade!
What matter if our shoes are worn?
What matter if our feet are torn?
"Quick-step! we're with him before dawn!"
  That's " 'Stonewall' Jackson's way."

1. Nathaniel Prentiss Banks was a Federal general who was pitted against Jackson in several engagements.

2. *In forma pauperis* is a Latin legal expression, meaning *as a poor man.*

3. Ambrose P. Hill was a prominent Confederate general.

The sun's bright lances rout the mists
   Of morning, and, by George!
Here's Longstreet[4] struggling in the lists,
   Hemmed in an ugly gorge.
Pope[5] and his Yankees, whipped before,—
"Bay'nets and grape!" hear "Stonewall" roar;
"Charge, Stuart![6] Pay off Ashby's[7] score!"
In " 'Stonewall' Jackson's way."

Ah! maiden, wait and watch and yearn
   For news of "Stonewall's" band!
Ah! widow, read with eyes that burn
   That ring upon thy hand.
Ah! wife, sew on, pray on, hope on!
Thy life shall not be all forlorn;
The foe had better ne'er been born
   That gets in " 'Stonewall's' way."

4. James Longstreet was one of the most distinguished of the Confederate generals.

5. John Pope, the Federal general, was badly defeated by Jackson and Robert E. Lee in the second battle of Bull Run, August 29 and 30, 1862.

6. James E. B. Stuart, a cavalry leader in the Confederate army, took a prominent part in the second battle of Bull Run, and was with Jackson in other engagements.

7. Turner Ashby, a Confederate general, had greatly aided Jackson by covering the latter's retreat before General Banks. He was killed in a skirmish in June, 1862.

BARON MUNCHAUSEN

INTRODUCTION

OLLECTED in a book called *The Travels of Baron Munchausen* is a series of the most extravagant stories imaginable. No one can possibly believe them to be true, and yet when we are reading them they do not appear so absurdly ridiculous as they seem afterward when we think of them. The book is said to have been written by a German named Rudolph Erich Raspe, but we cannot be sure of it, as there are no proofs. It is said, too, that there was a German officer, a Baron Hieronymous Karl Friedrich Munchausen who lived in the early part of the eighteenth century and who told such marvelous stories that he was very popular among his fellow officers and that his stories have been collected in a book. The book appeared first in 1793, and some have believed that it was written to ridicule the books of travel which had appeared from time to time, some of which contained narratives not much less incredible than some of the Baron's fanciful tales. It is probable, however, that the book is merely a collection of very old stories with many newer ones included among them, and that it was written solely for entertainment.

The Baron always insists upon the strict truthfulness and accuracy of his stories and grows quite indignant when his veracity is questioned. To verify his words he printed the following notice at the beginning of his book:

TO THE PUBLIC:—Having heard, for the first time, that my adventures have been doubted, and looked upon as jokes, I feel bound to come forward, and vindicate my character *for veracity,* by paying three shillings at the Mansion House of this great city for the affidavits hereto appended.

This I have been forced into in regard of my own honor, although I have retired for many years from public and private life; and I hope that this, my last edition, will place me in a proper light with my readers.

AT THE CITY OF LONDON, ENGLAND

We, the undersigned, as true believers in the *profit,* do most solemnly affirm, that all the adventures of our friend Baron Munchausen, in whatever country they may *lie,* are positive and simple facts. *And,* as we have been believed, whose adventures are tenfold more wonderful, *so* do we hope all true believers will give him their full faith and credence.

GULLIVER.   +
SINBAD.   +
ALADDIN.   +

Sworn at the Mansion House 9th November last, in the absence of the Lord Mayor.

JOHN *(the Porter).*

In this volume a few of his most amusing stories are printed—all, perhaps, that it is worth while to read.

I

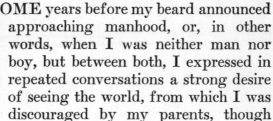OME years before my beard announced approaching manhood, or, in other words, when I was neither man nor boy, but between both, I expressed in repeated conversations a strong desire of seeing the world, from which I was discouraged by my parents, though my father had been no inconsiderable traveler himself, as will appear before I have reached the end of my singular, and, I may add, interesting adventures. A cousin, by my mother's side, took a liking to me, often said I was a fine, forward youth, and was much inclined to gratify my curiosity. His eloquence had more effect than mine, for my father consented to my accompanying him in a voyage to the island of Ceylon, where his uncle had resided as governor many years.

We sailed from Amsterdam with despatches from their High Mightinesses the States of Holland. The only circumstance which happened on our voyage worth relating was the wonderful effects of a storm, which had torn up by the roots a great number of trees of enormous bulk and height, in an island where we lay at anchor to take in wood and water; some of these trees weighed many tons, yet they were carried by the wind so amazingly high that they appeared like the feathers of small birds floating in the air, for they were at least five miles above the earth: however, as soon as the storm subsided they all fell perpendicularly into their respective places, and took root again, except the largest, which happened, when it was blown into

the air, to have a man and his wife, a very honest
old couple, upon its branches, gathering cucumbers
(in this part of the globe that useful vegetable
grows upon trees) : the weight of this couple, as the
tree descended, overbalanced the trunk, and brought
it down in a horizontal position: it fell upon the
chief man of the island, and killed him on the spot;
he had quitted his house in the storm, under an
apprehension of its falling upon him, and was returning through his own garden when this fortunate
accident happened. The word fortunate here re-
quires some explanation. This chief was a man
of a very avaricious and oppressive disposition, and
though he had no family, the natives of the island
were half starved by his oppressive and infamous
impositions.

The very goods which he had thus taken from
them were spoiling in his stores, while the poor
wretches from whom they were plundered were
pining in poverty. Though the destruction of this
tyrant was accidental, the people chose the cucum-
ber-gatherers for their governors, as a mark of their
gratitude for destroying, though accidentally, their
late tyrant.

After we had repaired the damages we sustained
in this remarkable storm, and taken leave of the
new governor and his lady, we sailed with a fair
wind for the object of our voyage.

In about six weeks we arrived at Ceylon, where
we were received with great marks of friendship and
true politeness. The following singular adventures
may not prove unentertaining.

After we had resided at Ceylon about a fortnight I accompanied one of the governor's brothers

upon a shooting party. He was a strong, athletic man, and being used to that climate (for he had resided there some years), he bore the violent heat of the sun much better than I could; in our excursion he had made a considerable progress through a thick wood when I was only at the entrance.

Near the banks of a large piece of water, which had engaged my attention, I thought I heard a rustling noise behind; on turning about I was almost petrified (as who would not be?) at the sight of a lion, which was evidently approaching with the intention of satisfying his appetite with my poor carcass, and that without asking my consent. What was to be done in this horrible dilemma? I had not even a moment for reflection; my piece was only charged with swan-shot, and I had no other about me; however, though I could have no idea of killing such an animal with that weak kind of ammunition, yet I had some hopes of frightening him by the report, and perhaps of wounding him also. I immediately let fly, without waiting till he was within reach, and the report did but enrage him, for he now quickened his pace, and seemed to approach me full speed: I attempted to escape, but that only added (if an addition could be made) to my distress; for the moment I turned about, I found a large crocodile, with his mouth extended almost ready to receive me. On my right hand was the piece of water before mentioned, and on my left a deep precipice, said to have, as I have since learned, a receptacle at the bottom for venomous creatures; in short, I gave myself up as lost, for the lion was now upon his hind legs, just in the act of seizing me; I fell involuntarily to the ground with fear, and, as it afterwards appeared, he sprang over me. I lay some time in a situation which no language can describe, expecting to feel his teeth or talons in some part of me every moment. After waiting in this prostrate situation a few seconds I heard a

THE LION HAD JUMPED INTO THE CROCODILE'S MOUTH

violent but unusual noise, different from any sound that had ever before assailed my ears; nor is it at all to be wondered at, when I inform you from whence it proceeded: after listening for some time I ventured to raise my head and look round, when, to my unspeakable joy, I perceived the lion had, by the eagerness with which he sprung at me, jumped forward as I fell, into the crocodile's mouth! which, as before observed, was wide open; the head of the one stuck in the throat of the other! and they were struggling to extricate themselves! I fortunately recollected my hunting knife, which was by my side; with this instrument I severed the lion's head at one blow, and the body fell at my feet! I then, with the butt end of my fowling piece, rammed the head farther into the throat of the crocodile, and destroyed him by suffocation, for he could neither gorge nor eject it.

Soon after I had thus gained a complete victory over my two powerful adversaries, my companion arrived in search of me; for finding I did not follow him into the wood, he returned, apprehending I had lost my way, or met with some accident.

After mutual congratulations we measured the crocodile, which was just forty feet in length.

As soon as we had related this extraordinary adventure to the governor, he sent a wagon and servants who brought home the two carcasses. The lion's skin was properly preserved with the hair on, after which it was made into tobacco pouches and presented by me, upon our return to Holland, to the burgomasters, who in return requested my acceptance of a thousand ducats.

The skin of the crocodile was stuffed in the usual manner, and makes a capital article in their public museum at Amsterdam, where the exhibitor relates the whole story to each spectator, with such additions as he thinks proper.

II

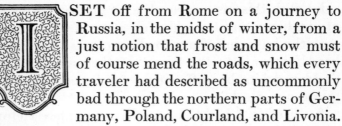

SET off from Rome on a journey to Russia, in the midst of winter, from a just notion that frost and snow must of course mend the roads, which every traveler had described as uncommonly bad through the northern parts of Germany, Poland, Courland, and Livonia. I went on horseback, as the most convenient manner of traveling: I was but lightly clothed, and of this I felt the inconvenience the more I advanced northeast. What must not a poor old man have suffered in that severe weather and climate, whom I saw on a bleak common in Poland, lying on the road, helpless, shivering and hardly having wherewithal to cover his nakedness? I pitied the poor soul: though I felt the severity of the air myself, I threw my mantle over him, and immediately I heard a voice from the heavens blessing me for that piece of charity, saying, "You will be rewarded, my son, for this in time."

I went on: night and darkness overtook me. No village was to be seen. The country was covered with snow, and I was unacquainted with the road.

Tired, I alighted and fastened my horse to something like a pointed stump of a tree, which appeared above the snow; for the sake of safety I placed my pistols under my arm, and lay down on the snow, where I slept so soundly that I did not open my eyes till full daylight. It is not easy to conceive my astonishment to find myself in the midst of a village, lying in a churchyard; nor was my horse to be seen, but I heard him soon after neigh somewhere above me. On looking upwards I beheld him hanging by his bridle to the weathercock of the steeple. Matters were now very plain to me: the village had been covered with snow over night; a sudden change of weather had taken place; I had sunk down to the churchyard whilst asleep, gently, and in the same proportion as the snow had melted away; and what in the dark I had taken to be a stump of a little tree appearing above the snow, to which I had tied my horse, proved to have been the cross or weathercock of the steeple!

Without long consideration, I took one of my pistols, shot the bridle in two, brought down the horse, and proceeded on my journey.

III

OR several months (as it was some time before I could obtain a commission in the army) I was perfectly at liberty to sport away my time and money in the most gentlemanlike manner. You may easily imagine that I spent much of both out of town with such gallant fellows as knew how to make the most of an open forest country. The very recollection of those amusements gives me fresh spirits, and creates a warm wish for a repetition of them. One morning I saw, through the windows of my bedroom, that a large pond not far off was covered with wild ducks. In an instant I took my gun from the corner, ran downstairs, and out of the house in such a hurry that I imprudently struck my face against the doorpost. Fire flew out of my eyes, but it did not prevent my intention; I soon came within shot,

when, leveling my piece, I observed to my sorrow, that even the flint had sprung from the cock by the violence of the shock I had just received. There was no time to be lost. I presently remembered the effect it had on my eyes, therefore opened the pan, leveled my piece against the wild fowls, and my fist against one of my eyes. A hearty blow drew sparks again; the shot went off, and I killed fifty brace of ducks, twenty widgeons, and three couple of teals.

IV

 I DARE say you have heard of the hunter and sportsman's saint and protector, Saint Hubert, and of the noble stag which appeared to him in the forest, with the holy cross between his antlers. I have paid my homage to that saint every year in good fellowship, and seen this stag a thousand times either painted in churches, or embroidered in the stars of his knights; so that, upon the honor and conscience of a good sportsman, I hardly know whether there may not have been formerly, or whether there are not such crossed stags even at this present day. But let me rather tell what I have seen myself. Having one day spent all my shot, I found myself unexpectedly in presence of a stately stag, looking at me as unconcernedly as if he had known of my empty pouches. I charged immediately with powder, and upon it a good handful of cherry-stones, for I had sucked the fruit as far as the hurry would permit. Thus I let fly at him, and hit him just on the middle of the forehead between

I BEHELD A NOBLE STAG

his antlers; it stunned him—he staggered—yet he
made off. A year or two after, being with a party
in the same forest, I beheld a noble stag with a fine
full-grown cherry tree above ten feet high between
his antlers. I immediately recollected my former
adventure, looked upon him as my property, and
brought him to the ground by one shot, which at

once gave me the haunch and cherry sauce; for the
tree was covered with the richest fruit, the like I
had never tasted before. Who knows but some
passionate holy sportsman, or sporting abbot or
bishop may have shot, planted and fixed the cross
between the antlers of Saint Hubert's stag, in a
manner similar to this?

V

REMEMBER with pleasure and tenderness a superb Lithuanian horse,
which no money could have bought.
He became mine by an accident, which
gave me an opportunity of showing my
horsemanship to a great advantage. I
was at Count Przobossky's noble
country seat in Lithuania, and remained with the
ladies at tea in the drawing-room, while the gentlemen were down in the yard to see a young horse of
blood which had just arrived from the stud. We
suddenly heard a noise of distress; I hastened
downstairs, and found the horse so unruly that nobody durst approach or mount him. The most
resolute horsemen stood dismayed and aghast; de-
spondency was expressed in every countenance,
when, in one leap, I was on his back, took him by
surprise, and worked him quite into gentleness and
obedience, with the best display of horsemanship I
was master of. Fully to show this to the ladies,
and save them unnecessary trouble, I forced him
to leap in at one of the open windows of the tea
room, walk round several times, pace, trot, and
gallop, and at last made him mount the tea table,
there to repeat his lessons in a pretty style of minia-

ture which was exceedingly pleasing to the ladies, for he performed them amazingly well, and did not break either cup or saucer. It placed me so high in their opinion, and so well in that of the noble lord, that, with his usual politeness, he begged I would accept of this young horse, and ride him to conquest and honor in the campaign against the Turks, which was soon to be opened, under the command of Count Munich.

We had very hot work once in the van of the army, when we drove the Turks into Oczakow. My spirited Lithuanian had almost brought me into a scrape: I had an advanced forepost, and saw the enemy coming against me in a cloud of dust, which left me rather uncertain about their actual numbers and real intentions: to wrap myself up in a similar cloud was common prudence, but would not have much advanced my knowledge, or answered the end for which I had been sent out; therefore I let my flankers on both wings spread to the right and left, and make what dust they could, and I myself led on straight upon the enemy, to have a nearer sight of them; in this I was gratified, for they stood and fought, till, for fear of my flankers, they began to move off rather disorderly. This was the moment to fall upon them with spirit; we broke them entirely—made a terrible havoc amongst them, and drove them not only back to a walled town in their rear, but even through it, contrary to our most sanguine expectation.

The swiftness of my Lithuanian enabled me to be foremost in the pursuit; and seeing the enemy fairly flying through the opposite gate, I thought it would be prudent to stop in the market place, to order the men to rendezvous. I stopped, gentlemen; but judge of my astonishment when in this market place I saw not one of my hussars about me! Are they scouring the other streets? or what is become of them? They could not be far off, and must, at all events, soon join me. In that expectation I walked my panting Lithuanian to a spring in this market place, and let him drink. He drank uncommonly, with an eagerness not to be satisfied, but natural enough; for when I looked round for my men, what should I see, gentlemen! the hind part of the poor creature—croup and legs—were missing, as if he had been cut in two, and the water ran out as it came in, without refreshing or doing him any good! How it could have happened was quite a mystery to me, till I returned with him to the town gate. There I saw that when I rushed in pell-mell with the flying enemy, they had dropped the portcullis (a heavy falling door, with sharp spikes at the bottom, let down suddenly to prevent the entrance of an enemy into a fortified town) unperceived by me, which had totally cut off his hind part, that still lay quivering on the outside of the gate. It would have been an irreparable loss, had not our farrier contrived to bring both parts together while hot. He sewed them up with sprigs and young shoots of laurels that were at hand; the wound healed, and, what could not have happened but to so glorious a horse, the sprigs took root in his body, grew up, and formed a bower over me; so that afterwards I could go upon many other expeditions in the shade of my own and my horse's laurels.

THE HIND PART OF THE POOR CREATURE WAS MISSING

VI

SUCCESS was not always with me. I had the misfortune to be overpowered by numbers, to be made prisoner of war; and, what is worse, but always usual among the Turks, to be sold for a slave. In that state of humiliation my daily task was not very hard and laborious, but rather singular and irksome. It was to drive the Sultan's bees every morning to their pasture grounds, to attend them all day long, and against night to drive them back to their hives. One evening I missed a bee, and soon observed that two bears had fallen upon her to tear her to pieces for the honey she carried. I had nothing like an offensive weapon in my hands but the silver hatchet, which is the badge of the Sultan's gardeners and farmers. I threw it at the robbers, with an intention to frighten them away, and set the poor bee at liberty; but, by an unlucky turn of my arm, it flew upwards, and continued rising till it reached the moon. How should I recover it? how fetch it down again? I recollected that Turkey-beans grow very quick, and run up to an astonishing height. I planted one immediately; it grew, and actually fastened itself to one of the moon's horns. I had no more to do now but to climb up by it into the moon, where I safely arrived, and had a troublesome piece of business before I could find my silver hatchet, in a place where everything has the brightness of silver; at last, however, I found it in a heap of chaff and chopped straw. I was now for returning: but, alas! the heat of the sun had dried up my

bean; it was totally useless for my descent; so I fell
to work and twisted me a rope of that chopped
straw, as long and as well as I could make it. This
I fastened to one of the moon's horns, and slid down
to the end of it. Here I held myself fast with the
left hand, and with the hatchet in my right, I cut
the long, now useless end of the upper part, which,
when tied to the lower end, brought me a good deal
lower: this repeated splicing and tying of the rope
did not improve its quality, or bring me down to the
Sultan's farm. I was four or five miles from the
earth at least when it broke; I fell to the ground
with such amazing violence that I found myself
stunned, and in a hole nine fathoms deep at least,
made by the weight of my body falling from so great
a height: I recovered, but knew not how to get out
again; however, I dug slopes or steps with my
finger-nails, and easily accomplished it.

Peace was soon after concluded with the Turks,
and gaining my liberty I left Saint Petersburg at
the time of that singular revolution, when the emperor in his cradle, his mother, the Duke of Bruns-
wick, her father, Field-Marshal Munich, and many
others were sent to Siberia. The winter was then
so uncommonly severe all over Europe that ever
since the sun seems to be frost-bitten. At my return
to this place I felt on the road greater inconveniences
than those I had experienced on my setting out.

I traveled post, and finding myself in a narrow
lane, bade the postilion give a signal with his horn,
that other travelers might not meet us in the narrow passage. He blew with all his might; but his
endeavors were in vain; he could not make the horn
sound, which was unaccountable, and rather un-

fortunate, for soon after we found ourselves in the presence of another coach coming the other way: there was no proceeding; however, I got out of my carriage, and being pretty strong, placed it, wheels and all, upon my head: I then jumped over a hedge about nine feet high (which, considering the weight of the coach, was rather difficult) into a field, and came out again by another jump into the road beyond the other carriage: I then went back for the horses, and placing one upon my head, and the other under my left arm, by the same means brought them to my coach, put to, and proceeded to an inn at the end of our stage. I should have told you that the horse under my arm was very spirited, and not above four years old; in making my second spring over the hedge, he expressed great dislike to that violent kind of motion by kicking and snorting; however, I confined his hind legs by putting them into my coat pocket. After we arrived at the inn my postilion and I refreshed ourselves; he hung his horn on a peg near the kitchen fire; I sat on the other side.

Suddenly we heard a *tereng! tereng! teng! teng!* We looked round, and now found the reason why the postilion had not been able to sound his horn; his tunes were frozen up in the horn, and came out now by thawing, plain enough, and much to the credit of the driver; so that the honest fellow entertained us for some time with a variety of tunes, without putting his mouth to the horn—The King of Prussia's March—Over the Hill and over the Dale—with many other favorite tunes; at length the thawing entertainment concluded, as I shall this short account of my Russian travels.

VII

EMBARKED at Portsmouth, in a first-rate English man-of-war, of one hundred guns, and fourteen hundred men, for North America. Nothing worth relating happened till we arrived within three hundred leagues of the river Saint Lawrence when the ship struck with amazing force against (as we supposed) a rock; however, upon heaving the lead, we could find no bottom, even with three hundred fathom. What made this circumstance the more wonderful, and indeed beyond all comprehension, was, that the violence of the shock was such that we lost our rudder, broke our bow-sprit in the middle, and split all our masts from top to bottom, two of which went by the board; a poor fellow, who was aloft, furling the main-sheet, was flung at least three leagues from the ship; but he fortunately saved his life by laying hold of the tail of a large sea-gull, who brought him back, and lodged him on the very spot from whence he was thrown. Another proof of the violence of the shock was the force with which the people between decks were driven against the floors above them; my head particularly was pressed into my stomach, where it continued some months before it recovered its natural situation. Whilst we were all in a state of astonishment at the general and unaccountable confusion in which we were involved, the whole was suddenly explained by the appearance of a large whale, who had been basking, asleep, within sixteen feet of the surface of the water. This animal was so much displeased with

the disturbance which our ship had given him, for
in our passage we had with our rudder scratched his
nose, that he beat in all the gallery and part of the
quarter deck with his tail, and almost at the same
instant took the main-sheet anchor, which was suspended, as it usually is, from the head, between his
teeth, and ran away with the ship, at least sixty
leagues, at the rate of twelve leagues an hour, when
fortunately the cable broke, and we lost both the
whale and the anchor.   However, upon our return
to Europe, some months after, we found the same
whale within a few leagues of the same spot, floating dead upon the water; it measured above half
a mile in length.   As we could take but a small
quantity of such a monstrous animal on board, we
got our boats out, and with much difficulty cut off
his head, where, to our great joy, we found the
anchor, and above forty fathom of the cable concealed on the left side of his mouth, just under his
tongue.   (Perhaps this was the cause of his death,
as that side of his tongue was much swelled, with
a great degree of inflammation.)   This was the only
extraordinary circumstance of this voyage.

VIII

E ALL remember Captain Phipp's
(now Lord Mulgrave) last voyage of
discovery to the north. I accompanied
the Captain, not as an officer, but a
private friend. When we arrived in a
high northern latitude I was viewing
the objects around me with the telescope, when I thought I saw two large white bears
in violent action upon a body of ice considerably

above the masts, and about half a league distant. I
immediately took my carbine, slung it across my
shoulder, and ascended the ice. When I arrived at
the top, the unevenness of the surface made my
approach to those animals troublesome and haz-
ardous beyond expression: sometimes hideous cav-
ities opposed me, which I was obliged to spring over;
in other parts the surface was as smooth as a mirror,
and I was continually falling: as I approached near
enough to reach them, I found they were only at
play. I immediately began to calculate the value of
their skins, for they were each as large as a well-fed
ox: unfortunately the very instant I was presenting
my carbine my right foot slipped, and I fell upon
my back, and the violence of the blow deprived me
totally of my senses for nearly half an hour; however, when I recovered, judge of my surprise at
finding one of those large animals I have just been
describing had turned me upon my face, and was
just laying hold of the waistband of my breeches,
which were then new and made of leather: he was
certainly going to carry me feet foremost, God
knows where, when I took this knife (showing a
large clasp knife) out of my side pocket, made a
chop at one of his hind feet, and cut off three of his
toes; he immediately let me drop, and roared most
horribly. I took up my carbine, and fired at him
as he ran off; he fell directly. The noise of the piece
roused several thousands of these white bears, who
were asleep upon the ice within half a mile of me;
they came immediately to the spot. There was no
time to be lost. A most fortunate thought arrived
in my pericranium just at that instant. I took
off the skin and head of the dead bear in half the

time that some people would be in skinning a rabbit, and wrapped myself in it, placing my own head directly under bruin's; the whole herd came round me immediately, and my apprehensions threw me into a most piteous situation to be sure: however, my scheme turned out a most admirable one for my own safety. They all came smelling, and evidently took me for a brother bruin: I wanted nothing but bulk to make an excellent counterfeit: however, I saw several cubs amongst them not much larger than myself. After they had all smelt me, and the body of their deceased companion, whose skin was now become my protector, we seemed very sociable, and I found I could mimic all their actions tolerably well; but at growling, roaring, and hugging, they were quite my masters. I began now to think how I might turn the general confidence which I had created amongst these animals to my advantage.

I had heard an old army surgeon say a wound in the spine was instant death. I now determined to try the experiment, and had again recourse to my knife, with which I struck the largest in the back of the neck, near the shoulders, but under great apprehensions, not doubting but the creature would, if he survived the stab, tear me to pieces. However, I was remarkably fortunate, for he fell dead at my feet without making the least noise. I was now resolved to demolish them every one in the same manner, which I accomplished without the least difficulty; for, although they saw their companions fall, they had no suspicion of either the cause or the effect. When they all lay dead before me, I felt myself a second Samson, having slain my thousands.

To make short of the story, I went back to the ship, and borrowed three parts of the crew to assist me in skinning them, and carrying the hams on board, which we did in a few hours, and loaded the ship with them. As to the other parts of the animals, they were thrown into the sea, though I doubt not but the whole would eat as well as the legs, were they properly cured.

IX

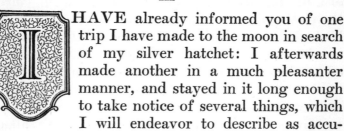HAVE already informed you of one trip I have made to the moon in search of my silver hatchet: I afterwards made another in a much pleasanter manner, and stayed in it long enough to take notice of several things, which I will endeavor to describe as accurately as my memory will permit.

I went on a voyage of discovery at the request of a distant relation, who had a strange notion that there were people to be found equal in magnitude to those described by Gulliver in the empire of Brobdingnag. For my part I always treated that account as fabulous; however, to oblige him, for he had made me his heir, I undertook it, and sailed for the South Seas, where we arrived without meeting with anything remarkable, except some flying men and women who were playing at leapfrog, and dancing minuets in the air.

On the eighteenth day, after we had passed the island of Otaheite, a hurricane blew our ship at least one thousand leagues above the surface of the water, and kept it at that height till a fresh gale arising filled the sails in every part, and onwards we traveled at a prodigious rate; thus we proceeded above the clouds for six weeks. At last we discovered a great land in the sky, like a shining island, round and bright, where, coming into a convenient harbor, we went on shore, and soon found it was inhabited. Below us we saw another earth, containing cities, trees, mountains, rivers, seas, etc., which we conjectured was this world, which we had left. Here we saw huge figures riding upon vultures of a prodigious size, and each of them having three heads. To form some idea of the magnitude of these birds, I must inform you that each of their wings is as wide and six times the length of the main-sheet of our vessel, which was about six hundred tons burden. Thus, instead of riding upon horses, as we do in this world, the inhabitants of the moon (for we now found we were in Madam Luna) fly about on these birds. The king, we found, was engaged in a war with the sun, and he offered me a commission, but I declined the honor his majesty intended me. Everything in *this* world is of extraordinary magnitude! a common flea being much larger than one of our sheep: in making war their principal weapons are radishes, which are used as darts: those who are wounded by them die immediately. Their shields are made of mushrooms, and their darts (when radishes are out of season) of the tops of asparagus. Some of the natives of the dog-star are to be seen here; commerce tempts them to ramble; and their faces are like large mastiffs', with their eyes near the lower end or tip of their noses: they have no eyelids, but cover their eyes with the end of their tongues when they go to sleep; they are generally twenty feet high. As to the natives of the moon; none of them are less in stature than thirty-six feet: they are not called the human species, but the cooking animals, for they all dress their food by fire, as we do, but lose no time at their meals, as they open their left side, and place the whole quantity at once in their stomach, then shut it again till the same day in the next month; for they never indulge themselves with food more than twelve times a year, or once a month. All but gluttons and epicures must prefer this method to ours.

There is but one sex either of the cooking or any other animals in the moon; they are all produced from trees of various sizes and foliage; that which produces the cooking animal, or human species, is much more beautiful than any of the others; it has large, straight boughs and flesh-colored leaves, and the fruit it produces are nuts or pods, with hard shells, at least two yards long; when they become ripe, which is known from their changing color, they are gathered with great care, and laid by as long as they think proper; when they choose to animate the seed of these nuts, they throw them into a large cauldron of boiling water, which opens the shells in a few hours, and out jumps the creature.

Nature forms their minds for different pursuits before they come into the world; from one shell comes forth a warrior, from another a philosopher, from a third a divine, from a fourth a lawyer, from a fifth a farmer, from a sixth a clown, etc., etc., and all of them immediately begin to perfect themselves by practicing what they before knew only in theory.

When they grow old they do not die, but turn into air and dissolve like smoke! As for their drink, they need none. They have but one finger upon

each hand, with which they perform everything in
as perfect a manner as we do who have four besides
the thumb. Their heads are placed under their right
arm, and when they are going to travel or about any
violent exercise, they generally leave them at home,
for they can consult them at any distance: this is a
very common practice; and when those of rank or

WARRIORS OF THE MOON

quality among the Lunarians have an inclination to
see what's going forward among the common people,
they stay at home, *i. e.,* the body stays at home and
sends the head only, which is suffered to be present
incog., and return at pleasure with an account of
what has passed.

Their eyes they can take in and out of their places
when they please, and can see as well with them in
their hand as in their heads! and if by any accident
they lose or damage one, they can borrow or pur-
chase another, and see as clearly with it as their own.
Dealers in eyes are on that account very numerous
in most parts of the moon, and in this article alone
all the inhabitants are whimsical: sometimes green
and sometimes yellow eyes are the fashion. I know
these things appear strange; but if the shadow of

a doubt can remain on any person's mind, I say, let him take a voyage there himself, and then he will know I am a traveler of veracity.

X

URING the early part of his present Majesty's reign I had some business with a distant relation who then lived on the Isle of Thanet; it was a family dispute, and not likely to be finished soon. I made it a practice during my residence there, the weather being fine, to walk out every morning. After a few of these excursions, I observed an object upon a great eminence about three miles distant: I extended my walk to it, and found the ruins of an ancient temple: I approached it with admiration and astonishment; the traces of grandeur and magnificence which yet remained were evident proofs of its former splendor: here I could not help lamenting the ravages and devastations of time, of which that once noble structure exhibited such a melancholy proof. I walked round it several times, meditating on the fleeting and transitory nature of all terrestrial things; on the eastern end were the remains of a lofty tower, near forty feet high, overgrown with ivy, the top apparently flat; I surveyed it on every side very minutely, thinking that if I could gain its summit I should enjoy the most delightful prospect of the circumjacent country. Animated with this hope, I resolved, if possible, to gain the summit, which I at length effected by means of the ivy, though not without great difficulty and danger; the top I found covered with this evergreen, except a large chasm in

the middle. After I had surveyed with pleasing wonder the beauties of art and nature that conspired to enrich the scene, curiosity prompted me to sound the opening in the middle, in order to ascertain its depth, as I entertained a suspicion that it might probably communicate with some unexplored subterranean cavern in the hill; but having no line, I was at a loss how to proceed. After revolving the matter in my thoughts for some time, I resolved to drop a stone down and listen to the echo; having found one that answered my purpose, I placed myself over the hole, with one foot on each side, and stooping down to listen, I dropped the stone, which I had no sooner done than I heard a rustling below, and suddenly a monstrous eagle put up its head right opposite my face, and rising up with irresistible force, carried me away, seated on its shoulders: I instantly grasped it around the neck, which was large enough to fill my arms, and its wings, when extended, were ten yards from one extremity to the other. As it rose with a regular ascent, my seat was perfectly easy, and I enjoyed the prospect below with inexpressible pleasure. It hovered over Margate for some time, was seen by several people, and many shots were fired at it; one ball hit the heel of my shoe, but did me no injury. It then directed its course to Dover Cliff, where it alighted, and I thought of dismounting, but was prevented by a sudden discharge of musketry from a party of marines that were exercising on the beach; the balls flew about my head, and rattled on the feathers of the eagle like hailstones, yet I could not perceive it had received any injury. It instantly reascended and flew over the sea towards Calais, but so very high that the Channel seemed to be no broader than the Thames at London Bridge. In a quarter of an hour I found myself over a thick wood in France, when the eagle descended very rapidly, which caused me to slip down to the back part of its head; but as it alighted on a large tree, and raised its head, I recovered my seat as before, but saw no possibility of disengaging myself without the danger of being killed by the fall; so I determined to sit fast, thinking it would carry me to the Alps, or some other high mountain, where I could dismount without any danger. After resting a few minutes it took wing, flew several times round the wood, and screamed loud enough to be heard across the English Channel. In a few minutes one of the same species arose out of the wood, and flew directly towards us; it surveyed me with evident marks of displeasure, and came very near me. After flying several times round, they both directed their course to the southwest. I soon observed that the one I rode upon could not keep pace with the other, but inclined towards the earth, on account of my weight; its companion perceiving this, turned round and placed itself in such a position that the other could rest its head on its rump; in this manner they proceeded till noon, when I saw the rock of Gibraltar very distinctly. The day being clear, the earth's surface appeared just like a map, where land, sea, lakes, rivers, mountains, and the like were perfectly distinguishable; and having some knowledge of geography, I was at no loss to determine what part of the globe I was in.

While I was contemplating this wonderful prospect a dreadful howling suddenly began all around me, and in a moment I was invested by thousands of small black, deformed, frightful-looking creatures, who pressed me on all sides in such a manner that I could neither move hand nor foot; but I had not been in their possession more than ten minutes when I heard the most delightful music that can possibly be imagined, which was suddenly changed into a noise the most awful and tremendous, to which the report of a cannon, or the loudest claps of thunder could bear no more proportion than the gentle zephyrs of the evening to the most dreadful hurricane; but the shortness of its duration prevented all those fatal effects which a prolongation of it would certainly have been attended with.

The music commenced, and I saw a great number of the most beautiful little creatures seize the other party, and throw them with great violence into something like a snuffbox, which they shut down, and one threw it away with incredible velocity; then turning to me, he said they whom he had secured were a party of devils, who had wandered from their proper habitation; and that the vehicle in which they were inclosed would fly with unabating rapidity for ten thousand years, when it would burst of its own accord, and the devils would recover their liberty and faculties, as at the present moment. He had no sooner finished this relation than the music ceased, and they all disappeared, leaving me in a state of mind bordering on the confines of despair.

When I had recomposed myself a little, I looked before me with inexpressible pleasure, and observed that the eagles were preparing to light on the peak of Teneriffe: they descended to the top of a rock, but seeing no possible means of escape if I dis-

mounted, I determined to remain where I was. The
eagles sat down seemingly fatigued, when the heat
of the sun soon caused them both to fall asleep, nor
did I long resist its fascinating power. In the cool
of the evening, when the sun had retired below the
horizon, I was aroused from sleep by the eagle moving under me; and have stretched myself along its
back, I sat up, and reassumed my traveling position,
when they both took wing, and having placed themselves as before, directed their course to South
America. The moon shining bright during the
whole night, I had a fine view of all the islands in
those seas.

About the break of day we reached the great
continent of America, that part called Terra-Firma,
and descended on the top of a very high mountain.
At this time, the moon, far distant in the west, and
obscured by dark clouds, but just afforded light
sufficient for me to discover a kind of shrubbery all
around bearing fruit something like cabbages, which
the eagles began to feed on very eagerly. I endeavored to discover my situation, but fogs and
passing clouds involved me in the thickest darkness,
and what rendered the scene still more shocking was
the tremendous howling of wild beasts, some of
which appeared to be very near: however, I determined to keep my seat, imagining that the eagle
would carry me away if any of them should make
a hostile attempt. When daylight began to appear
I thought of examining the fruit which I had seen
the eagles eat, and as some was hanging which I
could easily come at, I took out my knife and cut
a slice; but how great was my surprise to see that
it had all the appearance of roast beef regularly

mixed, both fat and lean! I tasted it, and found it well-flavored and delicious, then cut several large slices, and put in my pocket, where I found a crust of bread which I had brought from Margate; took it out, and found three musket-balls that had been lodged in it on Dover Cliff. I extracted them, and cutting a few slices more, made a hearty meal of bread and cold beef fruit. I then cut down two of the largest that grew near me, and tying them together with one of my garters, hung them over the eagle's neck for another occasion, filling my pockets at the same time. While I was settling these affairs, I observed a large fruit like an inflated bladder which I wished to try an experiment upon; and when I struck my knife into one of them, a fine pure liquor like Holland gin rushed out, which the eagles observing, eagerly drank up from the ground. I cut down the bladder as fast as I could, and saved about half a pint in the bottom of it, which I tasted, and could not distinguish it from the best mountain wine. I drank it all, and found myself greatly refreshed. By this time the eagles began to stagger against the shrubs. I endeavored to keep my seat, but was soon thrown to some distance among the bushes. In attempting to rise, I put my hand upon a large hedgehog, which happened to lie among the grass upon its back; it instantly closed round my hand, so that I found it impossible to shake it off. I struck it several times against the ground without effect; but while I was thus employed I heard a rustling among the shrubbery, and looking up, I saw a huge animal within three yards of me; I could make no defence, but held out both my hands, when it rushed upon me and seized that on which the hedgehog was fixed. My hand being soon released, I ran to some distance where I saw the creature suddenly drop down and expire with the hedgehog in its throat. When the danger was past, I went to view the eagles, and found them lying on the grass fast asleep, being intoxicated with the liquor they had drunk. Indeed, I found myself considerably elevated by it, and seeing everything quiet, I began to search for some more, which I soon found; and having cut down two large bladders, about a gallon each, I tied them together, and hung them over the neck of the other eagle, and the two smaller ones I tied with a cord round my own waist. Having secured a good stock of provisions, and perceiving the eagles begin to recover, I again took my seat. In half an hour they arose majestically from the place, without taking the least notice of their encumbrance. Each reassumed its former station; and directing their course to the northward, they crossed the Gulf of Mexico, entered North America, and steered directly for the Polar regions, which gave me the finest opportunity of viewing this vast continent that can possibly be imagined.

Before we entered the frigid zone the cold began to affect me; but piercing one of my bladders I took a draught, and found that it could make no impression on me afterwards. Passing over Hudson's Bay, I saw several of the company's ships lying at anchor, and many tribes of Indians marching with their furs to market.

By this time I was so reconciled to my seat, and become such an expert rider, that I could sit up and look around me; but in general I lay along the eagle's neck, grasping it in my arms, with my hands immersed in its feathers, in order to keep them warm.

In these cold climates I observed that the eagles flew with greater rapidity, in order, I suppose, to keep their blood in circulation. In passing Baffin's Bay I saw several large Greenlandmen to the eastward, and many surprising mountains of ice in those seas.

While I was surveying these wonders of nature it occurred to me that this was a good opportunity to discover the northwest passage, if any such thing existed, and not only obtain the reward offered by government, but the honor of a discovery pregnant with so many advantages to every European nation. But while my thoughts were absorbed in this pleasing reverie I was alarmed by the first eagle striking its head against a solid transparent substance, and in a moment that which I rode experienced the same fate, and both fell down seemingly dead.

Here our lives must inevitably have terminated, had not a sense of danger and the singularity of my situation inspired me with a degree of skill and dexterity which enabled us to fall near two miles perpendicular with as little inconvenience as if we had been let down with a rope; for no sooner did I perceive the eagles strike against a frozen cloud, which is very common near the poles, than (they being close together) I laid myself along the back of the foremost and took hold of its wings to keep them extended, at the same time stretching out my legs behind to support the wings of the other. This had the desired effect, and we descended very safe on a mountain of ice, which I supposed to be about three miles above the level of the sea.

I dismounted, unloading the eagles, opened one of the bladders, and administered some of the liquor to each of them, without once considering that the horrors of destruction seemed to have conspired against me. The roaring of waves, crashing of ice, and the howling of bears, conspired to form a scene the most awful and tremendous; but, notwithstanding this, my concern for the recovery of the eagles was so great that I was insensible of the danger to which I was exposed. Having rendered them every assistance in my power, I stood over them in painful anxiety, fully sensible that it was only by means of them that I could possibly be delivered from these abodes of despair.

But suddenly a monstrous bear began to roar behind me, with a voice like thunder. I turned round, and seeing the creature just ready to devour me, having the bladder of liquor in my hands, through fear I squeezed it so hard that it burst, and the liquor, flying in the eyes of the animal, totally deprived it of sight. It instantly turned from me, ran away in a state of distraction, and soon fell over a precipice of ice into the sea, where I saw it no more.

The danger being over, I again turned my attention to the eagles, whom I found in a fair way of recovery, and suspecting that they were faint for want of victuals, I took one of the beef fruit, cut it into small slices, and presented them with it, which they devoured with avidity.

Having given them plenty to eat and drink, and disposed of the remainder of my provisions, I took possession of my seat as before. After composing myself and adjusting everything in the best manner, I began to eat and drink very heartily; and through

the effects of the mountain, as I called it, was very
cheerful, and began to sing a few verses of a song
which I had learned when I was a boy: but the
noise soon alarmed the eagles, who had been asleep,
through the quantity of liquor which they had
drunk, and they arose seemingly much terrified.

WE DESCENDED SAFE ON A MOUNTAIN OF ICE

Happily for me, however, when I was feeding them
I had accidentally turned their heads towards the
southeast, which course they pursued with a rapid
motion. In a few hours I saw the Western Isles,
and soon after had the inexpressible pleasure of
seeing Old England. I took no notice of the seas
or islands over which I passed.

The eagles descended gradually as they drew near
the shore, intending, as I supposed, to alight on one

of the Welsh mountains; but when they came to the distance of about sixty yards, two guns were fired at them, loaded with balls, one of which penetrated a bladder of liquor that hung to my waist; the other entered the breast of the foremost eagle, who fell to the ground, while that which I rode, having received no injury, flew away with amazing swiftness.

This circumstance alarmed me exceedingly, and I began to think it was impossible for me to escape with my life; but recovering a little, I once more looked down upon the earth, when, to my inexpressible joy, I saw Margate at a little distance, and the eagle descending on the old tower whence it had carried me on the morning of the day before. It no sooner came down than I threw myself off, happy to find that I was once more restored to the world. The eagle flew away in a few minutes, and I sat down to compose my fluttering spirits, which I did in a few hours.

I soon paid a visit to my friends, and related these adventures. Amazement stood in every countenance; their congratulations on my returning in safety were repeated with an unaffected degree of pleasure, and we passed the evening as we are doing now, every person present paying the highest compliments to my COURAGE and VERACITY.

THE FIDDLING PARSON

ADAPTED FROM THE AUTOBIOGRAPHY OF

DAVY CROCKETT

ITTLE Rock lay on my way to Texas, and as I left it several companions accompanied me a short distance from the village. We were talking briskly together as we drew near the Washita River, and imagined ourselves the only travelers in that vicinity. In a lull in the conversation we were somewhat startled by the sound of music, evidently not far away. We checked our horses and listened, while the music continued.

"What can all that mean?" asked I.

"Blast my old shoes if I know," said one of the party.

We listened again and heard *Hail Columbia! Happy Land!* played in first-rate style.

"That's fine," said I.

"Fine as silk, Colonel, and a leetle finer," said another; "but hark! the tune is changed."

We listened again, and the musician struck up in a brisk and lively manner, *Over the Water to Charlie.*

"That's mighty mysterious," said one of my friends.

"Can't cipher it out nohow," said another.

"A notch beyant my measure," said a third.

"Then let's see what it is," said I, and off we dashed at a rapid gait.

As we approached the river, we saw to the right of the road a new clearing on a hill, from which several men were running down toward the river like wild Indians. There appeared no time to be lost, so we all cut ahead for the crossing. All this time the music kept growing stronger and stronger, every note distinctly saying, *Over the Water to Charlie*.

When we reached the crossing, we were astonished to see a man seated in a sulky in the middle of the river and playing for his life on a fiddle. The horse was up to his middle in water, and it seemed as if the flimsy vehicle was ready to be swept away by the current. Still the fiddler fiddled on composedly as if his life had been insured. We thought he was mad, and shouted to him. He heard us and stopped the music.

"You have missed the crossing," shouted one of the men.

"I know I have," replied the fiddler.

"If you go ten feet farther you will be drowned."

"I know I shall."

"Turn back," cried the man.

"I can't," said the fiddler.

"Then how the deuce will you get out?"

"I'm sure I don't know; come and help me."

The men from the clearing, who understood the river, took our horses, rode up to the sulky, and after some difficulty succeeded in bringing the traveler safe to shore. Then we recognized him as the worthy parson, who had played for us at a puppet show in Little Rock.

"You have had a narrow escape," said we.

"I found that out an hour ago," he said. "I have been fiddling to the fishes all the time, and played everything I can play without notes."

THE PARSON FIDDLED

"What made you think of fiddling in the time of such peril?" he was asked.

"I have found in my progress through life," said he, "that there is nothing so well calculated to draw people together as the sound of a fiddle. I might bawl for help till I was hoarse, and no one would stir a peg, but as soon as people hear the scraping of a fiddle, they will quit all other business and come to the spot in flocks."

We laughed heartily at the knowledge the parson showed of human nature; and he was right.

WE PLAN A RIVER TRIP[1]

By Jerome K. Jerome

THERE were four of us—George, and William Samuel Harris, and myself, and Montmorency. We were sitting in my room, smoking and talking about how bad we were—bad from a medical point of view I mean, of course.

We were all feeling seedy, and we were getting quite nervous about it. Harris said he felt such extraordinary fits of giddiness come over him at times, that he hardly knew what he was doing; and then George said that *he* had fits of giddiness, too, and hardly knew what he was doing. With me, it was my liver that was out of order. I knew it was my liver that was out of order, because I had just been reading a patent liver-pill circular, in which were detailed the various symptoms by which a man could tell when his liver was out of order. I had them all.

It is a most extraordinary thing, but I never read a patent medicine advertisement without being impelled to the conclusion that I am suffering from the particular disease therein dealt with, in its most virulent form. The diagnosis seems in every case to correspond exactly with all the sensations that I have ever felt.

1. This selection, with *On Comic Songs*, which follows, is taken from *Three Men in a Boat*, by Jerome K. Jerome. The complete title of the book is *Three Men in a Boat (To say nothing of the Dog)*.

I remember going to the British Museum one day to read up the treatment for some slight ailment of which I had a touch—hay fever, I fancy it was. I got down the book, and read all I came to read; and then, in an unthinking moment, I idly turned the leaves, and began indolently to study diseases generally. I forget which was the first distemper I plunged into—some fearful, devastating scourge, I know—and, before I had glanced half down the list of "premonitory symptoms," it was borne in upon me that I had fairly got it.

I sat for a while, frozen with horror; and then, in the listlessness of despair, I again turned over the pages. I came to typhoid fever—read the symptoms—discovered that I had typhoid fever, must have had it for months without knowing it—wondered what else I had got; turned up Saint Vitus's Dance—found, as I had expected, that I had that, too—began to get interested in my case, and determined to sift it to the bottom, and so started alphabetically—read up ague, and learned that I was sickening for it, and that the acute stage would commence in about another fortnight. Bright's disease, I was relieved to find, I had only in a modified form, and, so far as that was concerned, I might live for years. Cholera I had, with severe complications; and diphtheria I seemed to have been born with. I plodded conscientiously through the twenty-six letters, and the only malady I could conclude I had not got was housemaid's knee.

I felt rather hurt about this at first; it seemed somehow to be a sort of slight. Why hadn't I got housemaid's knee? Why this invidious reservation? After a while, however, less grasping feelings prevailed. I reflected that I had every other known malady in the pharmacology, and grew less selfish, and determined to do without housemaid's knee. Gout, in its most malignant stage, it would appear, had seized me without my being aware of it; and zymosis I had evidently been suffering with from boyhood. There were no more diseases after zymosis, so I concluded there was nothing else the matter with me. I sat and pondered. I thought what an interesting case I must be from a medical point of view, what an acquisition I should be to a class! Students would have no need to "walk the hospitals," if they had me. I was a hospital in myself. All they need do would be to walk round me, and, after that, take their diplomas.

Then I wondered how long I had to live. I tried to examine myself. I felt my pulse. I could not at first feel any pulse at all. Then, all of a sudden, it seemed to start off. I pulled out my watch and timed it. I made a hundred and forty-seven to the minute. I tried to feel my heart. I could not feel my heart. It had stopped beating. I have since been induced to come to the opinion that it must have been there all the time, and must have been beating, but I cannot account for it. I patted myself all over my front, from what I call my waist up to my head, and I went a bit round each side, and a little way up the back. But I could not feel or hear anything. I tried to look at my tongue. I stuck it out as far as ever it would go, and I shut one eye, and tried to examine it with the other. I could only see the tip, and the only thing that I could gain from that was to feel more certain than before that I had scarlet fever.

I had walked into that reading-room a happy, healthy man. I crawled out a decrepit wreck.

I went to my medical man. He was an old chum of mine, and feels my pulse, and looks at my tongue, and talks about the weather, all for nothing, when I fancy I'm ill; so I thought I would do him a good turn by going to him now. "What a doctor wants," I said, "is practice. He shall have me. He will get more practice out of me than out of seventeen hundred of your ordinary, commonplace patients, with only one or two diseases each." So I went straight up and saw him, and he said:

"Well, what's the matter with you?"

I said:

"I will not take up your time, dear boy, with telling you what is the matter with me. Life is brief, and you might pass away before I had finished. But I will tell you what is not the matter with me. I have not got housemaid's knee. Why I have not got housemaid's knee, I cannot tell you; but the fact remains that I have not got it. Everything, else, however, I *have* got.

And I told him how I came to discover it all.

Then he opened me and looked down me, and clutched hold of my wrist, and then hit me over the chest when I wasn't expecting it—a cowardly thing to do, I call it—and immediately afterward butted me with the side of his head. After that, he sat down and wrote out a prescription, and folded it up and gave it to me, and I put it in my pocket and went out.

I did not open it. I took it to the nearest chemist's, and handed it in. The man read it, and then handed it back.

He said he didn't keep it.

I said:

"You are a chemist?"

"I am a chemist. If I were a co-operative store and family hotel combined, I might be able to oblige you. Being only a chemist hampers me."

I read the prescription. It ran:

"1 lb. beefsteak, with
   1 pt. bitter beer
                every six hours.
1 ten-mile walk every morning.
1 bed at 11 sharp every night.
And don't stuff up your head with things you don't understand."

I followed the directions, with the happy result —speaking for myself—that my life was preserved, and is still going on.

* * * * * * *

George said:

"Let's go up the river."

He said we should have fresh air, exercise and quiet; the constant change of scene would occupy our minds (including what there was of Harris's); and the hard work would give us an appetite, and make us sleep well.

Harris said he didn't think George ought to do anything that would have a tendency to make him sleepier than he always was, as it might be dangerous. He said he didn't very well understand how George was going to sleep any more than he did now, seeing that there were only twenty-four hours in each day, summer and winter, alike; but thought that if he *did* sleep any more, he might just as well be dead, and so save his board and lodging.

Harris said, however, that the river would suit him to a "T." It suited me to a "T," too, and Harris and I both said it was a good idea of George's; and we said in a tone that seemed to imply somehow that we were surprised that George should have come out so sensible.

The only one who was not struck with the suggestion was Montmorency. He never did care for the river, did Montmorency.

"It's all very well for you fellows," he says; "you like it, but *I* don't. There's nothing for me to do. Scenery is not in my line, and I don't smoke. If I see a rat, you won't stop; and if I go to sleep, you get fooling about with the boat, and slop me overboard. If you ask me, I call the whole thing bally foolishness."

We were three to one, however, and the motion was carried.

* * * * * * * *

We made a list of the things to be taken, and a pretty lengthy one it was, before we parted that evening. The next day, which was Friday, we got them all together, and met in the evening to pack. We got a big Gladstone for the clothes, and a couple of hampers for the victuals and the cooking utensils. We moved the table up against the window, piled everything in a heap in the middle of the floor, and sat round and looked at it. I said I'd pack.

I rather pride myself on my packing. Packing is one of those many things that I feel I know more about than any other person living. (It surprises me myself, sometimes, how many of these subjects there are.) I impressed the fact upon George and Harris, and told them they had better leave the whole matter entirely to me. They fell into the suggestion with a readiness that had something uncanny about it. George put on a pipe and spread himself over the easy-chair, and Harris cocked his legs on the table and lit a cigar.

This was hardly what I intended. What I meant, of course, was, that I should boss the job, and that Harris and George should potter about under my directions, I pushing them aside every now and then with, "Oh, you——!" "Here, let me do it." "There you are, simple enough!"— really teaching them, as you might say. Their taking it in the way they did irritated me. There is nothing does irritate me more than seeing other people sitting about doing nothing when I'm working.

I lived with a man once who used to make me mad that way. He would loll on the sofa and watch me doing things by the hour together, following me round the room with his eyes, wherever I went. He said it did him real good to look on at me, messing about. He said it made him feel that life was not an idle dream to be gaped and yawned through, but a noble task, full of duty and stern work. He said he often wondered now how he could have gone on before he met me, never having anybody to look at while they worked.

Now, I'm not like that. I can't sit still and see another man slaving and working. I want to get up and superintend, and walk round with my hands in my pockets, and tell what to do. It is my energetic nature. I can't help it.

However, I did not say anything, but started the packing. It seemed a longer job than I had thought it was going to be, but I got the bag finished at last, and I sat on it and strapped it.

"Ain't you going to put the boots in?" said Harris.

And I looked round and found I had forgotten them. That's just like Harris. He couldn't have said a word until I'd got the bag shut and strapped, of course. And George laughed—one of those irritating, senseless, chuckle-headed, crack-jawed laughs of his. They do make me so wild.

I opened the bag and packed the boots in; and then, just as I was going to close it, a horrible idea occurred to me. Had I packed my toothbrush? I don't know how it is, but I never do know whether I've packed my toothbrush.

My toothbrush is a thing that haunts me when I'm traveling, and makes my life a misery. I dream that I haven't packed it, and wake up in a cold perspiration, and get out of bed and hunt for it. And, in the morning, I pack it before I have used it, and have to unpack again to get it, and it is always the last thing I turn out of the bag; and then I repack and forget it, and have to rush upstairs for it at the last moment and carry it to the railway station, wrapped up in my pocket handkerchief.

Of course I had to turn every mortal thing out now, and, of course, I could not find it. I rummaged the things up into much the same state that they must have been in before the world was created, and when chaos reigned. Of course, I found George's and Harris's eighteen times over, but I couldn't find my own. I put the things back one by one, and held everything up and shook it. Then

I found it inside a boot. I repacked once more.
When I had finished, George asked if the soap
was in. I said I didn't care a hang whether the soap
was in or whether it wasn't; and I slammed the bag
to and strapped it, and found that I had packed my
tobacco pouch in it and had to reopen it. It got
shut up finally at 10:05 p. m., and then there
remained the hampers to do. Harris said that we
should be wanting to start in less than twelve hours'
time, and thought that he and George had better
do the rest; and I agreed and sat down, and they
had a go.

They began in a light-hearted spirit, evidently
intending to show me how to do it. I made no com-
ment. I only waited. When George is hanged,
Harris will be the worst packer in this world; and
I looked at the piles of plates and cups, and kettles,
and bottles and jars, and pies, and stoves, and cakes,
and tomatoes, etc., and felt that the thing would
soon become exciting.

It did. They started with breaking a cup. That
was the first thing they did. They did that just
to show you what they *could* do, and to get you
interested.

Then Harris packed the strawberry jam on top
of a tomato and squashed it, and they had to pick
out the tomato with a teaspoon.

And then it was George's turn, and he trod on
the butter. I didn't say anything, but I came over
and sat on the edge of the table and watched them.
It irritated them more than anything I could have
said. I felt that. It made them nervous and excited,
and they stepped on things, and put things behind
them, and then couldn't find them when they wanted

them; and they packed the pies at the bottom, and put heavy things on top, and smashed the pies in.

They upset salt over everything, and as for the butter! I never saw two men do more with one-and-two pence worth of butter in my whole life than they did. After George had got it off his slipper, they tried to put it in the kettle. It wouldn't go in, and what *was* in wouldn't come out. They did scrape it out at last, and put it down on a chair, and Harris sat on it, and it stuck to him, and they went looking for it all over the room.

"I'll take my oath I put it down on that chair," said George, staring at the empty seat.

"I saw you do it myself, not a minute ago," said Harris.

Then they started round the room again looking for it; and then they met again in the center, and stared at one another.

"Most extraordinary thing I ever heard of," said George.

"So mysterious!" said Harris.

Then George got around at the back of Harris and saw it. "Why, here it is all the time," he exclaimed indignantly.

"Where?" cried Harris, spinning round.

"Stand still, can't you!" roared George, flying after him.

And they got it off, and packed it in the teapot.

Montmorency was in it all, of course. Montmorency's ambition in life is to get in the way and be sworn at. If he can squirm in anywhere where he particularly is not wanted, and be a perfect nuisance, and make people mad, and have things thrown at his head, then he feels his day has not been wasted.

"AIN'T YOU GOING TO PUT THE BOOTS IN?"

He came and sat down on things, just when they were wanted to be packed; and he labored under the fixed belief that, whenever Harris or George reached out a hand for anything, it was his cold, damp nose that they wanted. He put his leg into the jam, and he worried the teaspoons, and he pretended that the lemons were rats, and got into the hamper and killed three of them before Harris could land him with the frying-pan.

Harris said I encouraged him. I didn't encourage him. A dog like that doesn't want any encouragement. It's the natural, original sin that is born in him that makes him do things like that.

The packing was done at 12:50; and Harris sat on the big hamper, and said he hoped nothing would be found broken. George said that if anything was broken it *was* broken, which reflection seemed to comfort him. He also said he was ready for bed. We were all ready for bed.

ON COMIC SONGS

By Jerome K. Jerome

HARRIS has a fixed idea that he *can* sing a comic song; the fixed idea, on the contrary, among those of Harris's friends who have heard him try, is that he *can't,* and never will be able to, and that he ought not to be allowed to try.

When Harris is at a party and is asked to sing, he replies: "Well, I can only sing a *comic* song, you know"; and he says it in a tone that implies that his singing of *that,* however, is a thing that you ought to hear once, and then die.

"Oh, that *is* nice," says the hostess. "Do sing one, Mr. Harris," and Harris gets up and makes for the piano, with the beaming cheeriness of a generous-minded man who is just about to give somebody something.

"Now, silence, please, everybody," says the hostess, turning round; "Mr. Harris is going to sing a comic song!"

"Oh, how jolly!" they murmur; and they hurry in from the conservatory, and come up from the stairs, and go and fetch each other from all over the house, and crowd into the drawing-room, and sit round, all smirking in anticipation.

Then Harris begins.

Well, you don't look for much of a voice in a comic song. You don't expect correct phrasing or vocalization. You don't mind if a man does find out, when in the middle of a note, that he is too high, and comes down with a jerk. You don't bother about time. You don't mind a man being two bars in front of the accompaniment, and easing up in the middle of a line to argue it out with the pianist, and then starting the verse afresh. But you do expect the words.

You don't expect a man never to remember more than the first three lines of the first verse, and to keep on repeating these until it is time to begin the chorus. You don't expect a man to break off in the middle of a line, and snigger, and say, it's very funny, but he's blest if he can think of the rest of it, and then try and make it up for himself, and, afterward, suddenly recollect it, when he has got to an entirely different part of the song, and break off, without a word of warning, to go back and let you have it then and there. You don't—well, I will just give you an idea of Harris's comic singing, and then you can judge of it for yourself.

HARRIS (*standing up in front of piano and addressing the expectant mob*): "I'm afraid it's a very old thing, you know. I expect you all know it, you know. But it's the only thing I know. It's the Judge's song out of *Pinafore*—no, I don't mean *Pinafore*—I mean—you know what I mean—the other thing, you know. You must all join in the chorus, you know."

[*Murmurs of delight and anxiety to join in the chorus. Brilliant performance of prelude to the Judge's song in "Trial by Jury" by nervous pianist. Moment arrives for Harris to join in. Harris takes no notice of it. Nervous pianist commences prelude over again, and Harris, commencing singing at the same time, dashes off the first two lines of the First Lord's song out of "Pinafore." Nervous pianist tries to push on with prelude, gives it up, and tries to follow Harris with the accompaniment to the Judge's song out of "Trial by Jury," finds that doesn't answer, and tries to recollect what he is doing, and where he is, feels his mind giving way, and stops short.]*

HARRIS (*with kindly encouragement*): "It's all right. You're doing very well, indeed—go on."

NERVOUS PIANIST: "I'm afraid there's a mistake somewhere. What are you singing?"

HARRIS (*promptly*): "Why, the Judge's song out of *Trial by Jury*. Don't you know it?"

SOME FRIEND OF HARRIS'S (*from the back of the room*): "No, you're not, you chucklehead, you're singing the Admiral's song from *Pinafore*."

[Long argument between Harris and Harris's friend as to what Harris is really singing. Friend finally suggests that it doesn't matter what Harris is singing so long as Harris gets on and sings it, and Harris, with an evident sense of injustice rankling inside him, requests pianist to begin again. Pianist, thereupon, starts prelude to the Admiral's song, and Harris, seizing what he considers to be a favorable opening in the music, begins:

HARRIS:

" 'When I was young and called to the Bar.' "

[General roar of laughter, taken by Harris as

*a compliment. Pianist, thinking of his wife
and family, gives up the unequal contest and
retires: his place being taken by a stronger-
nerved man.*]

THE NEW PIANIST (*cheerily*): "Now then, old
man, you start off, and I'll follow. We won't bother
about any prelude."

HARRIS (*upon whom the explanation of matters
has slowly dawned—laughing*): "By Jove! I beg
your pardon. Of course—I've been mixing up the
two songs. It was Jenkins confused me, you know.
Now then."

[*Singing; his voice appearing to come from the
cellar, and suggesting the first low warnings
of an approaching earthquake.*]

" 'When I was young I served a term
     As office-boy to an attorney's firm.' "

(*Aside to pianist*): "It is too low, old man; we'll
have that over again, if you don't mind."

[*Sings first two lines over again, in a high falsetto
this time. Great surprise on the part of the
audience. Nervous old lady begins to cry,
and has to be led out.*]

HARRIS (*continuing*):

" 'I swept the windows and I swept the door,
     And I—' "

No—no, I cleaned the windows of the big front
door. And I polished up the floor—no, dash it—
I beg your pardon—funny thing, I can't think of
that line. And I—and I—oh, well, we'll get on the
chorus and chance it (*sings*):

" 'And I diddle-diddle-diddle-diddle-diddle-diddle-
     de,
     Till now I am the ruler of the Queen's navee.' "

"WHEN I WAS YOUNG"

Now then chorus—it's the last two lines repeated, you know."

General Chorus:

" 'And he diddle-diddle-diddle-diddle-diddle-diddle-dee'd,

Till now he is the ruler of the Queen's navee.' "

And Harris never sees what an ass he is making of himself, and how he is annoying a lot of people who never did him any harm. He honestly imagines that he has given them a treat, and says he will sing another comic song after supper.

Speaking of comic songs and parties, reminds me of a rather curious incident at which I once assisted; which, as it throws much light upon the inner mental working of human nature in general, ought, I think, to be recorded in these pages.

We were a fashionable and highly cultured party. We had on our best clothes, and we talked pretty, and were very happy—all except two young fellows, students, just returned from Germany, commonplace young men, who seemed restless and uncomfortable, as if they found the proceedings slow. The truth was, we were too clever for them. Our brilliant but polished conversation, and our high-class tastes, were beyond them. They were out of place among us. They never ought to have been there at all. Everybody agreed upon that, later on.

We discussed philosophy and ethics. We flirted with graceful dignity. We were even humorous—in a high-class way.

Somebody recited a French poem after supper, and we said it was beautiful; and then a lady sang a sentimental ballad in Spanish and it made one or two of us weep—it was so pathetic.

And then those two young men got up, and asked us if we had ever heard Herr Slossenn Boschen (who had just arrived, and was then down in the supper room) sing his great German comic song.

None of us had heard it, that we could remember.

The young men said it was the funniest song that had ever been written, and that, if we liked, they would get Herr Slossenn Boschen, whom they knew very well, to sing it. They said it was so funny that, when Herr Slossenn Boschen had sung it once before the German Emperor, he (the German Emperor) had had to be carried off to bed.

They said nobody could sing it like Herr Slossenn Boschen; he was so intensely serious all through it that you might fancy he was reciting a tragedy, and that, of course, made it all the funnier. They said he never once suggested by his tone or manner that he was singing anything funny—that would spoil it. It was his air of seriousness, almost of pathos, that made it so irresistibly amusing.

We said we yearned to hear it, that we wanted a good laugh; and they went downstairs, and fetched Herr Slossenn Boschen.

He appeared to be quite pleased to sing it, for he came up at once, and sat down to the piano without another word.

"Oh, it will amuse you. You will laugh," whispered the two young men, as they passed through the room and took up an unobtrusive position behind the Professor's back.

Herr Slossenn Boschen accompanied himself. The prelude did not suggest a comic song exactly. It was a weird, soulful air. It quite made one's flesh creep; but we murmured to one another that it was the German method, and prepared to enjoy it.

I don't understand German myself. I learned it at school, but forgot every word of it two years after I had left, and have felt much better ever since. Still, I did not want the people there to guess my ignorance; so I hit upon what I thought to be rather a good idea. I kept my eye on the two young students, and followed them. When they tittered, I tittered; when they roared, I roared; and I also threw in a little snigger all by myself now and then, as if I had seen a bit of humor that had escaped the others. I considered this particularly artful on my part.

I noticed, as the song progressed, that a good many other people seemed to have their eyes fixed on the two young men, as well as myself. These other people also tittered when the young men tittered, and roared when the young men roared; and, as the two young men tittered and roared and exploded with laughter pretty continuously all through the song, it went exceedingly well.

And yet that German professor did not seem happy. At first, when we began to laugh, the expression of his face was one of intense surprise, as if laughter were the very last thing he had expected to be greeted with. We thought this very funny: we said his earnest manner was half the humor. The slightest hint on his part that he knew how funny he was would have completely ruined it all. As we continued to laugh, his surprise gave way to an air of annoyance and indignation, and he scowled fiercely round upon us all (except the two young men, who, being behind him, could not be seen). That sent us into convulsions. We told

each other it would be the death of us, this thing.
The words alone, we said, were enough to send us
into fits, but added to his mock seriousness—oh, it
was too much!

In the last verse, he surpassed himself. He glow-
ered round upon us with a look of such concen-
trated ferocity that, but for our being forewarned
as to the German method of comic singing, we
should have been nervous; and he threw such a
wailing note of agony into the weird music that, if
we had not known it was a funny song, we might
have wept.

He finished amid a perfect shriek of laughter.
We said it was the funniest thing we had ever heard
in all our lives. We said how strange it was that,
in the face of things like these, there should be a
popular notion that the Germans hadn't any sense
of humor. And we asked the Professor why he
didn't translate the song into English, so that the
common people could understand it, and hear what
a real comic song was like.

Then Herr Slossenn Boschen got up, and went
on awful. He swore at us in German (which I
should judge to be a singularly effective language
for that purpose), and he danced, and shook his
fists, and called us all the English he knew. He
said he had never been so insulted in all his life.

It appeared that the song was not a comic song
at all. It was about a young girl who lived in the
Harz Mountains, and who had given up her life
to save her lover's soul; and he died, and met her
spirit in the air; and then, in the last verse, he jilted
her spirit, and went on with another spirit—I'm
not quite sure of the details, but it was something

very sad, I know. Herr Boschen said he had sung
it once before the German Emperor, and he (the
German Emperor) had sobbed like a little child.
He (Herr Boschen) said it was generally acknowledged to be one of the most tragic and pathetic
songs in the German language.

It was a trying situation for us—very trying.
There seemed to be no answer. We looked around
for the two young men who had done this thing,
but they had left the house in an unostentatious
manner immediately after the end of the song.

That was the end of that party. I never saw a
party break up so quietly, and with so little fuss.
We never said good-night even to one another. We
came downstairs one at a time, walking softly, and
keeping the shady side. We asked the servant for
our hats and coats in whispers, and opened the
door, and slipped out, and got round the corner
quickly, avoiding each other as much as possible.

I have never taken much interest in German songs
since then.

THE INCHCAPE ROCK

By ROBERT SOUTHEY

NOTE.—The Inchcape Rock, or Bell Rock, is a dangerous reef in the North Sea, east of the Firth of Tay, in Scotland, and twelves miles from all land. The story of the forethought of the abbot of Aberbrothok in placing the bell on the buoy as a warning to sailors is an ancient one, and one old writer thus gives the tradition made use of by Southey in this poem:

"In old times upon the said rocke there was a bell fixed upon a timber, which rang continually, being moved by the sea, giving notice to saylers of the danger. The bell was put there and maintained by the abbot of Aberbrothok, but being taken down by a sea-pirate, a yeare thereafter he perished upon the same rocke, with ship and goodes, in the righteous judgment of God."

A lighthouse, built with the greatest difficulty, has stood on the rock since 1810.

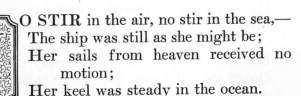

NO STIR in the air, no stir in the sea,—
The ship was still as she might be;
Her sails from heaven received no
    motion;
Her keel was steady in the ocean.

Without either sign or sound of their
  shock,
The waves flowed over the Inchcape Rock;
So little they rose, so little they fell,
They did not move the Inchcape bell.

The holy abbot of Aberbrothok
Had floated that bell on the Inchcape Rock;
On the waves of the storm it floated and swung,
And louder and louder its warning rung.

When the rock was hid by the tempest's swell,
The mariners heard the warning bell;
And then they knew the perilous rock,
And blessed the priest of Aberbrothok.

The sun in heaven shone so gay,—
All things were joyful on that day;
The sea-birds screamed as they sported round.
And there was pleasure in their sound.

The float of the Inchcape bell was seen,
A darker speck on the ocean green;
Sir Ralph, the rover, walked his deck,
And he fixed his eye on the darker speck.

He felt the cheering power of spring,—
It made him whistle, it made him sing;
His heart was mirthful to excess;
But the rover's mirth was wickedness.

His eye was on the bell and float:
Quoth he, "My men, pull out the boat;
And row me to the Inchcape Rock,
And I'll plague the priest of Aberbrothok."

The boat is lowered, the boatmen row,
And to the Inchcape Rock they go;
Sir Ralph bent over from the boat,
And cut the warning bell from the float.

Down sank the bell with a gurgling sound;
The bubbles rose, and burst around.
Quoth Sir Ralph, "The next who comes to the rock
Will not bless the priest of Aberbrothok."

Sir Ralph, the rover, sailed away,—
He scoured the seas for many a day;
And now, grown rich with plundered store,
He steers his course to Scotland's shore.

So thick a haze o'erspreads the sky
They could not see the sun on high;
The wind hath blown a gale all day;
At evening it hath died away.

On the deck the rover takes his stand;
So dark it is they see no land.
Quoth Sir Ralph, "It will be lighter soon,
For there is the dawn of the rising moon."

"Canst hear," said one, "the breakers roar?
For yonder, methinks, should be the shore.
Now where we are I cannot tell,
But I wish we could hear the Inchcape bell."

They hear no sound; the swell is strong,
Though the wind hath fallen, they drift along;
Till the vessel strikes with a shivering shock,—
O Christ! it is the Inchcape Rock!

Sir Ralph, the rover, tore his hair;
He beat himself in wild despair.
The waves rush in on every side;
The ship is sinking beneath the tide.

But ever in his dying fear
One dreadful sound he seemed to hear,—

ONE DREADFUL SOUND HE SEEMED TO HEAR

A sound as if with the Inchcape bell
The evil spirit was ringing his knell.

TOM BROWN AT RUGBY[1]

By Thomas Hughes

TOM AND ARTHUR

IT was a huge, high, airy room, with two large windows looking on to the school close.[2] There were twelve beds in the room, the one in the furthest corner by the fireplace occupied by the sixth-form[3] boy who was responsible for the discipline of the room, and the rest by boys in the lower-fifth and other junior

1. *Tom Brown's School Days*, a description of life at the great English public school of Rugby, is one of the best known and best-liked books ever written for boys. The author, Thomas Hughes, was himself a Rugby boy, and many of the incidents of the story are drawn from his own experience. One of the most interesting things about the book is the picture it gives of Thomas Arnold, head-master of Rugby from 1828 to 1842. The influence for good of this famous scholar and educator, called affectionately "the doctor," can scarcely be overestimated.

He held that fully as much attention should be paid to the development of manly character in the boys as to mental training, and that the prime object of a school was not to turn out scholars, but to turn out men. This Doctor Arnold was the father of Matthew Arnold, the poet.

2. Tom Brown, an old Rugby boy, has come back after his vacation, full of plans for the good times which he expects to have with his chum East and other cronies. He is, however, called into the housekeeper's room and introduced to a shy, frail boy, whom he is asked to receive as his roommate and to look out for in the early days of his life at Rugby. Although greatly disappointed, Tom sees no way to refuse the request, and at the beginning of the selection here given we find him with young Arthur in the boys' dormitory.

3. The word *form* is used in English schools instead of *class*.

forms, all fags[1] (for the fifth-form boys, as has been said, slept in rooms by themselves). Being fags, the eldest of them was not more than about sixteen years old, and all were bound to be up and in bed by ten; the sixth-form boys came to bed from ten to a quarter-past (at which time the old verger came round to put the candles out), except when they sat up to read.

Within a few minutes, therefore, of their entry, all the other boys who slept in Number 4, had come up. The little fellows went quietly to their own beds, and began undressing and talking to each other in whispers; while the elder, among whom was Tom, sat chatting about on one another's beds. Poor little Arthur was overwhelmed with the novelty of his position. The idea of sleeping in the room with strange boys had clearly never crossed his mind before, and was as painful as it was strange to him. He could hardly bear to take his jacket off; however, presently, with an effort, off it came, and then he paused and looked at Tom, who was sitting at the bottom of his bed talking and laughing.

"Please, Brown," he whispered, "may I wash my face and hands?"

"Of course, if you like," said Tom, staring; "that's your washhand-stand, under the window, second from your bed. You'll have to go down for more water in the morning if you use it all." And on he went with his talk, while Arthur stole timidly from between the beds out to his washhand-stand,

---

1. In English schools the name *fag* is applied to a boy who does, under compulsion, menial work for a boy of a higher form. The fagging system used to be greatly abused, the boys of the higher classes treating their fags with the greatest cruelty; but the bad points of the custom have been largely done away with.

and began his ablutions, thereby drawing for a
moment on himself the attention of the room.

On went the talk and laughter. Arthur finished
his washing and undressing, and put on his night-
gown. He then looked round more nervously than

THE BULLY CAUGHT IT ON HIS ELBOW

ever. Two or three of the little boys were already
in bed, sitting up with their chins on their knees.
The light burned clear, the noise went on. It was
a trying moment for the poor little lonely boy;
however, this time he didn't ask Tom what he might
or might not do, but dropped on his knees by his
bedside, as he had done every day from his childhood, to open his heart to Him who heareth the
cry and beareth the sorrows of the tender child, and
the strong man in agony.

Tom was sitting at the bottom of his bed unlacing his boots, so that his back was toward Arthur, and he didn't see what had happened, and looked up in wonder at the sudden silence. Then two or three boys laughed and sneered, and a big brutal fellow, who was standing in the middle of the room, picked up a slipper, and shied it at the kneeling boy, calling him a sniveling young shaver. Then Tom saw the whole, and the next moment the boot he had just pulled off flew straight at the head of the bully, who had just time to throw up his arm and catch it on his elbow.

"Confound you, Brown, what's that for?" roared he, stamping with pain.

"Never mind what I mean," said Tom, stepping on to the floor, every drop of blood in his body tingling; "if any fellow wants the other boot, he knows how to get it."

What would have been the result is doubtful, for at this moment the sixth-form boy came in, and not another word could be said. Tom and the rest rushed into bed and finished unrobing there, and the old verger, as punctual as the clock, had put out the candle in another minute, and toddled on to the next room, shutting the door with his usual "Good night, genl'm'n."

There were many boys in the room by whom that little scene was taken to heart before they slept. But sleep seemed to have deserted the pillow of poor Tom. For some time his excitement, and the flood of memories which chased one another through his brain, kept him from thinking or resolving. His head throbbed, his heart leaped, and he could hardly keep himself from springing out of bed and rushing

RUGBY SCHOOL

about the room. Then the thought of his own
mother came across him, and the promise he had
made at her knee, years ago, never to forget to
kneel by his bedside, and give himself up to his
Father, before he laid his head on the pillow, from
which it might never rise; and he lay down gently
and cried as if his heart would break. He was only
fourteen years old.

It was no light act of courage in those days, my
dear boys, for a little fellow to say his prayers pub-
licly even at Rugby. A few years later, when Arnold's manly piety had begun to leaven the school,
the tables turned; before he died, in the school-
house at least, and I believe in the other houses, the
rule was the other way. But poor Tom had come
to school in other times. The first few nights after
he came he did not kneel down because of the noise,
but sat up in bed till the candle was out, and then
stole out and said his prayers in fear, lest some one
should find him out. So did many another poor
little fellow. Then he began to think that he might
just as well say his prayers in bed, and then that
it didn't matter whether he was kneeling, or sitting,
or lying down. And so it had come to pass with
Tom as with all who will not confess their Lord
before men: and for the last year he had probably
not said his prayers in earnest a dozen times.

Poor Tom! the first and bitterest feeling which
was like to break his heart was the sense of his own
cowardice. The vice of all others which he loathed
was brought in and burned in on his own soul. He
had lied to his mother, to his conscience, to his God.
How could he bear it? And then the poor little
weak boy, whom he had pitied and almost scorned

for his weakness, had done that which he, braggart as he was, dared not do. The first dawn of comfort came to him in swearing to himself that he would stand by that boy through thick and thin, and cheer him, and help him, and bear his burdens, for the good deed done that night. Then he resolved to write home next day and tell his mother all, and what a coward her son had been. And then peace came to him as he resolved, lastly, to bear his testimony next morning. The morning would be harder than the night to begin with, but he felt that he could not afford to let one chance slip. Several times he faltered, for the devil showed him, first, all his old friends calling him "Saint" and "Squaretoes," and a dozen hard names, and whispered to him that his motives would be misunderstood, and he would only be left alone with the new boy; whereas it was his duty to keep all means of influence, that he might do good to the largest number. And then came the more subtle temptation, "Shall I not be showing myself braver than others by doing this? Have I any right to begin it now? Ought I not rather to pray in my own study, letting other boys know that I do so, and trying to lead them to it, while in public at least I should go on as I have done?" However, his good angel was too strong that night, and he turned on his side and slept, tired of trying to reason, but resolved to follow the impulse which had been so strong, and in which he had found peace.

Next morning he was up and washed and dressed, all but his jacket and waistcoat, just as the ten minute's bell began to ring, and then in the face of the whole room knelt down to pray. Not five words could he say—the bell mocked him; he was listening for every whisper in the room—what were they all thinking of him? He was ashamed to go on kneeling, ashamed to rise from his knees. At last, as it were from his inmost heart, a still small voice seemed to breathe forth words of the publican, "God be merciful to me a sinner!" He repeated them over and over, clinging to them as for his life, and rose from his knees comforted and humbled, and ready to face the whole world. It was not needed: two other boys besides Arthur had already followed his example, and he went down to the great school with a glimmering of another lesson in his heart—the lesson that he who has conquered his own coward spirit has conquered the whole outward world; and that other one which the old prophet learned in the cave of Mount Horeb, when he hid his face, and the still small voice asked, "What doest thou here, Elijah?" that however we may fancy ourselves alone on the side of good, the King and Lord of men is nowhere without His witnesses; for in every society, however seemingly corrupt and godless, there are those who have not bowed the knee to Baal.

He found too how greatly he had exaggerated the effect to be produced by his act. For a few nights there was a sneer or a laugh when he knelt down, but this passed off soon and one by one all the other boys but three or four followed the lead. I fear that this was in some measure owing to the fact, that Tom could probably have thrashed any boy in the room except the præpostor;[5] at any rate, every boy knew that he would try upon very slight

5. A præpostor is a monitor, a scholar appointed to oversee other scholars.

provocation, and didn't choose to run the risk of a hard fight because Tom Brown had taken a fancy to say his prayers.

THE FIGHT

 HERE is a certain sort of fellow—we who are used to studying boys all know him well enough—of whom you can predicate with almost positive certainty, after he has been a month at school, that he is sure to have a fight, and with almost equal certainty that he will have but one. Tom Brown was one of these; and as it is our well-weighed intention to give a full, true, and correct account of Tom's only single combat with a school-fellow, let those young persons whose stomachs are not strong, or who think a good set-to with the weapons which God has given to us all, an uncivilized, unchristian, or ungentlemanly, affair, just skip this chapter at once, for it won't be to their taste.

It was not at all usual in those days for two school-house boys to have a fight. Of course there were exceptions, when some cross-grained, hard-headed fellow came up, who would never be happy unless he was quarreling with his nearest neighbors, or when there was some class-dispute between the fifth-form and the fags, for instance, which required blood-letting; and a champion was picked out on each side tacitly, who settled the matter by a good, hearty mill. But for the most part the constant use of those surest keepers of the peace, the boxing-gloves, kept the school-house boys from fighting one another. Two or three nights in every week the gloves were brought out, either in the hall or fifth-form room; and every boy who was ever likely to fight at all, knew all his neighbors' prowess perfectly well, and could tell to a nicety what chance he would have in a stand-up fight with any other boy in the house. But of course no such experience could be gotten as regarded boys in other houses; and as most of the other houses were more or less jealous of the school-house, collisions were frequent.

After all, what would life be without fighting, I should like to know? From the cradle to the grave, fighting, rightly understood, is the business, the real, highest, honestest business of every son of man. Every one who is worth his salt has his enemies, who must be beaten, be they evil thoughts and habits in himself, or spiritual wickedness in high places, or Russians, or border-ruffians, or Bill, Tom, or Harry, who will not let him live his life in quiet till he has thrashed them.

It is no good for Quakers, or any other body of men to uplift their voices against fighting. Human nature is too strong for them, and they don't follow their own precepts. Every soul of them is doing his own piece of fighting, somehow and somewhere. The world might be a better world without fighting, for anything I know, but it wouldn't be our world; and therefore I am dead against crying peace when there is no peace, and isn't meant to be. I am as sorry as any man to see folk fighting the wrong people and the wrong things, but I'd a deal sooner see them doing that, than that they should have no fight in them. So having recorded, and being about to record, my hero's fights of all sorts, with all sorts of enemies, I shall now proceed to give an account of his passage-at-arms with the only one of his school-fellows whom he ever had to encounter in this manner.

It was drawing toward the close of Arthur's first half-year, and the May evenings were lengthening out. Locking-up was not till eight o'clock, and everybody was beginning to talk about what he would do in the holidays. The shell,[6] in which form all our *dramatis personae* now are, were reading among other things the last book of "Homer's Iliad," and had worked through it as far as the speeches of the women over Hector's body. It is a whole school-day, and four or five of the school-house boys (among whom are Arthur, Tom and East) are preparing third lesson together. They have finished the regulation forty lines, and are for the most part getting very tired, notwithstanding the exquisite pathos of Helen's lamentation. And now several long four-syllabled words come together, and the boy with the dictionary strikes work.

"I am not going to look out any more words," says he; "we've done the quantity. Ten to one we shan't get so far. Let's go out into the close."

"Come along, boys," cries East, always ready to leave the grind, as he called it; "our old coach is laid up, you know, and we shall have one of the new masters, who's sure to go slow and let us down easy."

So an adjournment to the close was carried *nem. con.*,[7] little Arthur not daring to lift up his voice;

6. *Shell* is the name applied, in some public schools, to a sort of intermediate class.

7. *Nemine contradicente* is a Latin expression meaning *no one speaking in opposition.*

but, being deeply interested in what they were reading, he stayed quietly behind, and learned on for
his own pleasure.

As East had said, the regular master of the form
was unwell, and they were to be heard by one of
the new masters, quite a young man, who had only
just left the university.   Certainly it would be hard
lines, if, by dawdling as much as possible in coming
in and taking their places, entering into long-winded
explanations of what was the usual course of the
regular master of the form, and others of the stock
contrivances of boys for wasting time in school, they
could not spin out the lesson so that he should not
work them through more than the forty lines; as to
which quantity there was a perpetual fight going
on between the master and his form, the latter insist-
ing, and enforcing by passive resistance, that it was
the prescribed quantity of Homer for a shell lesson,
the former that there was no fixed quantity, but
that they must always be ready to go on to fifty or
sixty lines if there were time within the hour.   However, notwithstanding all their efforts, the new master got on horribly quick; he seemed to have the
bad taste to be really interested in the lesson, and
to be trying to work them up into something like
appreciation of it, giving them good spirited English words, instead of the wretched bald stuff into
which they rendered poor old Homer; and construing over each piece himself to them, after each
boy, to show them how it should be done.

Now the clock strikes the three quarters; there is
only a quarter of an hour more; but the forty lines
are all but done.   So the boys, one after another,
who are called up, stick more and more, and make

balder and ever more bald work of it. The poor
young master is pretty near beat by this time, and
feels ready to knock his head against the wall, or
his fingers against somebody else's head. So he
gives up altogether the lower and middle parts of
the form, and looks round in despair at the boys
on the top bench to see if there is one out of whom
he can strike a spark or two, and who will be too
chivalrous to murder the most beautiful utterances
of the most beautiful woman of the old world. His
eye rests on Arthur, and he calls him up to finish
construing Helen's speech. Whereupon all the
other boys draw long breaths, and begin to stare
about and take it easy. They are all safe; Arthur
is the head of the form, and sure to be able to construe, and that will tide on safely till the hour strikes.

Arthur proceeds to read out the passage in Greek
before construing it, as the custom is. Tom, who
isn't paying much attention, is suddenly caught by
the falter in his voice as he reads the two lines:

ἀλλὰ σὺ τόν γ' ἐπέεσσι μαραιφάμενος κατέρυκες,

Σῆ τ' ἀγανοφροσύνη καὶ σοῖς ἀγανοῖς ἐπέεσσιν.[1]

He looks up at Arthur. "Why, bless us," thinks
he, "what can be the matter with the young 'un?
He's never going to get floored. He's sure to have
learned to the end." Next moment he is reassured
by the spirited tone in which Arthur begins construing, and betakes himself to drawing dogs' heads
in his notebook, while the master, evidently enjoying

---

1.   Pope's free rendering of these lines is as follows:
        If some proud brother eyed me with disdain,
        Or scornful sister with her sweeping train,
        Thy gentle accents softened all my pain.

the change, turns his back on the middle bench and stands before Arthur, beating a sort of time with his hand and foot and saying "Yes, yes," "very well," as Arthur goes on.

But as he nears the fatal two lines, Tom catches that falter and again looks up. He sees that there is something the matter—Arthur can hardly get on at all. What can it be?

Suddenly at this point Arthur breaks down altogether, and fairly bursts out crying, and dashes the cuff of his jacket across his eyes, blushing up to the roots of his hair, and feeling as if he should like to go down suddenly through the floor. The whole form are taken aback; most of them stare stupidly at him, while those who are gifted with presence of mind find their places and look steadily at their books, in hopes of not catching the master's eye and getting called up in Arthur's place.

The master looks puzzled for a moment, and then seeing, as the fact is, that the boy is really affected to tears by the most touching thing in Homer, perhaps in all profane poetry put together, steps up to him and lays his hand kindly on his shoulder, saying, "Never mind, my little man, you've construed very well. Stop a minute, there's no hurry."

Now, as luck would have it, there sat next above Tom that day, in the middle bench of the form, a big boy, by name Williams, generally supposed to be the cock of the shell, therefore, of all the school below the fifths. The small boys, who are great speculators on the prowess of their elders, used to hold forth to one another about Williams' great strength, and to discuss whether East or Brown would take a licking from him. He was called

Slogger Williams, from the force with which it was supposed he could hit. In the main, he was a rough, good-natured fellow enough, but very much alive to his own dignity. He reckoned himself the king of the form, and kept up his position with a strong hand, especially in the matter of forcing boys not to construe more than the legitimate forty lines. He had already grunted and grumbled to himself when Arthur went on reading beyond the forty lines. But now that he had broken down just in the middle of all the long words, the slogger's wrath was fairly roused.

"Sneaking little brute," muttered he, regardless of prudence, "clapping on the waterworks just in the hardest place; see if I don't punch his head after fourth lesson."

"Whose?" said Tom, to whom the remark seemed to be addressed.

"Why, that little sneak, Arthur's," replied Williams.

"No, you shan't," said Tom.

"Hullo!" exclaimed Williams, looking at Tom with great surprise for a moment, and then giving him a sudden dig in the ribs with his elbow, which sent Tom's books flying on the floor, and called the attention of the master, who turned suddenly round, and seeing the state of things, said:

"Williams, go down three places, and then go on."

The slogger found his legs very slowly, and proceeded to go below Tom and two other boys with great disgust, and then turning round and facing the master said:

"I haven't learned any more, sir; our lesson is only forty lines."

"Is that so?" said the master, appealing generally to the top bench. No answer.

"Who is the head boy of the form?" said he, waxing wroth.

"Arthur, sir," answered three or four boys, indicating our friend.

"Oh, your name's Arthur. Well now, what is the length of your regular lesson?"

Arthur hesitated a moment, and then said, "We call it only forty lines, sir."

"How do you mean, you call it?"

"Well, sir, Mr. Graham says we ain't to stop there, when there's time to construe more."

"I understand," said the master. "Williams, go down three more places, and write me out the lesson in Greek and English. And now, Arthur, finish construing."

"Oh! would I be in Arthur's shoes after fourth lesson?" said the little boys to one another; but Arthur finished Helen's speech without any further catastrophe, and the clock struck four, which ended third lesson. Another hour was occupied in preparing and saying fourth lesson, during which Williams was bottling up his wrath; and when five struck, and the lessons for the day were over, he prepared to take summary vengeance on the innocent cause of his misfortune.

Tom was detained in school a few minutes after the rest, and on coming out into the quadrangle, the first thing he saw was a small ring of boys, applauding Williams, who was holding Arthur by the collar.

"There, you young sneak," said he, giving Arthur a cuff on the head with his other hand, "what made you say that—"

"Hullo!" said Tom, shouldering into the crowd, "you drop that, Williams; you shan't touch him."

"Who'll stop me?" said the slogger, raising his hand again.

"I," said Tom; and suiting the action to the word, struck the arm which held Arthur's arm so sharply, that the slogger dropped it with a start, and turned the full current of his wrath on Tom.

"Will you fight?"

"Yes, of course."

"Huzza, there's going to be a fight between Slogger Williams and Tom Brown!"

The news ran like wild-fire about, and many boys were on their way to tea at their several houses turned back, and sought the back of the chapel, where the fights come off.

"Just run and tell East to come and back me," said Tom to a small school-house boy, who was off like a rocket to Harrowell's, just stopping for a moment to poke his head into the school-house hall, where the lower boys were already at tea, and sing out, "Fight! Tom Brown and Slogger Williams."

Up start half the boys at once, leaving bread, eggs, butter, sprats, and all the rest to take care of themselves. The greater part of the remainder follow in a minute, after swallowing their tea, carrying their food in their hands to consume as they go. Three or four only remain, who steal the butter of the more impetuous, and make to themselves an unctuous feast.

In another minute East and Martin tear through the quadrangle carrying a sponge, and arrive at the scene of action just as the combatants are beginning to strip.

Tom felt he had got his work cut out for him,
as he stripped off his jacket, waistcoat, and braces.
East tied his handkerchief round his waist, and
rolled up his shirt-sleeves for him: "Now, old boy,
don't you open your mouth to say a word, or try to
help yourself a bit, we'll do all that; you keep all
your breath and strength for the slogger." Martin

"A FIGHT!"

meanwhile folded the clothes, and put them under
the chapel rails; and now Tom, with East to handle
him and Martin to give him a knee, steps out on the
turf, and is ready for all that may come: and here
is the slogger too, all stripped, and thirsting for the
fray.

It doesn't look a fair match at first glance:
Williams is nearly two inches taller, and probably
a long year older than his opponent, and he is very
strongly made about the arms and shoulders; "peels
well," as the little knot of big fifth-form boys, the
amateurs, say; who stand outside the ring of little
boys, looking complacently on, but taking no
active part in the proceedings. But down below he
is not so good by any means; no spring from the
loins, and feebleish, not to say shipwrecky, about

the knees. Tom, on the contrary, though not half so strong in the arms, is good all over, straight, hard, and springy from neck to ankle, better perhaps in his legs than anywhere. Besides, you can see by the clear white of his eye and fresh bright look of his skin, that he is in tip-top training, able to do all he knows; while the slogger looks rather sodden, as if he didn't take much exercise and ate too much tuck.[9] The time-keeper is chosen, a large ring made, and the two stand up opposite one another for a moment, giving us time just to make our little observations.

"If Tom'll only condescend to fight with his head and heels," as East mutters to Martin, "we shall do."

But seemingly he won't for there he goes in, making play with both hands. Hard all, is the word; the two stand to one another like men; rally follows rally in quick succession, each fighting as if he thought to finish the whole thing out of hand. "Can't last at this rate," say the knowing ones, while the partisans of each make the air ring with their shouts and counter-shouts, of encouragement, approval and defiance.

"Take it easy, take it easy—keep away, let him come after you," implores East, as he wipes Tom's face after the first round with a wet sponge, while he sits back on Martin's knee, supported by the Madman's long arms, which tremble a little from excitement.

"Time's up," calls the time-keeper.

"There he goes again, hang it all!" growls East as his man is at it again as hard as ever. A very

9. *Tuck* is a slang name for pastry or sweetmeats.

TOM SITS ON MARTIN'S KNEE

severe round follows, in which Tom gets out and out
the worst of it, and is at last hit clean off his legs,
and deposited on the grass by a right-hander from
the slogger. Loud shouts rise from the boys of
slogger's house, and the school-house are silent and
vicious, ready to pick quarrels anywhere.

"Two to one in half-crowns on the big 'un," says
Rattle, one of the amateurs, a tall fellow, in thunder-
and-lightning waistcoat, and puffy, good-natured
face.

"Done!" says Groove, another amateur of quieter
look, taking out his note-book to enter it—for our
friend Rattle sometimes forgets these little things.

Meantime East is freshening up Tom with the
sponges for the next round, and has set two other
boys to rub his hands.

"Tom, old boy," whispers he, "this may be fun
for you, but it's death to me. He'll hit all the fight
out of you in another five minutes, and then I shall
go and drown myself in the island ditch. Feint
him—use your legs! draw him about! he'll lose his
wind then in no time, and you can go into him. Hit
at his body too, we'll take care of his frontispiece
by and by."

Tom felt the wisdom of the counsel, and saw already that he couldn't go in and finish the slogger
off at mere hammer and tongs, so changed his
tactics completely in the third round. He now fights
cautious, getting away from and parrying the slogger's lunging hits, instead of trying to counter, and
leading his enemy a dance all round the ring after
him. "He's funking; go in, Williams," "Catch
him up," "Finish him off," scream the small boys
of the slogger party.

"Just what we want," thinks East, chuckling to himself, as he sees Williams, excited by these shouts and thinking the game in his own hands, blowing himself in his exertions to get to close quarters again, while Tom is keeping away with perfect ease.

They quarter over the ground again and again, Tom always on the defensive.

The slogger pulls up at last for a moment, fairly blown.

"Now then, Tom," sings out East dancing with delight. Tom goes in in a twinkling, and hits two heavy body blows, and gets away again before the slogger can catch his wind; which when he does he rushes with blind fury at Tom, and being skillfully parried and avoided, over-reaches himself and falls on his face, amid terrific cheers from the school-house boys.

"Double your two to one?" says Groove to Rattle, note-book in hand.

"Stop a bit," says the hero, looking uncomfortably at Williams, who is puffing away on his second's knee, winded enough, but little the worse in any other way.

After another round the slogger too seems to see that he can't go in and win right off, and has met his match or thereabouts. So he too begins to use his head and tries to make Tom lose patience and come in before his time. And so the fight sways on, now one, and now the other, getting a trifling pull.

Tom's face begins to look very one-sided—there are little queer bumps on his forehead, and his mouth is bleeding; but East keeps the wet sponge going so scientifically, that he comes up looking as fresh

and bright as ever. Williams is only slightly
marked in the face, but by the nervous movement of
his elbows you can see that Tom's body blows are
telling. In fact, half the vice of the slogger's hit-
ting is neutralized, for he daren't lunge out freely
for fear of exposing his sides. It is too interesting
by this time for much shouting, and the whole ring
is very quiet.

"All right, Tommy," whispers East; "hold on's
the horse that's to win. We've got the last. Keep
your head, old boy."

But where is Arthur all this time? Words cannot paint the poor little fellow's distress. He
couldn't muster courage to come up to the ring, but
wandered up and down from the great fives'-court
to the corner of the chapel rails, now trying to make
up his mind to throw himself between them, and try
to stop them; then thinking of running in and telling Mary, the matron, who he knew would instantly
report it to the doctor. The stories he had heard of
men being killed in prize-fights rose up horribly
before him.

Once only, when the shouts of "Well done,
Brown!" "Huzza for the school-house!" rose higher
than ever, he ventured up to the ring, thinking the
victory was won. Catching sight of Tom's face in
the state I have described, all fear of consequences
vanishing out of his mind, he rushed straight off to
the matron's room, beseeching her to get the fight
stopped, or he should die.

But it's time for us to get back to the close. What
is this fierce tumult and confusion? The ring is
broken, and high and angry words are being
bandied about; "It's all fair,"—"It isn't"—"No

hugging"; the fight is stopped. The combatants, however, sit there quietly, tended by their seconds, while their adherents wrangle in the middle. East can't help shouting challenges to two or three of the other side, though he never leaves Tom for a moment, and plies the sponges as fast as ever.

The fact is, that at the end of the last round, Tom seeing a good opening, had closed with his opponent, and after a moment's struggle had thrown him heavily, by the help of the fall he had learned from his village rival in the vale of White Horse. Williams hadn't the ghost of a chance with Tom at wrestling; and the conviction broke at once on the slogger faction, that if this were allowed their man must be licked. There was a strong feeling in the school against catching hold and throwing, though it was generally ruled all fair within certain limits; so the ring was broken and the fight stopped.

The school-house are overruled—the fight is on again, but there is to be no throwing; and East in high wrath threatens to take his man away after the next round (which he don't mean to do, by the way), when suddenly young Brooke comes through the small gate at the end of the chapel. The school-house faction rush to him. "Oh, hurra! now we shall get fair play."

"Please, Brooke, come up, they won't let Tom Brown throw him."

"Throw whom?" says Brooke, coming up to the ring. "Oh! Williams, I see. Nonsense! of course he may throw him if he catches him fairly above the waist."

Now, young Brooke, you're in the sixth, you know, and you ought to stop all fights. He looks hard at both boys. "Anything wrong?" says he to East, nodding at Tom.

"Not a bit."

"Not beat at all?"

"Bless you, no! heaps of fight in him. Ain't there, Tom?"

Tom looks at Brooke and grins.

"How's he?" nodding at Williams.

"So, so; rather done, I think, since his last fall. He won't stand above two more. "

"Time's up!" the boys rise again and face one another. Brooke can't find it in his heart to stop them just yet, so the round goes on, the slogger waiting for Tom, and reserving all his strength to hit him out should he come in for the wrestling dodge again, for he feels that that must be stopped, or his sponge will soon go up in the air.

And now another newcomer appears on the field, to-wit, the under-porter, with his long brush and great wooden receptacle for dust under his arm. He has been sweeping out the schools.

"You'd better stop, gentlemen," he says; "the doctor knows that Brown's fighting—he'll be out in a minute."

"You go to Bath, Bill," is all that that excellent servitor gets by his advice. And being a man of his hands, and a stanch upholder of the school-house, he can't help stopping to look on for a bit, and see Tom Brown, their pet craftsman, fight a round.

It is grim earnest now, and no mistake. Both boys feel this, and summon every power of head, hand, and eye to their aid. A piece of luck on either side, a foot slipping, a blow getting well home, or another fall, may decide it. Tom works slowly round for an opening; he has all the legs, and can choose his own time: the slogger waits for the attack, and hopes to finish it by some heavy right-handed blow. As they quarter slowly over the ground, the evening sun comes out from behind a cloud and falls full on Williams' face. Tom starts in; the heavy right hand is delivered, but only grazes his head. A short rally at close quarters, and they close: in another moment the slogger is thrown again heavily for the third time.

"I'll give you three to two on the little one in half-crowns," said Groove to Rattle.

"No, thank 'ee," answers the other, diving his hands further into his coat-tails.

Just at this stage of the proceedings, the door of the doctor's library suddenly opens, and he steps into the close, and makes straight for the ring, in which Brown and the slogger are both seated on their seconds' knees for the last time.

"The doctor! the doctor!" shouts some small boy who catches sight of him, and the ring melts away in a few seconds, the small boys tearing off, Tom collaring his jacket and waistcoat, and slipping through the little gate by the chapel, and round the corner to Harrowell's with his backers, as lively as need be; Williams and his backers making off not quite so fast across the close; Groove, Rattle and the other bigger fellows trying to combine dignity and prudence in a comical manner, and walking off fast enough, they hope, not to be recognized, and not fast enough to look like running away.

Young Brooke alone remains on the ground by the time the doctor gets there, and touches his hat, not without a slight inward qualm.

"Hah! Brooke. I am surprised to see you here. Don't you know that I expect the sixth to stop fighting?"

Brooke felt much more uncomfortable than he had expected, but he was rather a favorite with the doctor for his openness and plainness of speech; so blurted out, as he walked by the doctor's side, who had already turned back:

"Yes, sir, generally. But I thought you wished us to exercise a discretion in the matter, too—not to interfere too soon."

"But they have been fighting this half-hour and more," said the doctor.

"Yes, sir, but neither was hurt. And they're the sort of boys who'll be all the better friends now, which they wouldn't have been if they had been stopped any earlier—before it was so equal."

"Who was fighting with Brown?" said the doctor.

"Williams, sir, of Thompson's. He is bigger than Brown, and had the best of it at first, but not when you came up, sir. There's a good deal of jealousy between our house and Thompson's, and there would have been more fights if this hadn't been let go on, or if either of them had had much the worst of it."

"Well but, Brooke," said the doctor, "doesn't this look a little as if you exercised your discretion by only stopping a fight when the school-house boy is getting the worst of it?"

Brooke, it must be confessed, felt rather graveled.

"Remember," added the doctor, as he stopped at the turret-door, "this fight is not to go on—you'll see to that. And I expect you to stop all fights in future at once."

"Very well, sir," said young Brooke, touching his hat, and not sorry to see the turret-door close, behind the doctor's back.

Meantime Tom and the stanchest of his adherents had reached Harrowell's, and Sally was bustling about to get them a late tea, while Stumps had been sent off to Tew, the butcher, to get a piece of raw beef for Tom's eye, so that he might show well in the morning. He was not a bit the worse except a slight difficulty in his vision, a singing in his ears, and a sprained thumb, which he kept in a cold-water bandage, while he drank lots of tea, and listened to the babel of voices talking and speculating of nothing but the fight, and how Williams would have given in after another fall (which he didn't in the least believe), and how on earth the doctor could have gotten to know of it—such bad luck! He couldn't help thinking to himself that he was glad he hadn't won; he liked it better as it was, and felt very friendly to the slogger. And then poor little Arthur crept in and sat down quietly near him, and kept looking at him and the raw beef with such plaintive looks, that Tom at last burst out laughing.

"Don't make such eyes, young 'un," said he, "there's nothing the matter."

"Oh, but Tom, are you much hurt? I can't bear thinking it was all for me."

"Not a bit of it, don't flatter yourself. We were sure to have had it out sooner or later."

"Well, but you won't go on, will you? You'll promise me you won't go on."

"Can't tell about that—all depends on the houses. We're in the hands of our countrymen, you know. Must fight for the school-house flag, if so be."

And now, boys all, three words before we quit the subject. I have put in this chapter on fighting of malice prepense, partly because I want to give you a true picture of what every-day school life was in my time and partly because of the cant and twaddle that's talked of boxing and fighting with fists now-a-days. Even Thackeray has given in to it; and only a few weeks ago there was some rampant stuff in the *Times* on the subject.

Boys will quarrel, and when they quarrel will sometimes fight. Fighting with fists is the natural English way for English boys to settle their quarrels. What substitute for it is there, or ever was there, among any nation under the sun? What would you like to see take its place?

Learn to box, then, as you learn to play cricket and football. Not one of you will be the worse, but very much the better for learning to box well. Should you never have to use it in earnest, there's no exercise in the world so good for the temper, and for the muscles of the back and legs.

As to fighting, keep out of it if you can, by all means. When the time comes, if it ever should, that you have to say "Yes" or "No" to a challenge to fight, say "No" if you can—only take care you make it clear to yourselves why you say "No." It's a proof of the highest courage, if done from true Christian motives. It's quite right and justifiable, if done from a simple aversion to physical pain and danger. But don't say "No" because you fear a licking, and say or think it's because you fear God, for that's neither Christian nor honest. And if you do fight, fight it out; and don't give in while you can stand and see.

PRONUNCIATION OF PROPER NAMES

NOTE.—The pronunciation of difficult words is indicated by respelling them phonetically. *N* is used to indicate the French nasal sound; *K* the sound of *ch* in German; *ü* the sound of the German *ü*, and French *u*; *ö* the sound of *ö* in foreign languages.

AGINCOURT, *aj' in kort*, or *ah zhaN koor'*
ATHELSTANE, *ath' el stane*
AYTOUN, (WM. E.) *ay' toon*
CAERLEON, *kahr le' on*
CHEYENNE, *shi en'*
DUQUESNE, *du kayn'*
FROUDE, *frood*
GALAHAD, *gal' a had*
GHENT, *gent*
GRANTMESNIL, *groN ma neel'*
GUINEVERE, *gwin' e veer*
HOUYHNHNMS, *hoo' in 'ms*
LEIODES, *le o' deez*
MARACAIBO, *mahr ah ki' bo*
OTAHEITE, *o tah he' te*
POITIERS, *pwaht ya'*
SEINE, *sayn*
SIOUX, *soo*
SKALD, *skawld*

Journeys Through Bookland